# WEAR

## 35TH ANNIVERSARY ISSUE
### Novel Aspects of Wear

# WEAR
## 35TH
## ANNIVERSARY ISSUE
## Novel Aspects of Wear

## EDITOR: DUNCAN DOWSON

Reprinted from
*Wear*
Vol. 153, No. 1

1992
ELSEVIER SEQUOIA S.A., LAUSANNE

ELSEVIER SEQUOIA S.A.
Avenue de la Gare 50, PO Box 564, 1001 Lausanne 1, Switzerland

ISBN 0-444-75090-8

**Library of Congress Cataloging-in-Publication Data applied for**

Printed in The Netherlands by Krips Repro B.V.

# Contents

Elsevier Sequoia

vi

*Wear, 153* (1992) 1–2

# Introduction

## 35th anniversary issue of *Wear*

In 1992 it will be 35 years since the journal *Wear* was launched under the Editorship of Geert Salomon. The initial launch provided an opportunity for papers on wear and associated topics to be published in a single journal and the response of authors clearly confirmed the need for such an innovation. When Dough Scott assumed the Editorship in 1968 the subject and the journal were well established, but his friendly and sympathetic approach did much to promote the journal until his untimely death in 1983.

One of my early tasks, on taking up the Editorship in 1983, was to plan the 100th volume of *Wear*. The centenary volume was published at the end of 1984 and we had thought that the 150th volume should also be recognised in 1991. However, the ever increasing interest in *Wear* and the increasing flow of material made this inappropriate and it was therefore decided to celebrate our 35th birthday with an issue of invited papers in 1992.

There have been exciting developments in wear research in recent times and the invited papers in this special issue reflect these trends. Scientific studies of events controlling wear, friction and lubrication on an atomic or molecular scale are contributing greatly to our understanding of the macroscopic manifestations of tribology. Professor Landman's opening paper reflects the developing interest in the atomic scale aspects of contact and adhesion, while Professor Israelachvili and his colleagues provide new and remarkable ideas on the mechanism of cavitation in very thin lubricating films. The significance of tribology in modern computing equipment has been widely discussed in recent times and the papers by Professor Bhushan and his colleagues provide an insight into the contact, friction and wear problems encountered in magnetic recording head applications.

The rheological behaviour of the lubricant in starved, highly stressed elastohydrodynamic contacts is examined by Dr. Spikes and his colleagues. This starved form of mixed lubrication is described as "parched"; a term originally used in relation to gyroscope ball bearings operating with minute quantities of lubricant. This interest in the behaviour of very thick lubricating films is further explored in the paper by Greenwood and Johnson, where they examine the extent of the flattening of transverse waves and the amplitude of the associated pressure perturbations in elastohydrodynamic line contacts.

The importance of the measurement and modelling of surface roughness is recognised by the contribution by Dr. Myshkin and colleagues from the Metal–Polymer Research Institute of the Byelorussian Academy of Science in Gomel. Professor Godet and colleagues from Lyon re-examine the features of fretting while Professor Czichos and colleagues from BAM, Berlin, contribute to our understanding of the wear behaviour of carbon coatings on both steel and ceramic. In their report on the friction and wear of plain carbon steels, Professor Rigney and Dr. Venkatesan relate their findings to the wear map of Lim and Ashby. The development of wear maps is another significant feature of developments in recent years.

Dr. Quinn takes the opportunity to introduce us to oxidative wear modelling while Dr. Gee of the National Physical Laboratory discusses the formation of aluminium

Elsevier Sequoia, Lausanne

hydroxide in the sliding of wear of alumina. Polymers and polymer composites are the subject of the paper by Professors Blanchet and Kennedy, while Professor Oxley and his colleagues from the University of New South Wales demonstrate deformation and sliding at asperity level in a model contact. Briscoe and his colleagues from Imperial College draw attention to the possibility of using vibrational spectroscopy in studies of the interface friction experienced by organic films. Professor Kato from Tohoku University rounds off the volume by discussing micromechanisms of wear in relation to wear modes.

The papers presented in this volume illustrate current trends in studies of basic wear processes in wear, friction and lubrication. Perhaps the outstanding feature of this volume is that it demonstrates that emphasis is now being placed upon studies of interacting surfaces at the atomic or nanometre level rather than the macro or micron level which was dominant in recent decades. On the theoretical side, molecular modelling is developing rapidly and confirming features of contacts which were widely assumed, but never observed in fine detail, in the development of our subject. Likewise, experimentalists now have the atomic force microscope to reveal fine details of surface forces and deformations. Perhaps the main challenge of the '90s will be to reconcile the revealing studies of surface interactions at the "nanometre" level with the overall observations at the "micrometre" level which have fascinated us in recent decades. It is now beginning to look as though the overall understanding of the engineering scale features of tribology will eventually be supported by a sound base of scientific knowledge of molecular interactions. If this turns out to be the case, the tribological house of truth will indeed be built on sound foundations.

*Duncan Dowson*, Editor

*Wear, 153* (1992) 3–30

# Atomistic mechanisms of adhesive contact formation and interfacial processes

Uzi Landman, W. D. Luedtke and Eric M. Ringer
*School of Physics, Georgia Institute of Technology, Atlanta, GA 30332 (USA)*

(Received July 30, 1991)

## Abstract

Investigations were undertaken using large-scale molecular dynamics simulations of atomistic mechanisms of adhesive contact formation, friction, and wear processes. These processes occur as a result of interactions between material tips and substrate surfaces and reveal the energetics and dynamics of various wear phenomena. These include jump-to-contact, elastic, plastic and yield processes, connective neck formation, wetting, reconstruction, atomic-scale stick–slip, and materials transfer. Results are presented for several tip and substrate materials, including intermetallic (nickel and gold), interionic (CaF$_2$), and thin alkane (*n*-hexadecane) films adsorbed on a metal (gold) surface and interacting with a metal (nickel) tip.

## 1. Introduction

Understanding the atomistic mechanisms, energetics, and dynamics underlying the interactions and physical processes that occur when two materials are brought together or separated is fundamentally important to basic and applied problems such as adhesion [1–8], contact formation [3–18], surface deformations [7, 8, 17–25], materials elastic and plastic response characteristics [3, 7, 8, 18–25], materials hardness [26–28], microindentation [6, 11, 27–30], friction and wear [17, 20, 31, 32], and fracture [33, 34]. These considerations have, for over a century [1, 3, 18–21], motivated extensive theoretical and experimental research endeavors of the above phenomena and their technological consequences. Most theoretical approaches to these problems, with a few exceptions [7, 8, 15–17], have been anchored in continuum elasticity and contact mechanics [18–26]. Similarly, until quite recently [35–38] experimental observations and measurements of surface forces and the consequent materials response to such interactions have been macroscopic in nature.

The history of studying frictional or tribological phenomena is long and interesting [39]. Leaping over centuries of empirical observations we start with the classical friction law presented by Amonton in 1699 and extended by Coulomb in 1781 (although it was actually known to da Vinci in the fifteenth century) which states that relative sliding of two bodies in contact will occur when the net tangential force reaches a critical value proportional to the net force pressing the two bodies together. Furthermore, this proportionality factor, the friction coefficient, is independent of the apparent contact area and depends only weakly on the surface roughness.

Elsevier Sequoia, Lausanne

The first to introduce the notion of cohesive forces between material bodies in contact and their contribution to the overall frictional resistance experienced by sliding bodies was Desagulier's, whose ideas on friction are contained in a book published in 1734, entitled *A Course of Experimental Philosophy*. His observations which introduced adhesion as a factor in the friction, additional to the idea of interlocking asperities favoured in France, were conceived in the context of the role of surface finish where he writes "... the flat surfaces of metals or other Bodies may be so far polish'd as to increase Friction and this is a mechanical Paradox: but the reason will appear when we consider that the Attraction of Cohesion becomes sensible as we bring the Surfaces of Bodies nearer and nearer to Contact."

While it was recognized for many years that the Amonton–Coulomb laws of friction are applicable only to the description of friction between effectively rigid bodies and gross sliding of one body relative to another, the concepts of stress and the elastostatics came only later, in the writings of Cauchy, Navier and others, and the formulation by Hertz in 1881 of elastic contact mechanics [18]. Extensions of Hertz's theory to the contact of two elastic bodies including the influence of friction of the contact interface were made first by Cattaneo [40] and independently later by Mindlin [41].

Although we are not attempting to give a complete historical account here, we do note the role of adhesive interactions, plastic deformation and yield in determining the mechanical response and friction between bodies in contact, which has been growing since the beginning of the century. The notion that the yield point of a ductile metal is governed by shear stress [22]; either the absolute maximum (Tresca criterion) or the octahedral shear stress (von Mises criterion) is particularly noted. The relationship between the interfacial adhesive formation and shearing of intermetallic junctions and friction, was succinctly summarized by Tabor and Bowden as follows [42]: "Friction is the force required to shear intermetallic junctions plus the force required to plow the surface of the softer metal by the asperities on the harder surface."

The first successful theory of the contact mechanics of adhesive contact was formulated by Johnson, Kendall and Roberts (JKR) [23] who observed, during an investigation into the friction of automobile windscreen wipers, that when two bodies are pressed together and one or both surfaces is very compliant, the radius of the contact circle exceeded the value predicted by Hertz. Moreover, when the load was removed, a measurable contact area remained, and it was necessary to apply a tensile force to separate the surfaces. The JKR theory considers the adhesion between the two interfacing bodies simply as a change in surface energy only where they are in contact (*i.e.* infinitely short-range attractive forces). An alternative formulation [24] by Derjaquin, Muller and Toporov (DMT) asserts that the attractive force between the solids must have a finite range, and in their original formulation they assume this interaction to act in a region just outside the contact zone. (In addition the DMT theory assumes that the deformed shape of the surfaces is hertzian, *i.e.* unaffected by the surface forces.) More complete formulations, which allow solid–solid interactions to be a prescribed function of the local separation between the surfaces, have also been suggested [43, 44]. Furthermore, Maugis and Pollock [12] have investigated, in the context of metal microcontacts, the development of plastic deformation and adherence under zero applied load by considering the influence of surface forces, and have derived conditions for ductile or brittle modes of separation after an elastoplastic or full plastic contact.

The quest to understand and observe natural phenomena on refined microscopic scales has led to the development of conceptual and technological devices allowing the interrogation of materials with increasing resolution. On the experimental front, the importance of investigating single asperity contact in order to study the fundamental micromechanical response of solids has long been recognized. Such conditions are usually associated (*i.e.* assumed to be valid) for tip-on-flat configurations, with a tip radius of 1–2 $\mu$m or less [11, 45–47]. This may very well be the case for clean metal contacts [48–50]. Indeed, evidence for continuous contact over an entire tip of several thousand angstroms radius was given first by Pollock *et al.* [10].

The recent emergence and proliferation of surface force apparatus (SFA) [36], of scanning tunneling microscopy (STM) [37], and of the related atomic force microscopy (AFM) [35] broaden our perspectives and abilities to probe the morphology, electronic structure, and nature of interatomic forces in materials, as well as enhance our ability to manipulate materials on the atomic scale [38].

On the theoretical front, recent advances in the formulation and evaluation of the energetics and interatomic interactions in materials [7, 51], coupled with the development and implementation of computational methods and simulation techniques [7, 8, 52], open new avenues for investigations of the microscopic origins of complex materials phenomena. In particular, large-scale molecular dynamics computer simulations (which are, in a sense, computer experiments) where the evolution of a system of interacting particles is simulated with high spatial and temporal resolution by means of direct integration of the particles' equations of motion, have greatly enhanced our understanding of a broad range of materials phenomena.

Although our knowledge of interfacial processes occurring when two material bodies are brought together has significantly progressed since the original presentation by Hertz [18], full microscopic understanding of these processes is still lacking. Moreover, it has been recognized that continuum mechanics is not fully applicable as the scale of the material bodies and the characteristic dimension of the contact between them is reduced [25, 45]. Furthermore, it has been observed [20, 28] that the mechanical properties of materials exhibit a strong dependence on the size of the sample (small specimens appear to be stronger than larger ones). Since the junctions between contacting solids can be small, their mechanical properties may be drastically different from those of the same materials in their bulk form. Consequently, the application of the newly developed theoretical and experimental techniques to these problems promises to provide significant insights concerning the microscopic mechanisms and the role of surface forces in the formation of microcontacts and to enhance our understanding of fundamental issues pertaining to interfacial adherence, microindentation, structural deformations, and the transition from elastic to elastoplastic or fully developed plastic response of materials. Additionally, studies such as those described in this paper allow critical assessment of the range of validity of continuum-based theories of these phenomena and could inspire improved analytical formulations. Finally, knowledge of the interactions and atomic-scale processes occurring between small tips and materials surfaces, and their consequences, is of crucial importance to optimize, control, interpret, and design experiments employing the novel tip-based microscopies [6, 7, 14, 15, 17, 35–38, 53–58].

In an attempt to address the above issues on an atomistic level, we have embarked on a series of investigations [7, 8, 17] of the energetics, mechanisms and consequences of interactions between material tips and substrate surfaces, using molecular dynamics simulations. Since material phenomena and processes are governed by the nature and magnitude of bonding and interatomic interactions, as well as by other materials characteristics (such as thermodynamic state, structure, and degree of compositional and structural perfection) a comprehensive study of any class of phenomena (interfacial processes in particular) requires systematic investigations for a range of material-dependent parameters. To this end we have investigated the dynamical interactions between tips and surfaces of various materials and geometries.

In our earlier studies [17(a, c)] we have investigated the interaction between silicon tips and silicon surfaces (*i.e.* a case of reactive tip–substrate system). Our simulations, in both the constant-tip height and constant-force scan modes, revealed that the local structure of the surface can be stressed and modified as a consequence of the tip–substrate dynamical interaction, even at tip–substrate separations which correspond to weak interaction. For large separations these perturbations anneal upon advancement of the tip while permanent damage can occur for smaller separations. For this system (employing the interatomic potentials constructed by Stillinger and Weber [59], which include two- and three-body interactions reflecting the directional bonding character in covalent materials) we did not find long-range elastic deformations, which may occur in other circumstances [56] depending upon the elastic properties of the material and the nature of interactions. Furthermore, we found that the characteristics of the data depend upon the geometry of the scan, the degree of perfection of the substrate, and the temperature. We identified various dynamical events including stick–slip phenomena, which could be experimentally resolved, using current estimates [35, 38].

In this paper we focus on metallic (gold and nickel) and ionic (CaF$_2$) systems, as well as present results of our most recent studies on thin alkane films confined between solid boundaries.

## 2. Methodology

Molecular dynamics (MD) simulations consist of integration of the equations of motion of a system of particles interacting via prescribed interaction potentials [52]. The interatomic interactions that govern the energetics and dynamics of the system are characteristic to the system under investigation. Thus, for an ionic material (*e.g.* CaF$_2$) the energy may be described rather adequately as a sum of pairwise interactions between the ions, with the potential $V_{\alpha\beta}(r)$ between ions of types $\alpha$ and $\beta$ taken to be

$$V_{\alpha\beta}(r) = z_\alpha z_\beta e^2/r + A_{\alpha\beta} e^{-r/\rho_{\alpha\beta}} - C_{\alpha\beta}/r^6 \qquad (1)$$

where the first two terms correspond to the Coulomb and overlap-repulsion contributions, and the last term represents the van der Waals dispersion interaction; the charge on ions of type $\alpha$, in units of the electron charge $e$, is denoted by $z_\alpha$. In our simulations of CaF$_2$ [61] we have employed a parametrization of the potential in eqn. (1) determined partly by fitting to selected experimental data for the low temperature bulk crystal (such as structure, lattice parameters, cohesive energy, elastic constants and defect formation energies) and partly by appeal to quantum-mechanical calculations [61].

The nature of cohesion in metals is rather different. Here, the dominant contribution to the total cohesive energy of the system ($E_{coh}$) is due to the electronic distribution interacting with the metal ions embedded in it. Based on the philosophy of density-functional theory [62], a description of metallic systems which is amenable to molecular dynamics simulations is provided by the embedded atom method (EAM) [63, 64]. The basic feature of this method is that the effect of the surroundings on each atom in the system can be described in terms of the average electron density which other atoms in the system provide around the atom in question. The electronic structure problem is then converted to that of the embedding of an atom in a homogeneous electron gas, which can be described in terms of a universal density-dependent energy function. Thus the density-dependent term gives rise to many-body interactions.

In the EAM the cohesive energy $E_{coh}$ of the metal is written as

$$E_{coh} = \sum_i \left[ F_i \left( \sum_{j \neq i} \rho_j^a(R_{ij}) + \frac{1}{2} \sum_{j \neq i} \phi_{ij}(R_{ij}) \right) \right] \tag{2}$$

where $\rho^a$ is the spherically averaged atomic electron density and $R_{ij}$ is the distance between atoms $i$ and $j$. In EAM the embedding function, $F$, and the pair-repulsion between the partially screened ions, $\phi$, are determined by choosing functional forms which meet certain general requirements, and fitting parameters [65] in these functions to a number of bulk equilibrium properties of the solid, such as lattice constant, heat of sublimation, elastic constants, vacancy formation energy, heat of solution (of alloys), etc. The EAM has been used with significant success in studies of metallic systems in various thermodynamic states and degrees of aggregation [63–66].

In our simulations of tip–substrate systems the surface part of the system is modeled by a slab containing $n_d$ layers of dynamic atoms, with $n$ atoms per layer, exposing an $(hkl)$ surface plane, and interacting with $n_s$ layers of the same material and crystallographical orientation. The surface atoms interact with a dynamic crystalline tip arranged initially in a pyramidal (tapered) geometry with the bottom layer (closest to the substrate surface) consisting of $n_1$ atoms, the next layer consisting of $n_2 > n_1$ atoms and so on. In addition the tip interacts with a static holder, made of the same material as the tip, consisting of $n_h$ atoms located in $n_{hl}$ layers. This system is periodically replicated in the two directions parallel to the surface plane, and no boundary conditions are imposed in the direction normal to the surface.

The simulations were performed at 300 K with temperature control imposed only on the deepest layer of the dynamic substrate (*i.e.* the one closest to the static substrate). No significant variations in temperature were observed during the simulations. The equations of motion were integrated using a fifth-order predictor–corrector algorithm with a time step $\Delta t$ ($\Delta t = 3 \times 10^{-15}$ fs for the metallic systems and $1 \times 10^{-15}$ fs for the ionic systems).

Following equilibration of the system at 300 K with the tip outside the range of interaction, the tip was lowered slowly towards the surface. Motion of the tip occurs by changing the position of the tip-holder assembly in increments of 0.25 Å over 500 $\Delta t$. After each increment the system is fully relaxed, that is dynamically evolved, until no discernable variations in system properties are observed beyond natural fluctuations.

Analysis of the phase-space trajectories generated during the simulations allows determination of energetic, structural and dynamical properties. For example the stress tensor and individual atomic contributions to it can be derived most generally from the Lagrangian of the system [67, 68]. For the particular case of pair interactions the matrix of the stress tensor $\sigma$ is given in dyadic tensor notation by

$$\sigma \equiv \sum_i \sigma_i = \sum_i \left[ m_i v_i v_i + \frac{1}{2} \sum_j \chi(r_{ij})(r_i - r_j)(r_i - r_j) \right] \Omega_i^{-1} \tag{3}$$

where $\Omega_i$ is the volume per particle $i$, $v_i$ is the velocity vector of the particle, $r_i$ is its position vector and $\chi(r) = -r^{-1} dV(r)/dr$, where $V(r)$ is the pair-potential. The expression for potentials beyond pair interactions are somewhat more complicated. From the atomic stresses, invariants of the stress tensor can be calculated; in particular the second invariant of the stress deviator, $J_2$, which is proportional to the stored strain energy and is related to the von Mises shear strain–energy criterion for the onset of plastic yielding [19, 22], is given by

$$J_2 = \tfrac{1}{2}\mathrm{Tr}[\boldsymbol{\Gamma} \cdot \boldsymbol{\Gamma}^{\mathrm{T}}] \tag{4a}$$

where Tr denotes the trace of the matrix product in square brackets, $\boldsymbol{\Gamma}^{\mathrm{T}}$ is the transpose of the matrix $\boldsymbol{\Gamma}$ defined as

$$\boldsymbol{\Gamma} = \sigma - p\mathbf{1} \tag{4b}$$

where the hydrostatic pressure $p = \tfrac{1}{3}\,\mathrm{Tr}\,\sigma$, and $\mathbf{1}$ is the unit matrix.

## 3. Case studies

### 3.1. Solid–solid interfaces

In this section the results of several investigations are summarized. We start with simulations of the approach to adhesive contact followed by retraction (pull-off) of a clean nickel tip interacting with a clean gold substrate (Ni/Au). Simulations for the same system but when the tip is lowered beyond the point of contact formation are also described (nano-indentation). Subsequently the materials in the tip and substrate are interchanged, *i.e.* a clean gold tip is lowered towards a clean nickel substrate (Au/Ni). We also give results for a modified nickel tip (*i.e.* the one obtained at the end of the Ni/Au nano-indentation, where the bottom of the tip is coated by an epitaxial gold layer) interacting with an undamaged gold substrate. Finally consequences of the interactions between a CaF$_2$ surface and a tip made of the same material are described for both vertical and tangential displacements of the tip relative to the surface.

#### 3.1.1. Clean nickel tip/gold surface [7]

Simulated force *vs.* distance curves for the system are shown in Fig. 1 as well as the calculated potential energy *vs.* distance (Fig. 1(c)). Results for tip-to-sample approach followed by separation are shown, for adhesive contact (Fig. 1(a)) and indentation (Figs. 1(b) and 1(c)) studies. In these simulations the substrate consists of $n_s = 3$, $n_d = 8$, $n = 450$ atoms/layer exposing the (001) face. The tip consists of a bottom layer of 72 atoms exposing a (001) facet, the next layer consists of 128 atoms and the remaining six layers contain 200 dynamic atoms each. The static holder consists of 1176 atoms arranged in three (001) layers. This gives the tip an effective radius of curvature of $\approx 30$ Å.

The simulations correspond to a case of a rigid cantilever and therefore the recorded properties of the system as the tip-holder assembly approaches or retracts from the sample portray directly the consequences of the interatomic interactions between the tip and the sample. The distance scale that we have chosen in presenting the calculated results is the separation (denoted as $d_{hs}$) between the rigid (static) holder of the tip and the static gold lattice underlying the dynamic substrate. The origin of the distance scale is chosen such that $d_{hs} = 0$ after jump-to-contact occurs ($d_{hs} \geqslant 0$ when the system is not advanced beyond the JC point and $d_{hs} < 0$ corresponds to indentation). Since the dynamic nickel tip and gold substrate atoms displace in response to the interaction between them, the distance $d_{hs}$ does not give directly the actual separation between regions in the dynamic tip and substrate material. The actual relative distances, $d_{ts}$, between the bottom part of the tip (averaged $z$-position of atoms in the bottom-most layer of the tip) and the surface (averaged $z$-position of the topmost layer of the gold surface, calculated for atoms in the first layer away from the perturbed region in the vicinity of the tip) are given by the letter symbols in Figs. 1(a) and 1(b). Note that the distance between the bottom of the tip and the

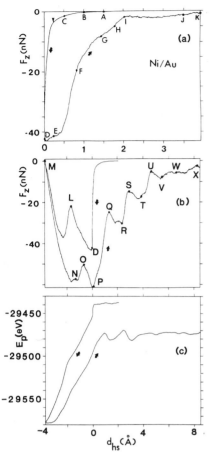

Fig. 1. Calculated force on the tip atoms, $F_z$, vs. tip-to-sample distance $d_{hs}$, between a nickel tip and gold sample for: (a) approach and jump-to-contact followed by separation; (b) approach, jump-to-contact, indentation, and subsequent separation; $d_{hs}$ denotes the distance between the rigid tip-holder assembly and the static substrate of the gold surface ($d_{hs} = 0$ at the jump-to-contact point marked D). The capital letters on the curves denote the actual distances, $d_{ts}$, between the bottom part of the nickel tip and the gold surface in (a): A = 5.7 Å, B = 5.2 Å, C = 4.7 Å, D = 3.8 Å, E = 4.4 Å, F = 4.85 Å, G = 5.5 Å, H = 5.9 Å, I = 6.2 Å, J = 7.5 Å and K = 8.0 Å; in (b): D = 3.8 Å, L = 2.4 Å, M = 0.8 Å, N = 2.6 Å, O = 3.0 Å, P = 3.8 Å, Q = 5.4 Å, R = 6.4 Å, S = 7.0 Å, T = 7.7 Å, U = 9.1 Å, V = 9.6 Å, W = 10.5 Å and X = 12.8 Å. (c) Potential energy of the system for a complete cycle of the tip approach, jump-to-contact, indentation, and subsequent separation. Forces in units of nN, energy in eV and distances in Å.

gold atoms in the region immediately underneath it may differ from $d_{ts}$. Thus for example when $d_{hs} = 0$ (point D in Figs. 1(a) and 1(b)) the tip to unperturbed gold distance, $d_{ts}$, is 3.8 Å, while the average distance between the bottom layer of the tip and the adherent gold layer in immediate contact with it is 2.1 Å.

*3.1.1.1. Tip–substrate approach.* Following an initial slow variation of the force between the gold substrate and the nickel tip we observe in the simulations the onset of an instability, signified by a sharp increase in the attraction between the two (see

Fig. 1(a) as well as Figs. 1(b) and 1(c) where the segments corresponding to lowering of the tip up to the point D describe the same stage as that shown in segment AD in Fig. 1(a)) which is accompanied by a marked decrease in the potential energy of the system (see sudden drop of $E_p$ in Fig. 1(c) as $d_{hs}$ approaches zero from the right). We note the rather sudden onset of the instability which occurs only for separations $d_{hs}$ smaller than 0.25 Å (marked by an arrow on the curve in Fig. 1(a)). Our simulations reveal that in response to the imbalance between the forces on atoms in each of the materials and those due to intermetallic interactions a jump-to-contact (JC) phenomenon occurs via a fast process where gold atoms in the region of the surface under the nickel tip displace by approximately 2 Å toward the tip in a short time span of $\simeq 1$ ps. After the jump-to-contact occurs the distance between the bottom layer of the nickel tip and the layer of adherent gold atoms in the region immediately underneath it decreases to 2.1 Å from a value of 4.2 Å. In addition to the adhesive contact formation between the two surfaces an adhesion-induced partial wetting of the edges of the nickel tip by gold atoms is observed.

The jump-to-contact phenomenon in metallic systems is driven by the marked tendency of the atoms at the interfacial regions of the tip and substrate materials to optimize their embedding energies (which are density dependent, deriving from the tails of the atomic electronic charge densities) while maintaining their individual material cohesive binding (in the nickel and gold) albeit strained due to the deformation caused by the atomic displacements during the JC process. In this context we note the difference between the surface energies of the two metals, with the one for nickel markedly larger than that of gold, and the differences in their mechanical properties, such as elastic moduli, yield, hardness, and strength parameters (for example, the elastic moduli are $21 \times 10^{10}$ and $8.2 \times 10^{10}$ N m$^{-2}$ for nickel and gold, respectively [69]).

Further insight into the JC process is provided by the local hydrostatic pressure in the materials (evaluated as the trace of the atomic stress tensors [67]) shown in Fig. 2(a) after contact formation (i.e. point D in Fig. 1(a)). The pressure contours reveal that atoms at the periphery of the contact zone (at $X = \pm 0.19$ and $Z = 0.27$) are under extreme tensile stress ($-10^5$ atm $= -10^{10}$ N m$^{-2} = -10$ GPa). In fact we observe that the tip as well as an extended region of the substrate in the vicinity of the contact zone are under tension. Both the structural deformation profile of the system and the pressure distribution which we find in our atomistic MD simulations are similar, in general terms, to those described by certain modern contact mechanics theories [19–22] where the influence of adhesive interactions is included.

*3.1.1.2. Tip–substrate separation after contact.* Starting from contact the force vs. distance ($F_z$ vs. $d_{hs}$) curve exhibits a marked hysteresis seen both experimentally and theoretically (Fig. 1(a)) as the surfaces are separated [7]. We remark that, in the simulation and the measurements [7], separating the surfaces prior to contact results in no hysteresis. The hysteresis is a consequence of the adhesive bonding between the two materials and, as demonstrated by the simulation, separation is accompanied by inelastic processes in which the topmost layer of the gold sample adheres to the nickel tip. The mechanism of the process is demonstrated by the pressure contours during liftoff of the tip shown in Fig. 2(b), recorded for the configuration marked G ($d_{ts} = 5.5$ Å in Fig. 1(a)). As seen the maximum tensile stress is located near the edges of the adhesive contact. We further observe that the diameter of the contact area decreases during lifting of the tip, resulting in the formation of a thin "adhesive neck" due to ductile extension, which stretches as the process continues, ultimately breaking

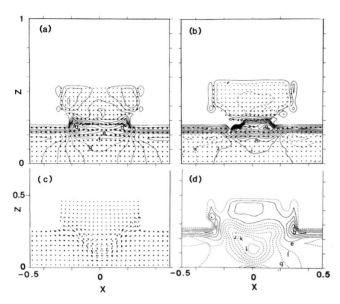

Fig. 2. Calculated pressure contours and atomic configurations viewed along the [010] direction, in slices through the system. The nickel tip occupies the topmost eight atomic layers. Short-time atomic trajectories appear as dots. Distance along the $X$ and $Z$ directions in units of $X=1$ and $Z=1$ corresponding to 61.2 Å each. Solid contours correspond to tensile stress (*i.e.* negative pressure) and dotted ones to compressive stress. (a) After jump-to-contact (point D in Fig. 1(a)). The maximum magnitude of the tensile (*i.e.* negative pressure), 10 GPa, is at the periphery of the contact, $(X,Z) = (\pm 0.19, 0.27)$. The contours are spaced with an increment, $\Delta$, of 1 GPa. Thus, the contours marked e, f and g correspond to $-6$, $-5$ and $-4$ GPa, respectively. (b) During separation following contact (point G in Fig. 1(a)). The maximum tensile pressure (marked a), $\approx -9$ GPa, is at the periphery of the contact at $(X,Z)$ equal to (0.1, 0.25) and $(-0.04, 0.25)$. $\Delta = 0.9$ GPa. The marked contours, h, i, j and k correspond to $-2.5$, $-1.6$, $-0.66$ and 0.27 GPa, respectively. (c) Short-time particle trajectories at the final stage of relaxation of the system, corresponding to point M in Fig. 1(b), (*i.e.* $F_z = 0$). Note slip along the [111] planes in the substrate. (d) Pressure contours corresponding to the final configuration shown in (c). Note the development of compressive pressure in the substrate which maximizes in the region of the contour marked l (8.2 GPa). The increment between contours $\Delta = 1.4$ GPa. The contours marked a and e correspond to $-6.4$ GPa and $-1.1$ GPa, respectively, and those marked f and g to 0.2 GPa and 1.6 GPa.

at a distance $d_{ts}$ of $\approx 9\text{--}10$ Å. The evolution of adhesion and tear mechanisms which we observe can be classified as mode-I fracture [33], re-emphasizing the importance of forces operating across the crack in modeling crack propagation [33, 34].

*3.1.1.3. Indentation.* We turn now to theoretical results recorded when the tip is allowed to advance past the jump-to-contact point, *i.e.* indentation (see Figs. 1(b) and 1(c), and Fig. 3). As evident from Fig. 1(b), decreasing the separation between the tip and the substrate causes first a decrease in the magnitude of the force on the tip (*i.e.* less attraction, see segment DL) and an increase in the binding energy (*i.e.* larger magnitude of the potential energy, shown in Fig. 1(c)). However, upon reaching the point marked L in Fig. 1(b) a sharp increase in the attraction occurs, followed by a monotonic decrease in the magnitude of the force until $F_z = 0$ (point M in Fig. 1(b)) at $d_{ts} = 0.8$ Å. The variations of the force (in the segment DLM) are correlated with

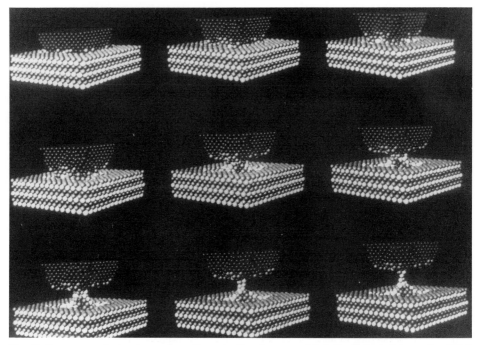

Fig. 3. Sequence of atomic configuration starting from a nickel tip indented in a Au (001) substrate (top left) and during the process of retraction of the tip (from left to right) accompanied by formation of a connective neck.

large deformations of the gold substrate. In particular, the nonmonotonic feature (near point L) results from tip-induced flow of gold atoms which relieve the increasing stress via wetting of the sides of the tip. Indeed the atomic configurations display a "piling-up" around the edges of the indenter due to atomic flow driven by the deformation of the gold substrate and the adhesive interactions between the gold and nickel atoms. Further indentation is accompanied by slip of gold layers (along (111) planes) and the generation of interstitial defects. In addition, the calculations predict that during the indentation process a small number of nickel atoms diffuse into the surrounding gold, occupying substitutional sites. Furthermore the calculated pressure contours at this stage of indentation, shown in Fig. 2(d), demonstrate that the substrate surface zone in the vicinity of the edges of the tip is under tensile stress, while the deformed region under the tip is compressed with the maximum pressure (8.2 GPa) occurring at about the fifth gold layer below the center of the nickel tip-indenter. The general characteristics of the pressure (and stress) distributions obtained in our indentation simulations correspond to those associated [12, 19, 23] with the onset and development of plastic deformation in the substrate.

Experimentally, advancing the sample past the contact point is noted by the change in slope of the force as the increasing repulsive forces push the tip and cantilever back towards their rest position. We remark that the calculated pressures from the simulations compare favorably with the average contact pressure of $\approx 3$ GPa determined experimentally by dividing the measured attractive force by the estimated circular contact area of radius 20 nm.

*3.1.1.4. Tip–substrate separation after indentation.* Reversal of the direction of the tip motion relative to the substrate from the point of zero force (point M in Fig. 1(b)) results in the force and potential energy *vs.* distance curves shown in Figs. 1(b) and 1(c). The force curve exhibits first a sharp monotonic increase in the magnitude of the attractive force (segment MN in Fig. 1(b)) with a corresponding increase in the potential energy (Fig. 1(c)). During this stage the response of the system is mostly elastic accompanied by the generation of a small number of vacancies and substitutional defects in the substrate. Past this stage the force and energy curves *vs.* tip-to-sample separation exhibit a nonmonotonic behaviour which is associated mainly with the process of elongation of the connective neck which forms between the substrate and the retracting tip.

To illustrate the neck formation and elongation process we show in Fig. 4 a sequence of atomic configurations corresponding to the maxima in the force curve (Fig. 1(b), points marked O, Q, S, U, W and X). As is evident, upon increased separation between the tip-holder and the substrate a connective neck forms consisting mainly of gold atoms (see atomic configurations shown in Fig. 3). The mechanism of elongation of the neck involves atomic structural transformations whereby in each

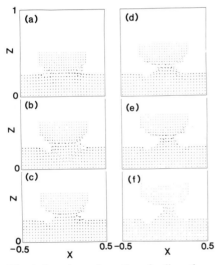

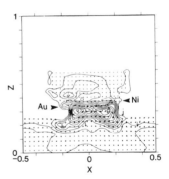

Fig. 4. Atomic configurations in slices through the system illustrating the formation of a connective neck between the nickel tip and the gold substrate during separation following indentation. The nickel tip occupies the topmost eight layers. The configurations (a)–(f) correspond to the stages marked O, Q, S, U, W and X in Fig. 1(b). Note the crystalline structure of the neck. Successive elongations of the neck, upon increased separation between the tip-holder assembly and the substrate, occur via structural transformation resulting in successive addition of layers in the neck accompanied by narrowing (*i.e.* reduction in cross-sectional area of the neck). Distance in units of $X$ and $Z$, with $X=1$ and $Z=1$ corresponding to 61.2 Å.

Fig. 5. Von Mises' shear stress ($J_2^{1/2}$) corresponding to the configuration marked T in Fig. 1(b) (that is, just before the structural transformation resulting in the configuration (d) in Fig. 4). The proximal interfacial layers of nickel and gold are marked by arrows. The maximum contours (2.9 GPa, marked a) occur on the periphery of the neck $(X,Z)=(\pm 0.1, 0.3)$. The increment between contours is 0.2 GPa. The contours marked h, i, j and k correspond to 1.1, 0.9, 0.7 and 0.5 GPa, respectively. Distance along $X$ and $Z$ in units of $X=1$ and $Z=1$ corresponding to 61.2 Å.

elongation stage atoms in adjacent layers in the neck disorder and then rearrange to form an added layer, *i.e.* a more extended neck of a smaller cross-sectional area. Throughout the process the neck maintains a layered crystalline structure (see Fig. 4) except for the rather short structural transformation periods, corresponding to the sharp variations in the force curve (see segments PQ, RS, TU and VW in Fig. 1(b)) and the associated features in the calculated potential energy shown in Fig. 1(c) where the minima correspond to ordered layered structures after the structural rearrangements. We note that beyond the initial formation stage the number of atoms in the connective neck region remains roughly constant throughout the elongation process.

Further insight into the microscopic mechanism of elongation of the connective neck can be gained via consideration of the variation of the second invariant of the stress deviator, $J_2$, which is related to the von Mises shear strain–energy criterion for the onset of plastic yielding [19, 22, 26]. Returning to the force and potential energy curves shown in Figs. 1(b) and 1(c), we have observed that between each of the elongation events (*i.e.* layer additions, points marked Q, S, U, W and X) the initial response of the system to the strain induced by the increased separation between the tip-holder and the substrate is mainly elastic (segments OP, QR, ST, UV in Fig. 1(b), and correspondingly the variations in Fig. 1(c)), accompanied by a gradual increase of $J_2^{1/2}$, and thus the stored strain energy. The onsets of the stages of structural rearrangements are found to be correlated with a critical maximum value of $J_2^{1/2}$ of about 3 GPa (occurring for states at the end of the intervals marked OP, QR, ST and UV in Fig. 1(b)) localized in the neck in the region of the ensuing structural transformation. After each of the elongation events the maximum value of $J_2^{1/2}$ (for the states marked Q, S, U, W and X in Fig. 1(b)) drops to approximately 2 GPa.

In this context, it is interesting to remark that the value of the normal component of the force per unit area in the narrowest region of the neck remains roughly constant ($\approx 1$ GPa) throughout the elongation process, increasing by about 20% prior to each of the aforementioned structural rearrangements. This value has been estimated both by using the data given in Fig. 1(b) and the cross-sectional areas from atomic configuration plots (such as given in Fig. 4), and via a calculation of the average axial component (*zz* element) of the atomic stress tensors [51] in the narrow region of the neck. We note that the above observations constitute atomic-scale realizations of basic concepts which underlie macroscopic theories of materials behaviour under load [18–24].

A typical distribution of the stress, $J_2^{1/2}$, prior to a structural transformation is shown in Fig. 5 (shown for the state corresponding to the point marked T in Fig. 1(b)). As seen, the maximum of $J_2^{1/2}$ is localized about a narrow region around the periphery in the strained neck. Comparison between the atomic configuration at this stage (see Fig. 5, or the very similar configuration shown in Fig. 4(c)) and the configuration after the structural transformation has occurred (see Fig. 4(d), corresponding to the point marked U in Fig. 1(b)) illustrates the elongation of the neck by the addition of a layer and accompanying reduction in areal cross-section. We note that as the height of the connective neck increases the magnitude of the variations in the force and potential energy during the elongation stages diminishes. The behaviour of the system past the state shown in Fig. 4(f) (corresponding to the point marked X in the force curve shown in Fig. 1(b)) is similar to that observed at the final stages of separation after jump-to-contact (Fig. 1(b)), characterized by strain-induced disordering and thinning in a narrow region of the neck near the gold-covered bottom of the tip and eventual fracture of the neck (occurring for a tip-to-substrate distance $d_{ts} \approx 18$ Å), resulting in a nickel tip whose bottom is covered by an adherent gold layer.

The theoretically predicted increased hysteresis upon tip–substrate separation following indentation, relative to that found after contact (compare Figs. 1(a) and 1(b)), is also observed experimentally [7]. In both theory and experiment the maximum attractive force after indentation is roughly 50% greater than when contact is first made. Note, however, that the nonmonotonic features found in the simulations (Fig. 1(b)) are not discernible in the experiment which is apparently not sufficiently sensitive to resolve such individual atomic-scale events when averaged over the entire contact area.

### 3.1.2. Gold-covered nickel tip/gold surface

Having described in the previous section the processes occurring as a result of the interaction between a clean nickel tip with a gold surface, we turn next to a system where a nickel tip "wetted" by a gold monolayer is lowered and subsequently retracted from a clean initially undamaged Au(001) surface.

As aforementioned, the retraction of the nickel tip from the gold surface after formation of an adhesive contact between the two is accompanied by wetting of the tip by gold atoms. The gold-coated nickel tip used in the present simulations was obtained following a slight indentation (see section 3.1.3). It is interesting to note in this context that the epitaxial gold monolayer coating the Ni(001) tip exhibits a (111) two-dimensional structure rotated with respect to the (001) mesh.

The force vs. distance curve obtained for the system, along with the one corresponding to the clean nickel tip (see also Fig. 1(a)) shown in Fig. 6 and inspection of atomic configurations reveal that while the adhesive interaction is reduced for the coated tip, jump-to-contact instability, formation of an adhesive contact and hysteresis during subsequent retraction occur in both cases. However we should note that in the present case while a connective neck, made solely of substrate gold atoms, is formed during retraction of the tip (of dimensions similar to that formed upon indentation, see Fig. 3), insignificant transfer of atoms from the surface to the tip occurs upon complete separation (i.e. while gold wets by adhering to a bare nickel tip, no wetting occurs for a gold-covered tip).

### 3.1.3. Clean gold tip/nickel surface [8]

In the studies discussed in section 3.1.1 the tip material (i.e. nickel) was the harder one, characterized additionally by a larger surface energy. In this section studies

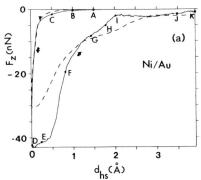

Fig. 6. Calculated force on the tip atoms, $F_z$, vs. tip-to-sample distance, $d_{hs}$, for the case of a gold-coated nickel tip approaching and then being retracted from a clean Au (001) surface (dashed line), as well as for the case of a clean nickel tip (see Fig. 1(a)).

where the materials composing the tip and surface are interchanged, *i.e.* a gold tip interacts with a Ni(001) surface, are described. In these investigations the substrate consists again of $n_s = 3$ and $n_d = 8$ layers, exposing the Ni(001) surface, but with a larger number of atoms per layer ($n = 800$) than in the previous studies to allow for spreading of the gold tip (see below). The gold tip, exposing a Au(001) facet, is prepared in a similar manner to that described in section 3.1.1.

*3.1.3.1. Contact formation and separation.* The simulated force on the tip and potential energy *vs.* distance curve are shown in Fig. 7, and atomic configurations of the system (*i.e.* short-time atomic trajectories, shown for a slice of 11 Å width through the system) recorded at selected stages during the tip-to-substrate approach and subsequent separation are shown in Fig. 8.

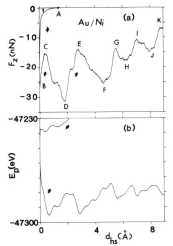

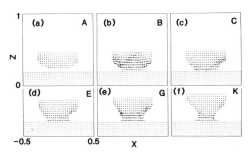

Fig. 7. Calculated force $F_z$ (a) and potential energy of the system $E_p$ (b), *vs.* tip-to-sample distance, $d_{hs}$, between a gold tip and a nickel sample for approach and jump-to-contact followed by separation. $d_{hs}$ denotes the distance between the rigid tip-holder assembly and the static substrate of the nickel surface ($d_{hs} = 0$ at the jump-to-contact point, marked B). The distance between the bottom layer of the tip and the top layer of the sample is 4.2 Å at the onset of the jump-to-contact, *i.e.* the last stable point upon tip lowering (marked by an arrowhead in (a)). That distance is 2.1 Å after contact formation (point marked B). The points marked C, E, G, I and K correspond to ordered configurations of the tip each containing an additional layer. Force in units of nN, energy in eV and distance in Å.

Fig. 8. Atomic configurations in a slice, in the *XZ* plane (*i.e.* containing the [100] and [001] directions), of width 11 Å through the system (in the [010] direction) illustrating the atomic arrangements in the system before and after jump-to-contact (in (a) and (b), respectively) and for the ordered configurations during the tip elongation processes which occur upon retraction of the tip from the point of adhesive contact (in (c)–(f)). The capital letters identify the corresponding points on the $F_z$ *vs.* distance curve given in Fig. 7(a). Note the crystalline structure of the neck. Successive elongations of the neck, upon increased separation between the tip-holder assembly and the substrate, occur by way of a structural transformation resulting in successive addition of layers in the neck, accompanied by narrowing (that is, reduction in cross-sectional area of the neck). Distance in units of $X$ and $Z$, with $X = 1$ and $Z = 1$ corresponding to 70.4 Å.

Following an initial slow variation of the force between the nickel substrate and the gold tip we observe the onset of an instability, signified by a sharp increase in the attraction between the two (see segment AB in Fig. 7(a)) which is accompanied by a marked decrease in the potential energy of the system (see sudden drop of $E_p$ in Fig. 7(b) as $d_{hs}$ approaches zero). We note the rather sudden onset of the instability which occurs only for separations $d_{hs}$ smaller than 0.25 Å (marked by an arrow on the curve in Fig. 7(a) and corresponding to $d_{ts} = 4.2$ Å). Our simulations reveal that in response to the imbalance between the forces on atoms in each of the materials and those due to intermetallic interactions a JC phenomenon occurs via a fast process where gold tip atoms displace by approximately 2 Å toward the surface in a short time span of $\approx 1$ ps (see Figs. 8(a) and 8(b) where the atomic configurations before and after the JC are depicted). After the JC occurs the distance between the bottom layer of the gold tip and the top layer of the nickel surface decreases to 2.1 Å from a value of 4.2 Å. The response in this system should be contrasted with that observed by us in simulations of a nickel tip approaching a gold surface (see section 3.1.1.) where the JC phenomenon involved a bulging of the gold surface underneath the tip.

Contours of the local pressure (evaluated as the trace of the atomic stress tensors) and the square root of $J_2$ (second invariant of the stress deviator), after JC had occurred, are shown in Figs. 9(a) and 9(b), respectively. We observe that the pressure

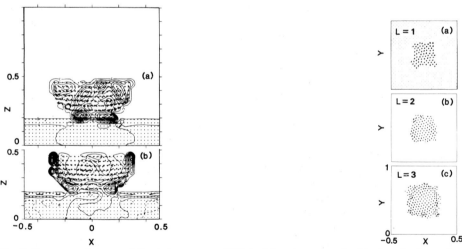

Fig. 9. Contours of the von Mises' shear stress ($J_2^{1/2}$) in (a) and pressure in (b) after the formation of adhesive contact between the gold tip and the nickel surface (corresponding to point B in Fig. 7(a)). Note the $J_2^{1/2}$ maximizes at the periphery of the contact achieving a value of 2 GPa. The increment between the contours in (a) is 0.17 GPa. The hydrostatic pressure in (b) is tensile and large on the periphery of the tip and achieves a value of $\approx -5$ GPa at the peripheral region of the contact. The increment between contours is 1 GPa. Distance along the $X$ and $Z$ directions in units of $X = 1$ and $Z = 1$ corresponding to 70.4 Å.

Fig. 10. Atomic configurations in layers of the gold tip closest to the nickel substrate after the formation of the adhesive contact (point B in Fig. 7(a)). $L = 1$ corresponds to the proximal layer (large dots in (a)) of the gold tip in contact with the Ni (001) substrate (small dots in (a)). Note the (111) reconstruction of the gold layers. $L = 2$ and $L = 3$ are the two layers above the proximal layer. Distance along the $X$ ([100]) and $Y$ ([001]) directions in units of 70.4 Å.

on the periphery of the tip is large and negative (tensile), achieving values up to $-1 \times 10^5$ atm $= -10^{10}$ N m$^{-1}$ = 10 GPa, while the middle core of the tip is under a small compressive pressure. The $J_2^{1/2}$ maximizes in the interfacial contact region achieving a value of $2.0 \times 10^4$ atm = 2 GPa.

As a consequence of the formation of the adhesive contact between the two materials, the interfacial region of the gold tip exhibits large structural rearrangements, both in the normal and lateral directions. The atomic configurations in the three layers of the tip closest to the nickel surface are shown in Fig. 10. The structure of the proximal gold layer (large dots in Fig. 10(a), superimposed on the atomic structure of the underlying Ni (001) surface) exhibits a marked tendency towards a (111) reconstruction (in this context we remark that only a small tendency towards a (111) structure was observed by us for a patch of a gold monolayer deposited on a Ni (001) surface). Furthermore, the (111) reconstruction extends 3–4 layers from the interface into the gold tip. Accompanying the epitaxial surface structural rearrangement in the gold, which is partially driven by the lattice constant mismatch between gold and nickel, an increase in interlayer spacing occurs ($d_{12} = 2.44$ Å, $d_{23} = d_{34} = d_{45} = 2.53$ Å, $d_{56} = d_{67} = 2.2$ Å and $d_{78} = 2.1$ Å, compared with the interlayer spacing between (001) layers in the bulk gold of 2.04 Å where $d_{n\,n+1}$ is the spacing between layers $n$ and $n+1$, and layer number 1 corresponds to the gold layer proximal to the nickel topmost surface layer). The (111) reconstruction and expanded interlayer spacings in the interfacial region of the gold tip persist throughout the separation process.

Starting from contact the force $vs.$ distance ($F_z$ $vs.$ $d_{hs}$) curve exhibits a marked hysteresis as the tip is retracted from the substrate (see Fig. 7(a)). We remark that separating the surfaces prior to jump-to-contact results in no hysteresis. The hysteresis is a consequence of the adhesive bonding between the two materials and, as demonstrated by the simulation, separation is accompanied by inelastic processes and the formation of an extended gold connective neck (see Figs. 8(c)–8(f)).

The hysteresis in the force $vs.$ distance curve exhibits marked variations (see Fig. 7(a)) which portray the atomistic processes of gold neck formation and elongation. In this context we remark that our earlier simulations (and accompanying AFM experiments) of a nickel tip interacting with a gold surface have also shown a marked hysteresis upon separation from adhesive contact. However in that case the variation of the force $F_z$ $vs.$ distance curve was monotonic, and the extension of the connective neck was rather limited. Variations similar to those shown in Fig. 1(a) were observed by us before (section 3.1.1) only upon tip–sample separation following a slight indentation (see Fig. 1(b)) of the gold surface by the nickel tip.

The maxima in Fig. 7(a) (points marked C, E, G, I and K) are associated with ordered structures of the elongated connective neck, each corresponding to a neck consisting of one more layer than the previous one. Thus the number of gold layers at point C is 9 (one more than the original 8-layer tip), 10 layers at point E, etc. (see Fig. 8).

The mechanism of elongation of the neck is similar to that discussed before (see section 3.1.1) involving atomic structural transformations whereby in each elongation stage atoms in adjacent layers in the neck disorder and then rearrange to form an added layer which is a more extended neck of a smaller cross-sectional area. Throughout the process the neck maintains a layered crystalline structure except for the rather short structural transformation periods, corresponding to the sharp variations in the force curve (see segments BC, DE, FG, HI and JK in Fig. 7(a) and the associated features in the calculated potential energy shown in Fig. 7(b), where the minima correspond to ordered layered structures after the structural rearrangements).

As we mentioned before, associated with the formation of the adhesive neck and throughout the elongation stage the interfacial region of the neck is structurally reconstructed laterally (*i.e.* (111) reconstruction in layers) accompanied by expanding interlayer spacings compared with that in Au (001). The depth of the reconstructed region tends to be larger during the stretching stages, prior to the reordering which results in an additional layer. The reconstruction and increased interlayer spacings are related to the coupled effects of lattice constant mismatch between gold and nickel and the fact that the tensile stress in the normal direction acts on interfacial layers whose areas are smaller than those in the region of the tip close to the static holder, resulting in a larger strain in the former region.

*3.1.3.2. Tip compression.* Having discussed the processes of contact formation and pull-off, we show in Fig. 11 the force and potential energy curves obtained when the motion of the gold tip towards the nickel substrate is continued past contact formation (point marked B, $d_{hs}=0$, in Fig. 11). (In this figure $d_{hs}<0$ corresponds to continued motion towards the surface.) The force curve exhibits nonmonotonic variations and reverses sign, signifying the onset of a repulsive interaction.

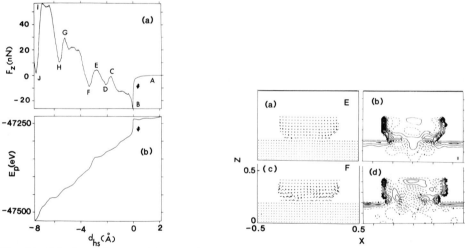

Fig. 11. Calculated force $F_z$ (a) and potential energy of the system $E_p$ (b) *vs.* tip-to-sample distance, $d_{hs}$, for a gold tip lowered towards a Ni (001) surface. The point marked B ($d_{hs}=0$) corresponds to the adhesive contact. $d_{hs}<0$ corresponds to continued motion of the tip toward the surface past the contact point. The points marked E, G and I correspond to ordered configurations of the compressed tip, each containing one atomic layer less than the previous one (starting with 8 layers at point E). Force in units of nN, energy in eV and distance in Å.

Fig. 12. Atomic configurations and pressure contours in an 11 Å slice through the system, corresponding to the points marked E and F in Fig. 11(a). Note that in (a) the tip consists of eight gold layers, while in (b), the peripheral region rearranges to form seven layers, while the core region still consists of eight layers, thus containing an interstitial defect layer. In (b), corresponding to point E, the compressive pressure (dashed contours) concentrates and maximizes just below the nickel surface, achieving a value of 6 GPa. The increment between contours is 1.2 GPa. Solid contours correspond to tensile pressure. The pressure contours during the intermediate state between ordered configurations (point F in Fig. 11(a)) exhibit concentration of compressive pressure in the core defect region (achieving a maximum value of 4.8 GPa inside the tip) and just below the surface. The increment between contours is 1 GPa.

We observe that a continued compression of the tip results in an increase in the interfacial contact area between the tip and the substrate, and a "flattening" of the tip. To illustrate the process we show in Figs. 12 and 13 atomic configurations and pressure contours of the system, corresponding to the points marked E, F, G and H on the force curve (Fig. 11(a)). As can be seen the number of layers in the gold tip corresponding to points E and G (Figs. 12(a) and 13(a), respectively) decreases from 8 to 7 (contact areas $\simeq 1100$ Å$^2$ and 1750 Å$^2$, respectively). The pressure contours corresponding to these configurations show tensile (negative) pressure on the sides of the tip and a concentration of compressive pressure in the interfacial substrate region.

The evolution of the structural transformation, induced by continued compression, between the ordered structures involves the generation of interstitial-layer partial dislocations in the central region (core) of the tip and subsequent transformation, as may be seen from Figs. 12(c) and 13(c) (the latter one rearranges to a six-layer tip upon continued compression (point marked I in Fig. 11(a)), with a contact surface area of $\simeq 2400$ Å$^2$). In the course of lowering of the tip (between ordered configurations) the outer regions of the tip rearrange first to reduce the number of crystalline layers leaving an interstitial-layer defect in the core of the tip which is characterized as a

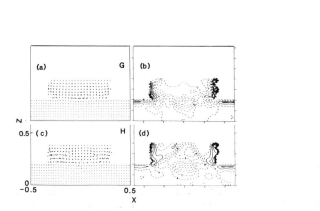

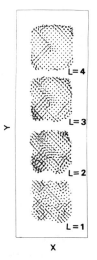

Fig. 13. Same as Fig. 12 for the configurations marked G and H in Fig. 11(a). The ordered configuration marked G contains seven layers in the gold tip and evolves from configuration F (see Fig. 12(c)). Note the increase in contact area. Configuration H contains six layers at the outside region of the tip and an interstitial defect layer at the tip core region. As in Fig. 12 the compressive pressure (dashed contours) maximizes just below the surface region for the ordered configuration (in (b)) achieving a value of 7.6 GPa. During the intermediate stage (in (d)) compressive pressure concentrates near the surface region (where it achieves a maximum value of 7.7 GPa) and in the core of the tip (where a maximum value of 6.2 GPa is achieved). The increment between contours is 1.5 GPa.

Fig. 14. Atomic trajectories in the interfacial layers of the compressed gold tip, recorded during part of the segment FG in Fig. 11(a), *i.e.* between configurations starting from one which contains a core interstitial defect layer and ending in an ordered configuration (compare Figs. 12(c) and 13(a)). $L=1$ corresponds to the proximal gold layer. The trajectories illustrate the atomic mechanism by which the core interstitial layer defect is expelled.

high compressive pressure region (see Figs. 12(d) and 13(d)). Continued lowering of the tip results in a "dissolution" (or annealing) of the interstitial-layer defect which is achieved by fast correlated atomic motions along preferred (110) directions (see Fig. 14, showing short-time trajectories in layers 1–4 of the tip, recorded in the segment FG of Fig. 11(a)). Accompanying the annealing of the defect the compressive pressure transfers from the tip to the interfacial substrate region. The initial atomic rearrangement of the peripheral region of the tip and the eventual expulsion of the remaining interstitial layer atoms from the core, contribute to the increase of the contact area between the tip and the substrate.

### 3.1.4. CaF₂ tip/CaF₂ surface

In the previous sections results pertaining to intermetallic contacts were discussed. Here we turn to results obtained in simulations of a $CaF_2$ tip interacting with a $CaF_2$ (111) surface. As remarked in section 2, the nature of bonding in ionic materials is different from that in metallic systems, including long-range Coulombic interactions.

In these simulations the substrate is modeled by three static layers interacting with 12 layers of dynamic atoms, with 242 $Ca^{2+}$ cations in each calcium layer and 242 $F^-$ anions in each fluorine layer, exposing the (111) surface of a $CaF_2$ crystal (the stacking sequence is ABAABA... where A and B correspond to all $F^-$ and all $Ca^{2+}$ layers, respectively. The top surface layer is an A layer). The $CaF_2$ tip is prepared as a (111) faceted microcrystal containing nine (111) layers, with the bottom layer containing 18 $F^-$ anions, the one above it 18 $Ca^{2+}$ cations followed by a layer of 18 $F^-$ anions. The next three layers contain 50 ions per layer, and the three layers above it contain 98 ions in each layer. The static holder of the tip is made of 3 $CaF_2$ (111) layers (242 ions total). The system is periodically replicated in the two directions parallel to the surface plane and no periodic boundary conditions are imposed in the normal, z, direction. The long-range Coulomb interactions are treated via the Ewald summation method and temperature is controlled to 300 K via scaling of the velocities of atoms in the three layers closest to the static substrate. The integration time step $\Delta t = 1.0 \times 10^{-15}$ s and motion of the tip occurs in increments of 0.5 Å over a time span of 1 ps ($10^{-12}$ s). As before, after each increment in the position of the tip-holder assembly the system is allowed to dynamically relax.

Curves of the average force, $F_z$, on the tip atoms recorded for the fully relaxed configurations, vs. distance $d_{ns}$, are shown in Fig. 15(a) along with the corresponding variations in the potential energy of the tip atoms (Fig. 15(b)). From Fig. 15(a) we observe, following a gradual increase in the attraction upon approach of the tip to the surface, the onset of an instability marked by a sharp increase in attraction occurring when the bottom layer of the tip approaches a distance $d_{ts} \simeq 3.75$ Å from the top layer of the surface. This stage is accompanied by an increase in the interlayer spacing in the tip material, i.e. tip elongation, and is reminiscent of the jump-to-contact phenomenon which we discussed in the context of intermetallic contacts, although the elongation found in the present case($\approx 0.35$ Å) is much smaller than that obtained for the metallic systems.

Decreasing the distance between the tip-holder assembly and the substrate past the distance corresponding to maximum adhesive interaction (which occurs at $d_{ts} \simeq 2.3$ Å) results in a decrease in the attractive interaction, which eventually turns slightly repulsive (positive value of $F_z$), accompanied by a slight compression of the tip material. Starting from that point ($d_{hs} = 26.5$ Å, $d_{ts} \simeq 1.4$ Å) and reversing the direction of motion of the tip-holder assembly (i.e. detracting it from the surface) results in the force curve denoted by crosses in Figs. 15(a) and 15(b).

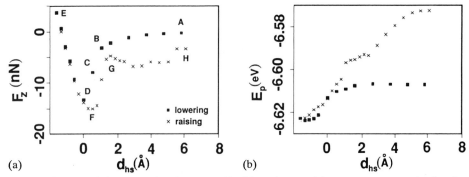

(a)  (b)

Fig. 15. Calculated force on the tip atoms, $F_z$, (a) and potential energy per atom in the tip, $E_p$, *vs.* tip-to-sample distance, $d_{hs}$, for a $CaF_2$ tip approaching (filled squares) and subsequently retracting (crosses) from a $CaF_2$ (111) surface. The distance from the bottom layer of the tip to the topmost surface layer, $d_{ts}$, for the points marked by letters is: A (8.6 Å), B (3.8 Å), C (3.0 Å), D (2.3 Å), E (1.43 Å), F (2.54 Å), G (2.7 Å) and H (3.3 Å). Distance in Å, energy in eV, and force in nN.

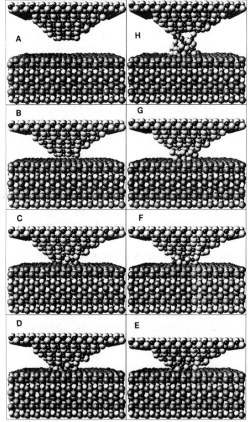

Fig. 16. Atomic configurations corresponding to the marked points in Fig. 15(a). Small and large balls correspond to $Ca^{2+}$ and $F^-$ ions, respectively. The images were obtained for a cut in the middle of the system.

As clearly observed from Fig. 15(a), the force *vs.* distance relationship upon tip-to-substrate approach and subsequent separation exhibits a pronounced hysteresis. The origin of this behaviour, which is also reflected in the tip potential energy *vs.* distance curve shown in Fig. 15(b), is a plastic deformation of the crystalline tip, leading to eventual fracture. At the end of the lifting processes part of the tip remains bonded to the substrate. Atomic configurations corresponding to those stages marked by letter on the force curve (Fig. 15(a)) are shown in Fig. 16.

*3.1.4.1. Tip sliding.* Starting from the tip–substrate configuration under a slight attractive load ($h_{ts}$ = 1.7 Å, $F_z$ = −3.0 nN), lateral motion of the tip parallel to the surface plane is initiated by translating the tip-holder assembly in the $\langle \bar{1},1,0 \rangle$ direction in increments of 0.5 Å followed by a period of relaxation, while maintaining the vertical distance between the tip-holder and the substrate at a constant value. This then corresponds to a constant-height scan in the language of atomic-force microscopy. We have also performed constant-load simulations which will not be discussed here.

The recorded component of the force on the tip atoms in the direction of the lateral motion, as a function of the displacement of the tip-holder assembly, is shown in Fig. 17(a) and the corresponding potential energy of the tip atoms is given in Fig. 17(b). As is seen, the force on the tip exhibits an oscillatory variation as a function of lateral displacement which is a characteristic of atomic-scale stick–slip behaviour. Inspection of the atomic configurations along the trajectory of the system reveals that the lateral displacement results in shear-cleavage of the tip. The sequence of atomic configurations shown in Fig. 18 reveals that the bottom part of the tip remains bonded to the substrate, and sliding occurs between that portion of the tip material and the adjacent layers. This result indicates that under the conditions of the simulation (*i.e.* small load), atomic layers of the tip may be transferred to the substrate upon sliding resulting in tip wear. From the average value of the recorded variation in the tangential force on the tip (see Fig. 17(a)), and the contact area, we estimate that the critical yield stress associated with the initiation of slip in the system is $\approx 9$ GPa, in good correspondence with other simulations of shear deformations of perfect bulk crystalline $CaF_2$.

## 3.2. Tip–liquid film–solid substrate

Our discussion up to this point was confined to the interaction between material tips and bare crystalline substrates. Motivated by the fundamental and practical importance of understanding the properties of adsorbed molecularly thin films and phenomena occurring when films are confined between two solid surfaces, pertaining to diverse fields [70–73] such as lubrication, prevention of degradation and wear, wetting, spreading and drainage, we have initiated most recently investigations of such systems [74]. Among the issues which we attempted to address are the structure, dynamics, and response of confined complex films, their rheological properties, and modifications which they may cause to adhesive and tribological phenomena, such as inhibition of jump-to-contact instabilities and prevention of contact junction formation. Furthermore, these studies are of importance in the light of recent AFM experiments on adsorbed polymeric films [75]. In the following we highlight certain of our results.

The molecular film which we studied, n-hexadecane ($C_{16}H_{34}$)) is modeled by interaction potentials developed by Ryckaert and Bellmans [76] and which have been employed before in investigations of the thermodynamic, structural and rheological properties of bulk liquid n-alkanes [77]. In this model the $CH_2$ and $CH_3$ groups are represented by pseudo-atoms of mass $2.41 \times 10^{-23}$ g, and the intermolecular bond-

24

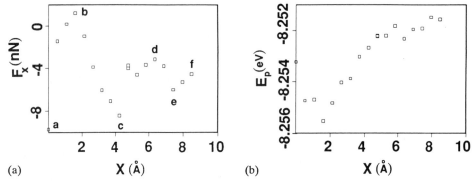

Fig. 17. Tangential force on the tip atoms, $F_x$, in the $\langle 1\bar{1}0 \rangle$ direction, and per-ion potential energy in the tip, $E_p$ $vs.$ distance ($X$, along the $\langle 1\bar{1}0 \rangle$ direction), calculated for a $CaF_2$ tip translated at constant height parallel to a $CaF_2$ (111) substrate surface in the $\langle 1\bar{1}0 \rangle$ direction. Note the oscillatory character of the force curve, portraying an atomic stick–slip process. Note also the increase in $E_p$ with translated distance. The marked points in (a) correspond to minima and maxima of the $F_x$ curve along the $\langle 1\bar{1}0 \rangle$ ($X$) direction. Distance in Å, energy in eV and force in nN.

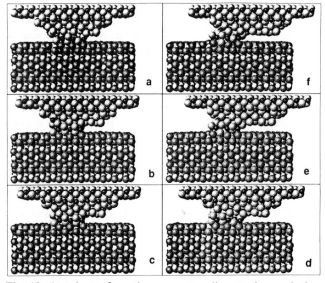

Fig. 18. Atomic configurations corresponding to the marked points in Fig. 17(a). Note the interlayer slip occurring in the tip as the tip-holder assembly is translated from left to right. The bottom three layers of the tip adhere to the surface leading to an adhesive wear process of the sliding tip.

lengths are fixed at 1.53 Å and the bond-angles at 109° 28′. A 6–12 Lennard–Jones (LJ) potential describes the intermolecular interaction between sites (pseudo-atoms) in different molecules and the intramolecular interactions between sites more than three apart. The LJ potential well-depth parameter $\epsilon_2 = 6.2 \times 10^{-3}$ eV, and the distance parameter $\sigma_2 = 3.923$ Å. The range of the LJ interaction is cut-off at 9.8075 Å. An angle-dependent dihedral potential is used to model the effect of missing hydrogen atoms on the molecular conformation.

The substrate (Au(001)) and tip (nickel) which we use are described using the EAM potentials as in our aforementioned studies of Ni/Au (001) (see section 3.1.1). The interaction between the n-hexadecane molecules and the metallic tip and substrate is modeled using a LJ potential with $\epsilon_3 = 3\epsilon_2 = 18.6 \times 10^{-3}$ eV and $\sigma_3 = 3.0715$ Å. The cut-off distance of the molecule–surface interaction is 7.679 Å. We remark that the choice of $\epsilon_3$ corresponds to an enhanced adsorption tendency of the alkane molecules onto the metals, which is a reasonable assumption, based on theoretical estimates obtained using the theory of dispersion interactions [70].

All details of the simulation pertaining to the metallic tip and substrate are as those given in section 3.1.1. The hexadecane film is composed of 73 alkane molecules (1168 pseudo-atoms) equilibrated initially on the Au (001) surface at a temperature of 300 K. The constrained equations of motion for the molecules are solved using a recently proposed method [78], employing the Gear fifth-order predictor–corrector algorithm.

The equilibrated adsorbed molecular film prior to interaction with the nickel tip is layered (see Fig. 19(a)) with the interfacial layer (the one closest to the Au (001) substrate) exhibiting a high degree of orientational order (the molecules in this layer tend to be oriented parallel to the surface plane, see Fig. 19(b)).

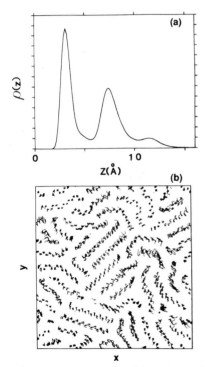

Fig. 19. Density profile (a) and top view of the first molecular layer adsorbed on the surface (b) for a thin film of n-hexadecane adsorbed on a Au (001) surface at 300 K. Distance in units of Å. The dimension along the $x$- and $y$-axis in (b) is 61.2 Å. The origin of the $z$-axis (normal to the surface) is at the average position of the centers of the gold atoms in the topmost surface layer.

Lowering of the (001) faceted nickel tip to within the range of interaction with the film causes first adherence of some of the alkane molecules to the tip resulting in partial "swelling" of the film [75, 79] and a small attractive force on the tip. Continued approach of the tip towards the substrate causes "flattening" of the molecular film, accompanied by partial wetting of the sides of the tip, and reduced mobility of the molecules directly underneath it (see short-time trajectories shown in Fig. 20(a), corresponding to a distance $d_{ts} = 9.5$ Å between the bottom layer of the tip and the topmost layer of the Au (001) surface). The arrangement of molecules in the interfacial layer of the film is shown in Fig. 21(a). At this stage the tip experiences a repulsive force $F_z = 2$ nN.

Continued lowering of the tip induces drainage of the second layer molecules under the tip, increased wetting of the sides of the tip and "pinning" of hexadecane molecules under it. Side views for several tip-lowering stages are shown in Figs. 20(b)–20(d), corresponding to $d_{ts} \simeq 6.5$ Å (in (b)), 5.1 Å (in (c)), and 4.0 Å (in (d) and (e)). (The corresponding recorded forces on the tip, after relaxation, for these values of the tip-to-surface separations are 0 nN, 25 nN, and −5 nN, respectively.) Note that for $d_{ts} = 5.1$ Å and $d_{ts} = 4.0$ Å the region of the surface of the gold substrate

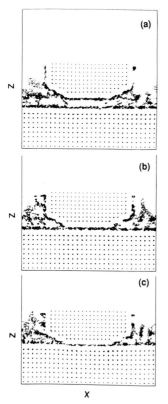

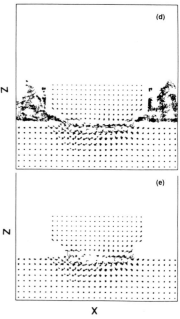

Fig. 20. Side views of short-time trajectories of the nickel tip-hexadecane film–Au (001) surface system at four stages of the tip-lowering process: (a) $d_{ts} = 9.5$ Å, (b) $d_{ts} = 6.5$ Å, (c) $d_{ts} = 5.1$ Å, (d, e) $d_{ts} = 4.0$ Å, where in (d) both the metal atoms and alkane molecules are displayed and in (e) only the metal atoms are shown. These values of $d_{ts}$ are average distances between atoms in the bottom layer of the nickel tip and those in the topmost layer of the gold substrate.

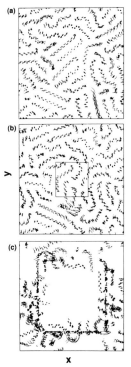

x

Fig. 21. (a) Arrangement of molecules in the first interfacial layer adsorbed on the Au (001) substrate for $d_{ts} = 9.5$ Å and in the first molecular layer (b) and the region above it (c), at $d_{ts} = 6.5$ Å. Note that molecules above the first layer drained from under the tip. The inner marked square in (b) denotes the projected area of the bottom layer of the tip.

directly under the tip is deformed and the above $d_{ts}$ values represent averages over the whole surface area (in this context we mention that for $d_{ts} = 5.1$ Å the average pressure in the contact area between the tip and the sample is $\approx 2$ GPa). We also remark that we have observed that during the later stages of the tip-lowering process, drainage of entangled, or "stapled", molecules from under the tip is assisted by transient local inward deformations of the substrate which apparently lower the barriers for the relaxation of such unfavorable conformations of the confined alkane molecules. The arrangement of molecules in the first adsorbed alkane layer and in the region above it for $d_{ts} = 6.5$ Å is shown in Figs. 21(b) and 21(c). The molecules are oriented preferentially parallel to the surface, particularly in the region under the tip (exhibiting in addition a reduced mobility).

Comparison of the response of the system with that described in section 3.1.1 for the bare gold surface (see Fig. 1(a)) reveals that while in the latter case the force between the tip and the substrate is attractive throughout (and remains attractive even for a slight indentation of the surface, see Fig. 1(b)), the overall force on the tip in the presence of the adsorbed alkane film is repulsive for relative tip-to-substrate distances for which it was attractive in the other case (except for the initial stages of the tip approach process). However we note for the smallest tip-to-substrate separation which we investigated here (average distance $d_{ts} = 4.0$ Å before relaxation) the onset of intermetallic contact formation, occurring by displacement of gold atoms towards the nickel tip accompanied by partial drainage of alkane molecules, resulting in a net attractive force on the tip of about $-5$ nN (the intermetallic contribution to this force is about $-20$ nN and the alkane repulsive contribution is about 15 nN).

From these preliminary results we conclude that lowering of a faceted nickel tip towards a gold surface covered by a thin adsorbed n-hexadecane film results first in small attraction between the film and the tip followed, upon further lowering of the tip, by ordering (layering) of the molecular film. During continued approach of the tip toward the surface the total interaction between the tip and the substrate (metal plus film) is repulsive, and the process is accompanied by molecular drainage from the region directly under the tip, wetting of the sides of the tip, and orientational ordering of the adsorbed molecular monolayer under the tip. Further lowering of the tip is accompanied by inward deformation of the substrate and eventual formation of intermetallic contact (occurring via displacement of surface gold atoms towards the tip) which is accompanied by partial molecular drainage and results in a net attractive force on the tip. The implications of these results to the analysis of AFM measurements of the thickness of adsorbed films [75], and the dependence of the results on the extent of the film, and on the nature of the adsorbed molecular film and its interaction with the substrate and tip, are currently under investigation in our laboratory.

## Acknowledgments

This work was supported by the US Department of Energy, the Air Force Office of Scientific Research and the National Science Foundation. Simulations were performed on the Cray Research, Inc. computers at the National Energy Research Supercomputer Center, Livermore, CA, through a grant from DOE, and at the Pittsburgh Supercomputer Center.

## References

1 D. Tabor, *J. Colloid Interface Sci., 58* (1977) 2; M. D. Pashley and D. Tabor, *Vacuum, 31* (1981) 619.
2 N. Gane, P. F. Pfaelzer and D. Tabor, *Proc. R. Soc. London A, 340* (1974) 395.
3 H. M. Pollock, *Vacuum, 31* (1981) 609.
4 D. Maugis, *Le Vide, 186* (1977) 1.
5 R. G. Horn, J. N. Israelachvili and F. Pribac, *J. Colloid Interface Sci., 115* (1987) 480 and references therein.
6 N. A. Burnham and R. J. Colton, *J. Vac. Sci. Technol. A, 7* (1989) 2906.
7 U. Landman, W. D. Luedtke, N. A. Burnham and R. J. Colton, *Science, 248* (1990) 454.
8 U. Landman and W. D. Luedtke, *J. Vac. Sci. Technol., 9* (1991) 414.
9 D. Tabor and R. H. S. Winterton, *Proc. R. Soc. London A, 312* (1969) 435.
10 H. M. Pollock, P. Shufflebottom and J. Skinner, *J. Phys. D, 10* (1977) 127; H. M. Pollock, *J. Phys. D, 11* (1978) 39.
11 N. Gane and F. P. Bowden, *J. Appl. Phys., 39* (1968) 1432.
12 D. Maugis and H. M. Pollock, *Acta Metall., 32* (1984) 1323 and references therein.
13 U. Durig, J. K. Gimzewski and D. W. Pohl, *Phys. Rev. Lett., 57* (1986) 2403; U. During, O. Zuger and D. W. Pohl, *J. Microsc., 152* (1988) 259.
14 J. M. Gimzewski and R. Moller, *Phys. Rev. B, 36* (1987) 1284.

15  J. B. Pethica and A. P. Sutton, *J. Vac. Sci. Technol. A, 6* (1988) 2494.
16  J. R. Smith, G. Bozzolo, A. Banerjea and J. Ferrante, *Phys. Rev. Lett., 63* (1989) 1269.
17  (a) U. Landman, W. D. Luedtke and M. W. Ribarsky, *J. Vac. Sci. Technol. A, 7* (1989) 2829; *Mater. Res. Soc. Symp. Proc., 140* (1989) 101; see also (b) M. W. Ribarsky and U. Landman, *Phys. Rev. B, 38* (1988) 9522; (c) U. Landman, W. D. Luedtke and A. Nitzan, *Surf. Sci., 210* (1989) L177.
18  H. Hertz, *J. Reine Angew. Math., 92* (1882) 156; also in *Miscellaneous Papers,* Macmillan, London, 1896, p. 146; see review by K. L. Johnson, *Proc. Instrum. Mech. Eng., 196* (1982) 363.
19  G. Dieter, *Mechanical Metallurgy,* McGraw-Hill, New York, 1967.
20  E. Rabinowicz, *Friction and Wear of Materials,* Wiley, New York, 1965.
21  S. P. Timoshenko and J. N. Goodier, *Theory of Elasticity,* McGraw-Hill, New York, 3rd edn., 1970.
22  K. L. Johnson, *Contact Mechanics,* Cambridge Univ. Press, Cambridge, 1985.
23  K. L. Johnson, K. Kendall and A. D. Roberts, *Proc. R. Soc. London A, 324* (1971) 301.
24  B. V. Derjaguin V. M. Muller and Yu. P. Toporov, *J. Colloid Interface Sci., 53* (1975) 314; V. M. Muller, B. V. Derjaguin and Yu. P. Toporov, *Colloids Surf., 7* (1983) 251.
25  P. A. Pashley, *Colloids Surf., 12* (1984) 69.
26  D. Tabor, *The Hardness of Metals,* Clarendon, Oxford, 1951.
27  J. B. Pethica, R. Hutchings and W. C. Oliver, *Philos. Mag. A, 48* (1983) 593.
28  N. Gane, *Proc. R. Soc. London A, 317* (1970) 367 and references therein.
29  P. J. Blau and B. R. Lawn (eds.), *Microindentation Techniques in Materials Science and Engineering,* Am. Soc. for Testing and Materials, Philadelphia, PA, 1985.
30  M. F. Doerner and W. D. Nix, *J. Mater. Res., 1* (1988) 601.
31  See articles in L. E. Pope, L. L. Fehrenbacher and W. O. Winer (eds.), *Mater. Res. Soc. Symp. Proc., 140* (1989) 101, Materials Research Soc., Pittsburgh, PA, 1989; F. P. Bowden and D. Tabor, *Friction and Lubrication of Solids,* Clarendon, Oxford, 1950.
32  C. W. Mate, G. M. McClelland, R. Erlandsson and S. Chiang, *Phys. Rev. Lett., 59* (1987) 1942.
33  R. Thomson, *Solid State Phys., 9* (1986) 1.
34  B. R. Lawn, *Appl. Phys. Lett., 47* (1985) 809.
35  G. Binning, C. F. Quate and Ch. Gerber, *Phys. Rev. Lett., 56* (1986) 930.
36  J. N. Israelachvili, *Acc. Chem. Res., 20* (1987) 415; *Proc. Natl. Acad. Sci. U.S.A., 84* (1987) 4722; J. N. Israelachvili, P. M. McGuiggan and A. M. Homola, *Science, 240* (1988) 189.
37  G. Binning, H. Rohrer, Ch. Gerber and E. Weibel, *Phys. Rev. Lett., 50* (1983) 120.
38  See reviews by: P. K. Hansma and J. Tersoff, *J. Appl. Phys., 61* (1986) R1; R. J. Colton and J. S. Murday, *Naval Res. Rev, 40* (1988) 2; J. S. Murday and R. J. Colton, *Mater. Sci. Eng. B, 6* (1990) 77; J. S. Murday and R. J. Colton, in R. Vanselow and R. Howe (eds.), *Chemistry and Physics of Solid Surfaces, VIII,* Springer, Berlin, 1990.
39  D. Dowson, *History of Tribology,* Longman, London, 1979.
40  C. Cattaneo, *Rend. Accad. Naz. dei Lincei, Ser. 6, 27* (1938) Part I, pp. 342–348, Part II, pp. 434–436, Part III, pp. 474–478.
41  R. D. Mindlin, *J. Appl. Mech., 16* (1949) 259; see also J. L. Lubkin, in W. Flugge (ed.), *Handbook of Engineering Mechanics,* McGraw-Hill, New York, 1962.
42  F. P. Bowden and D. Tabor, *Friction,* Anchor Press/Doubleday, Garden City, NY, 1973, p. 62.
43  V. M. Muller, V. S. Yushchenko and B. V. Derjaguin, *J. Colloid Interface Sci., 77* (1980) 91; *J. Colloid Interface Sci., 92* (1983) 92.
44  B. D. Hughes and L. R. White, *Q. J. Mech. Appl. Math., 32* (1979) 445.
45  M. D. Pashley, J. B. Pethica and D. Tabor, *Wear, 100* (1984) 7.
46  J. Skinner and N. Gane, *J. Phys. D, 5* (1972) 2087.
47  D. Maugis, G. Desatos-Andarelli, A. Heurtel and R. Courtel, *ASLE Trans., 21* (1976) 1.
48  J. B. Pethica and W. C. Oliver, *Phys. Scr., T19* (1987) 61.
49  J. B. Pethica, *Phys. Rev. Lett., 57* (1986) 323.
50  Q. Guo, J. D. J. Ross and H. M. Pollock, *Mater. Res. Soc. Proc., 140* (1989) 51.

30

51 See articles in V. Vitek and D. J. Srolovitz (eds.), *Atomistic Simulations of Materials, Beyond Pair Potentials,* Plenum, New York, 1989; R. M. Nieminen, M. J. Puska and M. J. Manninen (eds.), *Many Body Interactions in Solids,* Plenum, New York, 1989.

52 See reviews by F. F. Abraham, *Adv. Phys., 35* (1986) 1; *J. Vac. Sci. Technol. B, 2* (1984) 534; U. Landman, in D. P. Landau, K. K. Mon and H. B. Schuttler (eds.), *Computer Simulation Studies in Condensed Matter Physics: Recent Developments,* Springer, Berlin, 1988, p. 108.

53 F. F. Abraham, I. P. Batra and S. Ciraci, *Phys. Rev. Lett., 60* (1988) 1314.

54 R. J. Colton, S. M. Baker, R. J. Driscoll, M. G. Youngquist, J. D. Baldeschwieler and W. J. Kaiser, *J. Vac. Sci. Technol. A, 6* (1988) 349.

55 D. Tomanek, C. Overney, H. Miyazaki, S. D. Mahanti and H. J. Guntherodt, *Phys. Rev. Lett., 63* (1989) 876.

56 J. M. Soler, A. M. Baro, N. Garcia and H. Rohrer, *Phys. Rev. Lett., 57* (1986) 444; see comment by J. B. Pethica, *Phys. Rev. Lett., 57* (1986) 3235.

57 N. A. Burnham, D. D. Dominguez, R. L. Mowery and R. J. Colton, *Phys. Rev. Lett., 64* (1990) 1931.

58 W. Zhong and D. Tomanek, *Phys. Rev. Lett., 64* (1990) 3054.

59 F. H. Stillinger and T. A. Weber, *Phys. Rev. B, 31* (1985) 5262.

60 E. Ringer and U. Landman (to be published).

61 C. R. A. Catlow, M. Dixon and W. C. Mackrodt, in *Computer Simulations of Solids, Lecture Notes in Physics, Vol. 166,* Springer, Berlin, 1982, p. 130; see also M. Gillan, in A. M. Stoneham (ed.), *Ionic Solids at High Temperatures,* World Scientific, Singapore, 1989, p. 57.

62 P. Hohenberg and W. Kohn, *Phys. Rev. B, 136* (1964) 864.

63 See review by M. Baskas, M. Daw, B. Dodson and S. Foiles, *Mater. Res. Soc. Bull., 13* (1988) 28.

64 S. M. Foiles, M. I. Baskes and M. S. Daw, *Phys. Rev. B, 33* (1986) 7983.

65 The parametrization used in our calculations is due to J. B. Adams, S. M. Foiles and W. G. Wolfer, *J. Mater. Res. Soc., 4* (1989) 102.

66 E. T. Chen, R. N. Barnett and U. Landman, *Phys. Rev. B, 40* (1989) 924; *Phys. Rev. B, 41* (1990) 439; C. L. Cleveland and U. Landman, *J. Chem. Phys., 94* (1991) 7376; W. D. Luedtke and U. Landman, *Phys. Rev. B, 44* (1991) 5970.

67 T. Egami and D. D. Srolovitz, *J. Phys., 12* (1982) 2141.

68 M. Parrinello and A. Rahman, *Phys. Rev. Lett., 45* (1980) 1196.

69 *Mater. Eng., 90* (1979) C120.

70 J. N. Israelachvili, *Intermolecular and Surface Forces,* Academic Press, London, 1985; R. G. Horn, *J. Am. Ceram. Soc., 73* (1990) 1117; R. J. Hunter, *Foundations of Colloid Science, Vols. 1 and 2,* Oxford University Press, Oxford, 1987 and 1989; I. B. Ivanov (ed.), *Thin Liquid Films,* Dekker, New York, 1988.

71 D. Y. Chan and R. G. Horn, *J. Chem. Phys., 83* (1985) 5311.

72 J. N. Israelachvili, P. M. McGuiggan and A. M. Homola, *Science, 240* (1988) 189; A. M. Homola, J. N. Israelachvili, P. M. McGuiggan and M. L. Gee, *Wear, 136* (1990) 65.

73 J. Van Alsten and S. Granick, *Phys. Rev. Lett., 61* (1988) 2570; H.-W. Hu, G. A. Carson and S. Granick, *Phys. Rev. Lett., 66* (1991) 2758; S. Granick, *Science, 253* (1991) 1374.

74 For simulations of the structural and dynamical properties of thin alkane films confined between two solid boundaries and the dynamics of film collapse upon application of load see M. W. Ribarsky and U. Landman, *J. Chem. Phys.* (1992); for simulations of metal tips interacting with thin alkane films adsorbed on metal surfaces see W. D. Luedtke and U. Landman, *J. Chem. Phys.* (1992).

75 C. M. Mate, M. R. Lorenz and V. J. Novotny, *J. Chem. Phys., 90* (1989) 7550; C. M. Mate and V. J. Novotny, *J. Chem. Phys., 94* (1991) 8420.

76 J. P. Ryckaert and A. Bellmans, *Discuss. Faraday Soc., 66* (1978) 96.

77 J. H. R. Clark and D. Brown, *J. Chem. Phys., 86* (1987) 1542; R. Edberg, G. P. Morriss and D. J. Evans, *J. Chem. Phys., 86* (1987) 4555.

78 R. Edberg, D. J. Evans and G. P. Morriss, *J. Chem. Phys., 84* (1986) 6933.

79 M. L. Forcada, M. M. Jakas and A. Gras-Marti, *J. Chem. Phys., 95* (1991) 706.

# Mechanism of cavitation damage in thin liquid films: collapse damage *vs.* inception damage

You Lung Chen, Tonya Kuhl and Jacob Israelachvili

*Department of Chemical and Nuclear Engineering, and Materials Department, University of California, Santa Barbara, CA 93106 (USA)*

(Received July 28, 1991)

## Abstract

Much experimental and theoretical work has been done on the collapse or bursting of vapour bubbles onto solid surfaces in liquids, and it is generally held that this is also the underlying cause of surface damage ("cavitation" damage). However, due to experimental difficulties, much less work has been done on the time-evolution of bubbles and cavities in thin liquid films, *e.g.* in thin lubricating films during shear. Thus, the intuition gained from experiments on, for example, hydrofoils in water tunnels, may not apply to tribological situations. We have used the surface forces apparatus technique to observe, at the submicroscopic level, the rapid growth and disappearance of vapour cavities between two moving surfaces while simultaneously monitoring their effects on the deformations and wear of the surfaces. We find that under these conditions the inception of cavities is a much more violent event than their collapse. The sudden nucleation and growth of cavities is associated with the relaxation of high local stresses on nearby surfaces, and it is at this point that damage occurs rather than during the much smoother subsequent collapse of cavities. Time-lapse video photos taken during the life cycles of cavities are presented. These clearly show the highly complex and inter-related processes that occur in the liquid and nearby surfaces during cavitation.

## 1. Introduction: critical historical review

The first high-speed ship propellers, introduced in the mid-nineteenth century, were disappointingly inefficient. After some research, it was found that the impingement of thousands of tiny air or vapour bubbles on the rapidly moving surfaces was causing severe surface erosion and thus a decreased efficiency and, ultimately, serious damage. This empirical knowledge was fortified by Rayleigh's theoretical analysis in 1917 [1] showing that implosive pressures of the order of 10 000 atm can develop during the final stages of bubble collapse, and since then it has generally been held that collapsing bubbles or cavities are the underlying cause of "cavitation damage" of surfaces in liquids.

Cavitation damage (and cavitation noise) reduce the working life and/or efficiency of a moving part, and as such is an important industrial and biological problem. For example, it is responsible for the erosion of propeller blades, of high-speed lubricated bearings and metal surfaces subjected to ultrasonic vibrations, in the wear of knee joints, and in decompression sickness (the bends).

On the basis of Rayleigh's classic paper, cavitation damage was thought to be due solely to the extremely high implosive pressure generated at the moment when a vacuum cavity or vapour bubble collapses, and the results of subsequent studies tended to confirm this view. Most of the work on cavitation and cavitation damage has been carried out with hydrofoils or with artificially created bubbles near surfaces. Thus, during the 1960s, it was shown that imploding bubbles deform into thin rapidly moving liquid jets, and that these jets cause damage on striking a surface, producing tiny pits or craters on the surfaces [2]. The original idea of Rayleigh of a bubble remaining spherical as it collapses (Fig. 1, top) was thus changed into a non-spherical collapse (Fig. 1, bottom) where the disruptive energy could be more highly concentrated at the tip of a high-speed jet.

The most direct experimental evidence linking surface damage with bubble collapse has come from experiments with hydrofoils in water tunnels. These generally show that regions of maximum erosion usually occur where cavitation bubbles are seen to collapse [3], as shown in Fig. 2. We return to consider whether this is the whole story later, but here it is worth pointing out that the source of energy in such systems does not come from the external hydrostatic pressure on these bubbles, nor from surface tension forces, but also from the kinetic energy of the rapidly moving liquids which directs the bubbles onto the surfaces where this energy (or some of it) is released on impingement. As we shall see, our results indicate that (1) the source of energy

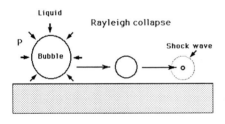

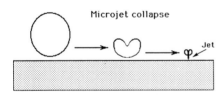

Fig 1. Deformations of collapsing vapour bubbles near surfaces according to Rayleigh's original theoretical analysis (top) and more likely mechanism as observed experimentally using high-speed cameras (bottom). In such controlled experiments, bubbles are nucleated near surfaces by focusing the intense light from a laser beam just above the surface, or by applying a brief high-voltage electric spark in the liquid (usually water).

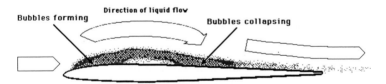

Fig. 2. Flow stream of water and bubbles across the top surface of a hydrofoil as ascertained in water tunnel experiments. The bubbles usually form towards the leading edge after which they are transported towards the trailing edge where they impinge violently on the surface, collapse and disappear, causing microscopic damage pits.

(whether due to hydrostatic, mechanical or viscous forces) and how it is transmitted to and subsequently released from a bubble, is important in determining when and where damage will occur in different systems, and (2) that there is therefore no unique time during a bubble's life when it causes cavitation damage.

Less direct, but more detailed information has been gained in laboratory experiments in which high-voltage electric sparks or pulsed laser beams are used to artificially nucleate individual bubbles at specific locations within a liquid close to a surface. Their subsequent time evolution is then recorded with a high-speed camera attached to an optical microscope [4, 5]. What one typically sees in such experiments is illustrated in Fig. 1 (bottom part), where the bubble forms and collapses in the same place. The whole growth and collapse processes usually occurs very rapidly ($10^{-6}$ to $10^{-3}$ s), and all of the interesting features have submicroscopic dimensions. After the experiments, the surfaces are examined for damage, usually using an electron microscope since the damage is too small to be seen as it occurs. These studies have so far not been able to determine exactly at what stage of the inception–growth–collapse cycle of bubbles that damage occurs [6], though it is generally believed that it occurs only during the collapse stage [4–7]. That high stresses are transmitted during a bubble's brief life have been ascertained by recording the noise (acoustically) as well as the shock waves (optically) emanating from the cavitation zone. It is noteworthy, however, that shock waves can also be seen as a bubble nucleates (Fig. 3), and not only during their collapse.

A further noteworthy aspect of such experiments is that the energy of forming the bubbles is transmitted to the liquid via light or an electric shock. This is very different from the kinetic energy arising from fluid flow in hydrofoils, or from the viscous shear energy of two rapidly moving surface as occurs in a thin liquid film. In the former situations the nearby surfaces are not involved in the bubble formation, while in the latter they are intimately involved (since it is through these surfaces or boundaries that the energy is supplied to nucleate the bubbles). Unfortunately, most experiments are designed to focus almost entirely on the collapse stage, with very little attention given to the growth stage. Thus, there is very little published data on the shock waves, noise generated, elastohydrodynamic surface deformations and other potentially important information on the inception of cavities.

The subject has also received much theoretical attention, but it has proved too difficult to arrive at a general theory that satisfactorily accounts for many of the observed phenomena [6, 8]. As in the case of the experiments, most theoretical treatments start from the point where cavities or gas bubbles are already present in the liquid, and then attempt to determine the course and consequence of their collapse. Curiously, little theoretical or experimental attention appears to have been given to how bubbles form under natural conditions, and the effects of the first shock wave produced by the rapidly growing bubbles [6]. The general consensus is that nothing very dramatic occurs when bubbles grow since the energy or stresses needed are generally low (witness the ease with which small air bubbles form on a glass surface in contact with water). While this is true, it is also the case that most cavitation damage is not caused by such lethargic bubbles, but by others that have been produced with a much greater and a more sudden input of energy.

Most experiments and theory have focused on single, isolated surfaces, and there is surprisingly little information on the relation between cavitation and wear during lubricated sliding or in tribological processes in general. During the course of our studies on the friction, lubrication and elastohydrodynamic deformations of two surfaces using the surface forces apparatus (SFA) technique [9], we noticed that when two

34

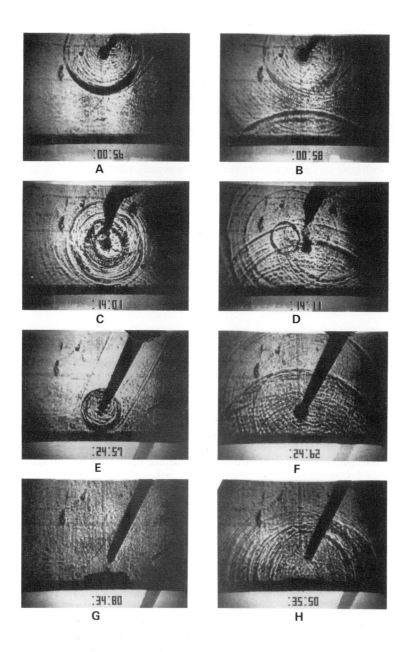

Fig. 3. Shock waves produced during inception (nucleation) and collapse of vapour bubbles in water near a surface. The bubbles were produced by the generation of a high-voltage spark. Time scale: 00:02 unit corresponds to about $10^{-6}$ s. A, B: inception at 4.8 mm from surface. C, D: collapse away from surface. E, F: inception at 1.1 mm from surface. G, H: collapse on surface. [Taken from a video recording by Professor Ellis of University of California, San Diego, who kindly loaned it to the authors and in whose possession it remained on Professor Ellis' recent death. The authors will gladly supply a copy of the tape to anyone interested.]

initially curved surfaces are rapidly moved towards or away from each other in a liquid, a vapour cavity often develops between the surfaces. Since the SFA technique [10] enables one to record how vapour or liquid cavities form between two surfaces [13] as well as how the surfaces deform in real time at the nanometer level [11, 12], we decided to study the phenomenon of cavitation and cavitation damage in more detail.

## 2. Experimental methods

The SFA with its molecular smooth surfaces and ångstrom resolution capability has been extensively used to measure the forces between surfaces in vapours and liquids, as well as for measuring various adhesion and tribological phenomena involving model (molecularly smooth) surfaces. The optical interference technique, using "fringes of equal chromatic order" (FECO), allows one to measure not only the distance between the two surfaces at any point to within 1 Å [10, 12], but also their changing shape with time [11] and the evolution of liquid bridges and vapour cavities [13, 14] between the surfaces. This technique is therefore particularly suitable for observing exactly when and where cavities form and collapse and where damage occurs in relation to these processes. By using liquids of very high viscosities we have found that all of these processes can be slowed down so that detailed video recordings [11] of these events could be made.

A conventional SFA was used with two separate video cameras (Fig. 4). One was used as a normal optical microscope for directly viewing the surfaces, while the other monitored the moving FECO fringes. The former provided a top view of the two opposing surfaces and of the cavities between them, and the latter provided ångstrom-scale resolution of surface profiles and refractive index discontinuities in the liquid

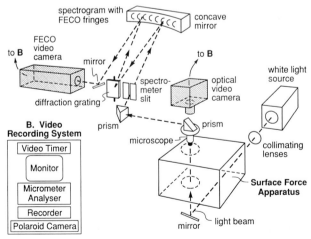

Fig. 4. Surface forces apparatus (SFA) system showing path of light and location of two video cameras for visualizing the region between the two surfaces. Optical video camera: for recording top view of moving surfaces in transmitted white light. FECO video camera: for recording the moving FECO fringes. Video recording system (B): receives output from cameras for monitoring, recording (storing) and analyzing video pictures.

[10, 13, 14]. The liquids used were pure hydrocarbons of polybutadiene (PBD) with molecular weight in the range $4 \times 10^3$ to $10 \times 10^3$ and viscosities in the range 10 to 180 P [15]. These "oils" were found to be particularly suitable for these experiments since they are chemically inert hydrocarbons, transparent to visible light, and available in a wide range of viscosities that exhibit no non-Newtonian behavior in the range of shear rates used in these experiments [15]. They were kindly provided by Dr. Lew Fetter of Exxon Research and Engineering Co., Clinton, NJ, USA.

The two surfaces were arranged to face each other in a crossed cylinder configuration. Because the radius $R$ of each surface ($\approx 1$ cm) is much greater than their separation $D$, this geometry is equivalent to a sphere near a flat surface or to two spheres close together. A large droplet of the liquid was injected between the two curved surfaces, and the atmosphere inside the chamber was controlled so that the gases dissolved in the liquids were either atmospheric air, dry nitrogen, no gases at all, or water. The molecularly smooth surfaces were either bare mica (a high-energy polar surface having strong adhesion to the liquid — ref. 17), or surfactant-coated mica (a low-energy inert hydrocarbon surface having weak adhesion to the liquid).

Some experiments were conducted using a SFA equipped with a sliding attachment for tribological studies [22]. With this attachment, one surface can be slid (sheared) laterally past the other, while simultaneously measuring the normal force, the frictional force, the sliding velocity, the surface separation (film thickness) to $\pm 1$ Å, the exact contact area when the two surfaces are parallel to each other over the contact zone or, when they are not parallel, their elastically deformed shapes. Only some preliminary results obtained with this attachment will be described here.


## 3. Results

### 3.1. Stresses and strains at low speed

We first describe the stresses and resulting deformations experienced by two surfaces approaching or separating from each other at low to intermediate velocities in a normal (Newtonian) liquid. In these experiments the curved surfaces are initially brought together at a constant driving velocity $v$ (typically between 0.01 and 5 mm s$^{-1}$ in our experiments). As the liquid between the two surfaces is squeezed out at a progressively increasing rate, the viscous forces acting on the surfaces increase. The material supporting the surfaces (mica sheets, glue layer, glass discs) responds by becoming elastically compressed ("elastohydrodynamically" deformed). This manifests itself as a flattening of the surfaces which therefore slows down their approach towards each other. The surface separation at which flattening begins depends on the elastic modulus of the underlying material, on the velocity of approach, and on the viscosity of the liquid. In our experiments flattening of the surfaces was observed to start at some finite surface separation of $D = 10$ to 200 nm.

On separating two surfaces from close approach, they again undergo elastohydrodynamic deformations, but these are different from those on approach (*i.e.* the surfaces do not retrace their path). These deformations are now characterized by a bulging outward, rather than inward, and it is this feature that becomes important for cavitation (discussed below).

The general features described above were found to be the same for all the surfaces and liquids studied, and are shown in Fig. 5.

Initially (Fig. 5(A)) the surfaces approach each other at a steady velocity $v$ but do not deform. When the surfaces are about 50 nm apart (Fig. 5(B)) they begin to slow down relative to each other due to the flattening/compression of the supporting material. From Figs. 5(B) to 5(C) the surfaces bulge inward, that is, they become "bell-shaped" — a characteristic feature of elastohydrodynamic deformations of two approaching surfaces [16]. At Fig. 5(C) the driving velocity was reduced to zero, so that from Figs. 5(C) to 5(D) the surfaces relax naturally to equilibrium. The surfaces end up in a flattened configuration at an equilibrium separation of $D=5$ nm, this value being determined by a short-range repulsive force between the two surfaces across the liquid film [17].

The reverse process of separating two surfaces after they have been brought together is shown in Figs. 5(E) to 5(F). We immediately note that the way the surfaces deform back to their original curved shapes is not simply by reversing the path taken on approach — a phenomenon that does not appear to have been much studied or its importance fully appreciated. In addition, when two surfaces are separated in liquid, two different paths can be taken depending on the speed of the separation: the first does not involve the formation of cavities and occurs at low velocities, the second does involve the formation of cavities and occurs above some critical velocity at which the surfaces are separated (pulled apart). We first consider the low velocity case.

At low speeds ($v < 0.1$ $\mu$m s$^{-1}$), the separation is "continuous" or "smooth", as shown in Figs. 5(E)–5(H). During separation the initially flattened mica surfaces go through a stage where they become pointed, that is where they bulge outward. Actually, the surfaces do not really bulge outward (even though it appears so); but rather the outermost regions of the contact zone come away from each other much faster than do the innermost (closest) regions, which remain almost unmoved. The net effect is that the surfaces become increasingly more pointed in shape. Eventually, the closest regions start moving apart, and these now accelerate very rapidly as they try to "catch up" with the furthermost regions. As the two surfaces move away their shape thus becomes less pointed as it returns to the original undeformed shape.

Judging from the surface deformation during the approach–separation cycle, it appears that the most highly strained region is where the surfaces are closest to each other and pointed. It is also noteworthy that maximum pointedness occurs just before these regions begin to move apart (Fig. 5(F)). We may expect, therefore, that this is also the place and time where the surfaces and the liquid experience their maximum (tensile) stress.

### 3.2. Stresses and strains at high speed

If the speed of separation is increased, the surfaces become increasingly more pointed just before they rapidly move apart. Then, above some critical speed $v_c$ (here about 1 $\mu$m s$^{-1}$) a completely new separation mechanism takes over, as shown in Figs. 6 and 7. Instead of separating smoothly, the liquid "fractures" or "cracks" open like a solid. It is known that when subjected to very high shear rates, liquids begin to behave mechanically like solids, for example fracturing like a brittle solid [18]. In our experiments, the point and time at which this "fracture" occurred was just as the surfaces were about to separate from their most highly pointed configuration (Fig. 6(B)) — for had the separation velocity been any smaller than $v_c$ they would have separated smoothly without fracturing. We consider that in the present case, the "fracturing" or "cracking" of the liquid between the surfaces must be considered as synonymous with the "nucleation" or "inception" of a vapour cavity.

Many things all happen at the same time immediately following the nucleation of the cavity. The surfaces now find themselves separated by a region of vapour (of low viscosity) rather than liquid, so that the inertia to motion is suddenly much reduced.

38

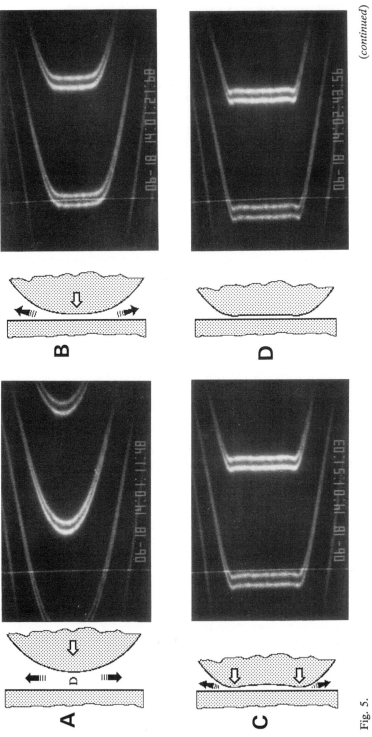

Fig. 5.

*(continued)*

39

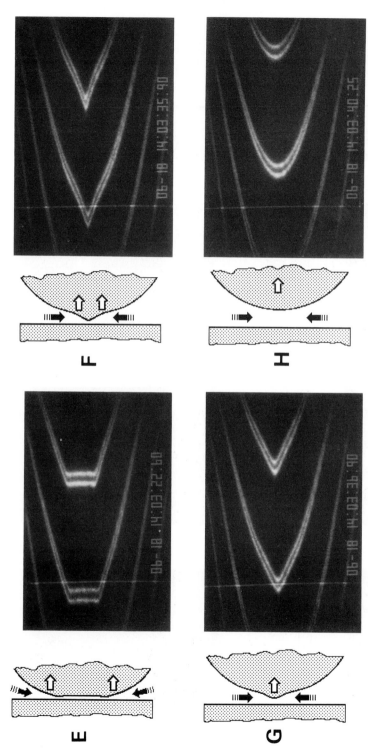

Fig. 5. Changing FECO fringe pattern with time as two curved surfaces with initial (undeformed) radii of $R \approx 1$ cm approach then separate from each other in liquid polybutadiene (PBD, viscosity 180 P) at a driving velocity of $v = 0.02$ $\mu$m s$^{-1}$. No cavities or surface damage occur at this low velocity ($v < v_c$). The shapes of the FECO fringes (white fringes on dark background) give the distance $D$ between the two surfaces and the surface profiles on approach and separation, which are shown schematically by the line drawings. Approach: A ($t = 0$ s, $D = 109$ nm), B ($t = 10.2$ s, $D = 40.6$ nm), C ($t = 39.55$ s, $D = 27.3$ nm), D ($t = 92.08$ s, $D = 21.7$ nm). Separation: E ($t = 131.12$ s, $D = 22$ nm), F ($t = 144.42$ s, $D = 22$ nm), G ($t = 145.42$ s, $D = 40.6$ nm), H ($t = 148.77$ s, $D = 97$ nm). Note that the highest stresses on both the surfaces and liquid probably occurs at the highly pointed central region in F.

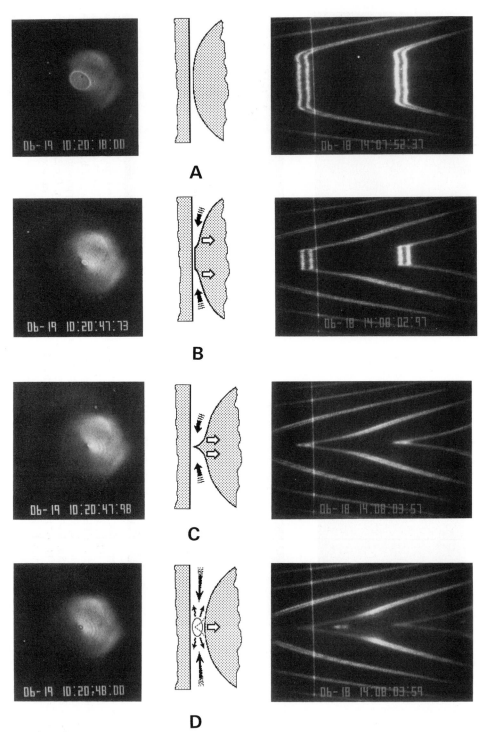

Fig. 6.

(*continued*)

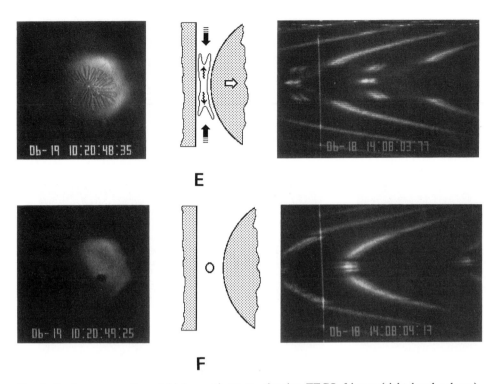

Fig. 6. Surfaces separating at high speed, $v > v_c$, showing FECO fringes (right hand column), schematic side-view (middle column), and optical microscope view (left hand column) of surfaces. Homogeneous nucleation of vapour cavity occurs at D ($t = 0$ s) which grows rapidly then collapses, as shown in more detail in Fig. 7. Note that at F ($t = 1.25$ s after inception) the cavity has still not totally disappeared (evaporated or collapsed).

This allows the high tensile stresses acting on both the solid and the liquid to be relaxed. Accordingly, the pointed surfaces suddenly snap back to their original rounded shape. The gap between the two recoiling surfaces therefore increases and this causes (i) the cavity to grow, and (ii) more liquid to rush in. The growing cavity surface is therefore met by in-rushing liquid and, since the viscosity of the liquid is much higher than that of the vapour, the surface of the cavity fingers its way into the liquid. All this happens in a split second, as shown in Figs. 6 and 7 where a 100 nm thick and $> 10$ $\mu$m wide cavity formed so rapidly that the whole process described above appeared on the same frame of our 0.02 s resolution video recording.

No such dramatic changes were observed after the bubbles formed. Instead, the fingers slowly retracted until the cavities became rounded, after which they slowly disappear ("collapse") but with no noticeable surface deformations. In fact, the surfaces could be moved towards each other before the bubbles had collapsed so that they were forced out to some place well away from the "contact zone".

Clearly, in this system, the stresses released by the growing cavities and the simultaneous impact pressures developed by the recoiling surfaces must be much higher than any implosion or jet impact pressure of the subsequently collapsing bubbles.

When the speed of separating two surfaces is increased further to well above $v_c$, the outermost surface regions now peel away so rapidly that it is here that the

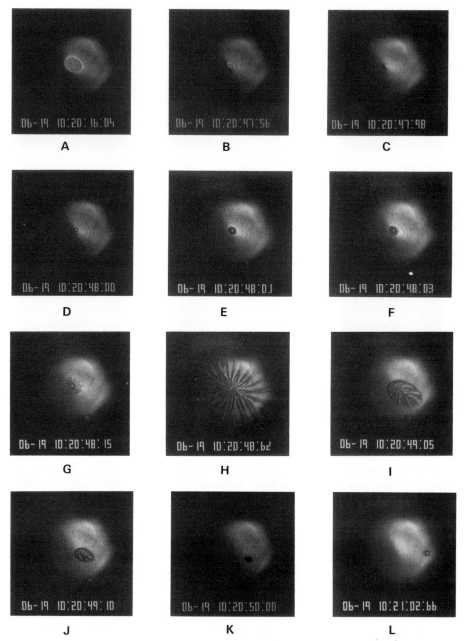

Fig. 7. Top view showing details of growth and collapse stages of Fig. 6. A to C: decrease in "contact" area. D: inception of spherical bubble at centre at $t = 0$ s. E: Rapid growth of bubble to a diameter of 30 $\mu$m at $t = 0.01$ s after inception. F to G: onset of fingering instability (dendritic growth). H: bubble continues to grow mainly via finger-like protrusions, reaching its maximum size at $t = 0.6$ s after inception. I to J: rapid collapse of bubble (retraction of fingers) until spherical shape is regained at about $t = 1.2$ s after inception. K to L: much slower collapse of now spherical bubble ($> 10$ s) as it drifts away from contact zone.

bifurcation becomes most sharp, i.e. "pointed" along a circle. Cavitation now occurs on this circle even before the elastically deforming surfaces have reached the centrally pointed stage (Fig. 8, top row). At the instant of cavitation the surface geometry is like that of two circular craters, one turned over the other, and it is now the rims of the craters that snap back, leaving behind a doughnut-shaped cavity. This cavity rapidly coalesces into a single disc-like cavity while simultaneously growing outwards by fingering as before. Time-lapse optical microscope photographs of these collapsing cavities are shown in Fig. 8, bottom row. It is interesting that very similar rosette-shaped cavities as shown in Figs. 6 to 8 have previously been photographed by Dowson and Taylor on a similar but more macroscopic system [19].

### 3.3. Effects of different surfaces

The processes just described indicate that, at sufficiently high separation speeds, two contacting surfaces deform elastically such that maximum negative pressure is reached either at the centre or at some finite radial distance from the center. It is at these places where the surfaces snap back (recoil), where cavities form (but do not necessarily collapse), and where damage occurs (as described below). It is important to stress that the two about-to-be-separated surfaces do not have to be in contact for all this to happen. All the above is true even if they are not in true contact but are separated by a very thin film of liquid. The thicker the initial film thickness the higher the value of $v_c$, and we have found it possible to nucleate cavities even when the surfaces were moved apart from an initial separation distance of $>100$ Å.

We have found that cavitation bubbles can occur either totally within the liquid, that is away from the surfaces, or at the solid/liquid interfaces. In the case of untreated (polar) mica surfaces, previous studies have shown that PBD liquids "wet" mica, which indicates that the adhesion of PBD to mica is stronger than its cohesion to itself. Indeed, two mica surfaces immersed in PBD strongly repel each other at short-range ($D<30$–100 Å), again indicative of strong bonding of the liquid to these surfaces. It is probably for this reason that all the cavities so far described formed totally within the liquid. This was ascertained by the ease with which they could be "pushed out" from between the surfaces, and — more directly — by the observation that when two surfaces were brought together with a cavity between them the short-range forces remained as before, a clear indication that a thin (but $>50$ Å thick) film of liquid was still present on the mica surfaces.

In contrast, when the mica surfaces are coated with a surfactant monolayer, they now expose non-polar, low-energy hydrocarbon groups that adhere only weakly to the PBD liquids [20]. With such surfaces, we have found the cavities now form at the interfaces, as shown in Fig. 9, which bridge the two surfaces in the same way as does a capillary condensed liquid or vapour bridge [13, 14]. When two such surfaces are connected by a cavity, they can now be brought into true molecular contact (at $D=0$) as shown in Fig. 9(A). The ability to do this enables one to quickly ascertain whether cavities have formed within the liquid film or attached to the surfaces.

### 3.4. Effects of water in the oil: heterogeneous nucleation of cavities

We have also made some preliminary studies on the effects of changing the nature of the liquid — in this case by introducing some water into the PBD liquid. Water and PBD are highly incompatible, the one being highly polar, the other a highly non-polar oil. Their mutual solubility has not been measured but is probably no higher than 100 ppm. When water is present in hydrocarbon liquids it migrates to any nearby polar surfaces, such as mica. This has three important effects that are relevant to the

44

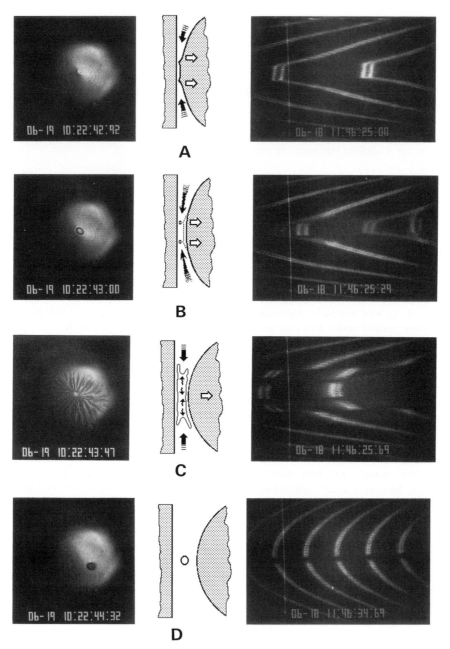

Fig. 8. Surface geometry and shapes of growing cavities at sufficiently high separation speeds ($v \gg v_c$) where toroidal-shaped cavities form around, rather than at the centre, of the contact zone. Such doughnut-shaped cavities rapidly coalesce into a single disc-like cavity as before, after which they proceed to grow and collapse also as before. B: surfaces snap back at the circular rim where the cavity initially forms; this is also where damage occurs (see later). C: coalescence of toroid into single dendritic cavity that grows as in Figs. 6 and 7, reaching maximum bubble size at $t=0.5$ s. D: remnant bubble after rapid collapse.

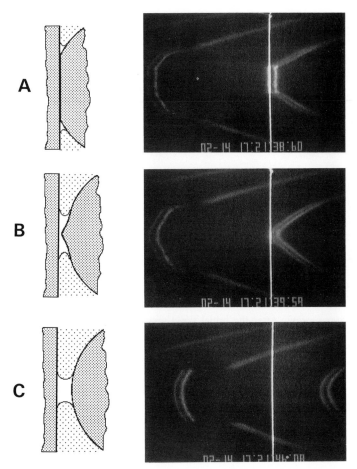

Fig. 9. Growth of vapour cavities between two low-energy hydrocarbon surfaces. The cavities "dewet" the surfaces and so remain attached to them as they grow and collapse. A: vapour annulus condenses at contact rim. B to C: vapour cavity bridging two surfaces during snap-back and subsequent growth of cavity.

cavitation and tribological mechanisms being considered here: first, a thin water film (often no more than 3–6 Å thick) forms at the mica–oil interface; second, this film is highly lubricious (its frictional coefficient is as low as ice, namely $\simeq 0.03$); and third, by the mere presence of another component in the liquid, our system has become a two-component system and so, by definition, any nucleation process must now be considered as being heterogeneous rather than homogeneous.

The thin lubricating water film enabled the PBD liquid to flow in or out of the gap between two surfaces much faster than in the absence of water. In effect, the water appeared to change the boundary conditions from non-slip to slip. This meant that under the same conditions as in the absence of water (e.g. same driving velocity) much lower stresses and strains were generated. Thus, the hydrodynamic deformations were now much less, and cavities did not form until much higher velocities were used. Once formed, the cavities quickly filled with water vapour and then bulk water which then proceeded to bridge the two surfaces (Fig. 10). The situation was thus similar

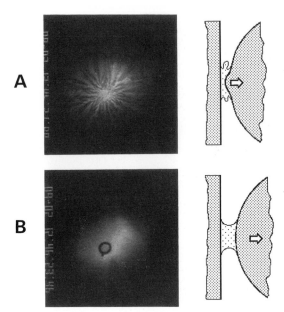

Fig. 10. Cavitation with water present. After the initial rapid growth and collapse phases, the remnant bubble disappears much more slowly as bulk liquid and saturated vapour diffuse slowly out of the bubble into the bulk liquid and onto the surfaces.

to that shown in Fig. 9, except that the bridge was one of water. The water bridges would eventually disappear by diffusing back into the liquid and the surfaces, but this took a long time (many minutes). It was not possible to initiate surface damage in this experiment, and all the processes proceeded much more slowly than in the absence of water in the oil.

### 3.5. Cavitation damage

Damage was generally seen to occur only during the formation of cavities, when the surfaces recoil, but not during the collapse of cavities, nor at the place of collapse. This was ascertained in two ways:

(1) At high separation velocities, when cavities occurred at the center of the contact zone, the surfaces could be brought back together again before the bubbles had disappeared. From the deformed shapes of the FECO fringes (Figs. 11(A)–11(C)), one could discern that two initially undamaged surfaces were already damaged at the center. Additionally, the bubbles usually moved to another place before disappearing, though without causing any discernable damage there.

(2) At even higher separation speeds where cavities formed in a ring around the contact region, this was also the region where damage occurred (Figs. 11(D)–11(F)). As previously mentioned, when doughnut-shaped cavities formed at $v \gg v_c$ they immediately coalesced into a single disc-like cavity, after which they collapsed in the same way as cavities that were not initially doughnut-shaped ($v > v_c$). Thus, the collapse process was generally the same regardless of the initial shape of the cavity, and yet the shape of the damage reflected the initial cavity shape. These observations clearly indicate that the surface damage is caused at some very early stage of a cavity's life.

One may well ask whether the damage could have preceded the inception of cavities, indeed even be the cause of cavity formation. Given the very high local

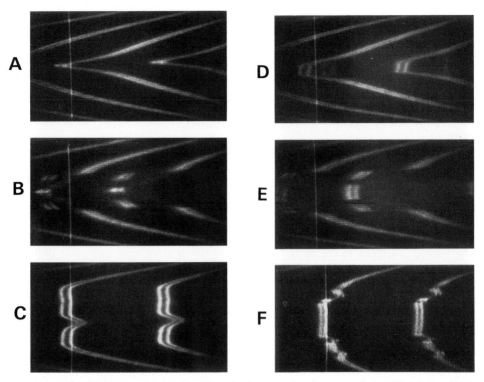

Fig. 11. Erosion damage, seen as irregular ripples on otherwise smooth FECO fringes which show a cut through the centre of the contact zone. A to C: damage occurs at the centre of the contact zone when $v \geqslant v_c$. Note that the fringes are smooth except for the "bump" at the centre, which represents a damaged flake about 500 Å high. D to F: damage occurring on a circular rim around the centre when $v \gg v_c$. The fringes are now smooth in the central region but rippled on either side of the centre.

elastohydrodynamic stresses on the surfaces one could imagine that these surfaces could crack, thereby exposing sharp edges that would be ideal sites for nucleating cavities. Two observations argue against this scenario. First, damage did not occur every time a cavity formed. This indicates that damage does not cause nor does it precede cavitation. Second, as already mentioned, between bare mica surfaces the cavities formed totally within the liquid; again, this would be inconsistent with a direct surface-induced cavitation mechanism.

Thus, our experiments show that the time that damage is caused in relation to cavity formation, it appears that both occur simultaneously (within the resolution of our experiments), coinciding with the sudden snap-back or recoil of the surfaces.

## 4. Discussion and conclusions

One way of describing our results is as follows: When two curved surfaces are moving away from each other at high speed in a liquid, a large negative pressure builds up in the region where the surfaces are closest to each other. This tensile pressure acts both on the liquid and on the surfaces, causing them to bulge outward (towards the liquid). If these stresses are sufficiently high, either the surface or the liquid will fracture or "crack" open like a solid. If the fracture occurs in the liquid, it will propagate in different directions, including towards the surfaces and when it reaches a surface it may or may not continue into the bulk material. All this happens in a split second. After the damage has been done and all stresses have been released, the "crack" in the liquid quickly changes its shape into a normal rounded bubble, while the surface is condemned to remain in its damaged state. The bubble may then move away and/or "collapse", but generally not with the same impact as heralded its birth.

Our results indicate that bubbles often collapse in two stages, depending on the presence of dissolved solute molecules in the cavitating liquid. When a cavity initially forms and grows explosively, it is essentially a vacuum cavity since no dissolved solute molecules or gases have had time to enter into the rapidly growing cavity. During the growth and collapse process, these molecules have time to enter into the bubble, which arrests the final collapse phase. From our observations, this arrest appears to occur fairly abruptly once the bubble has shrunk to some small but finite size. After this, the bubble continues to shrink but much more slowly since now molecular diffusion out of the bubble determines the collapse rate.

By analyzing the shapes of the FECO fringes, it should be possible to determine the profiles of the deformed surfaces, and from that obtain all the strains and stresses on the surfaces (and adjacent liquid) during any part of the cavitation cycle. We hope to do that in the near future, along the lines of ref. 12. Qualitatively, the greatest stresses are expected to occur at the most sharply curved regions, for example the tips of the surfaces in Figs. 5 and 6, where we estimate the local pressure to be a few hundred atmospheres. It would also be useful to have electron microscope pictures of the damaged regions, to ascertain the nature of the damage and whether it fits in with the idea of a crack propagating into the surface, or peeling (delamination) damage, whether some healing is occurring (none was ever observed in our experiments), etc.

In the case of two surfaces sliding (shearing) laterally past each other, rather than moving towards or away from each other, our initial results using the friction attachment of the SFA is that elastohydrodynamic deformations occur even at the submicroscopic level (Fig. 12), which may have important consequences for our understanding of the mechanism of cavitation damage in such situations.

Even when no damage occurs at rapidly moving surfaces, our results show that large elastohydrodynamic deformations may be occurring at the submicroscopic level. Since the surface material is likely to be imperfectly elastic, *i.e.* to exhibit some energy dissipating hysteresis, then even in the absence of damage there could be a significant loss of energy and/or a drop in efficiency. Put in purely thermodynamic terms, this type of "irreversible" process manifests itself in the dissipation of nonrecoverable heat, but with no visible sign of material or structural change, whereas the irreversibility caused when damage occurs is both thermal and mechanical.

Our findings and their interpretations are somewhat contrary to the conventional explanation of how cavitation damage is caused, *i.e.* during bubble collapse. However, since much less work is done on cavitation in thin films than on single surfaces adjacent to bulk liquid (whether stationary or flowing as in water tunnels), there is really no reason to believe that the same mechanism should be operating in both systems. In fact, one important difference between cavitation in thin films and in water tunnels is that in the former the microscopically shearing protrusions may well result in homogeneous cavitation rather than heterogeneous cavitation as is more usual when larger areas and volumes are involved. Since homogeneous nucleation is generally

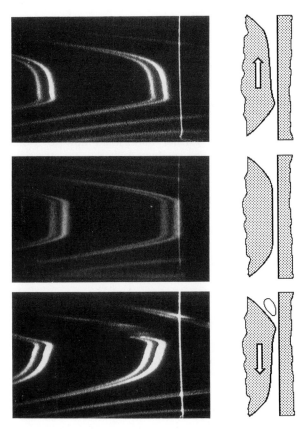

Fig. 12. Surface deformations and cavitation during the sliding of two surfaces. Centre: stationary surfaces. Top: surfaces sliding at low speed. Bottom: surfaces sliding at high speed where the (transient) discontinuity in the FECO fringes indicates a discontinuity in the refractive index in the film, and thus to cavity growth (and collapse) just behind the trailing end. The pointed trailing region of two shearing surfaces may be thought of as two receding surfaces, as in the geometry of the earlier figures. It is interesting that it is in this region that cavitation bubbles have previously been observed to occur [19].

associated with much larger stresses, these can now cause damage that may be absent under different experimental conditions.

Basically, what our results suggest is that both the birth and death of cavities are traumatic events, and that damage may be caused at either stage.

Another difference between thin film cavitation and the type usually studied lies in the way that the energy is transmitted to the liquid to produce the cavities. This may be just as important as the way in which the energy is dissipated when the bubbles collapse. It is reasonable to expect that if the energy is transmitted to the liquid through the surfaces, then this energy could be greater than that subsequently transmitted back again to the surfaces. In such situations, one would expect the greatest shock to occur at the beginning rather than the end of the cavitation process. This is the situation that applies to many tribological processes. On the other hand, when bubbles acquire their energy in a liquid from a different source, for example from electric

50

sparks, highly focused light beams or by being accelerated in a rapidly flowing liquid, then the energy they release on collapsing onto a surface may well exceed any energy they received from a surface during their formation.

It must not be forgotten that cavitation damage on extended surfaces often occurs throughout the surface, and not only where bubbles collapse. For example, while most damage of hydrofoils and rotor blades appears at the downstream end of the bubble cloud (Fig. 2), there is often a significant amount also at the leading edge, where the bubbles are formed (see, for example, Fig. 1 in ref. 4).

In conclusion, our findings suggest that to further understand how to avoid cavitation damage new types of experiments need to be conducted where more attention is given to the elastohydrodynamic deformations of surfaces not only during but also before, and in the absence of, cavity formation. The new mechanism suggested here most likely applies to tribological processes more than it does to other processes where cavitation damage occurs, and it implicates the importance of the material and wettability properties of surfaces and any surface-active additives in the lubricating liquids, all of which determine where bubbles are most likely to occur and the stresses associated with their inception.

## Acknowledgments

We thank L. J. Fetters and Exxon Research Labs for providing the PBD liquids, and the Office of Naval Research for supporting this work under research grant N00014-89-J-1101.

## References

1 Lord Rayleigh, *Philos. Mag., 34* (1917) 94.
2 T. B. Benjamin and A. T. Ellis, *Philos. Trans. R. Soc. London, Ser. A, 260* (1966) 221.
3 R. T. Knapp, J. W. Daily and F. G. Hammitt, *Cavitation,* McGraw-Hill, New York, 1970, ch. 8; J. H. J. Van der Meulen and Y. Nakashima, in *Cavitation,* S. P. Hutton (ed.), Mechanical Engineering Publishers, London, 1983, pp. 13–19; R. Simoneau, F. Avellan and Y. Kuhn de Chizelle, *Int. Symp. on Cavitation Noise and Erosion in Fluid Systems,* R. E. A. Arndt (ed.), ASME, New York, 1989, vol. 88, pp. 95–102.
4 J. R. Blake and D. C. Gibson, *Ann. Rev. Fluid Mech., 19* (1987) 99–123.
5 D. H. Trevena, *Cavitation and Tension in Liquids,* Adam Hilger, Bristol, 1987, Chap. 6 and 8.
6 A. Vogel, W. Lauterborn and R. Timm, *J. Fluid Mech., 206* (1989) 299; Y. Tomita and A. Shima, *J. Fluid Mech., 169* (1986) 535.
7 P. A. Lush, *J. Fluid Mech., 135* (1983) 373.
8 S. Fujikawa and T. Akamatsu, *J. Fluid. Mech., 97* (1980) 481.
9 J. N. Israelachvili and G. E. Adams, *J. Chem. Soc. Faraday Trans. I, 74* (1978) 975.
10 J. Israelachvili, *Nature, 229* (1971) 4, 85; J. N. Istraelachvili, *J. Colloid Interface Sci., 44* (1973) 259.
11 C. A. Helm, J. N. Israelachvili and P. M. McGuiggan, *Science, 246* (1989) 919.
12 R. G. Horn, J. N. Israelachvili and F. Pribac, *J. Colloid Interface Sci., 115* (1987) 480.
13 H. K. Christenson and P. M. Claesson, *Science, 239* (1988) 390.
14 L. R. Fisher and J. N. Israelachvili, *Colloid Surf., 3* (1981) 303; H. K. Christenson, *J. Colloid Interface Sci., 104* (1985) 234.

15 R. H. Colby, L. J. Fetters and W. W. Graessly, *Macromolecules, 20* (1987) 2226.
16 R. Gohar, *Elastohydrodynamics,* Horwood, Chichester, 1988; D. Dowson and G. R. Higginson, *Elasto-hydrodynamic Lubrication,* Pergamon, Oxford, 1977.
17 J. N. Israelachvili and S. J. Kott, *J. Chem. Phys., 88* (1988) 7162.
18 J. C. Fisher, *J. Appl. Phys., 19* (1948) 1062.
19 D. Dowson and C. M. Taylor, *Ann. Rev. Fluid Mech., 11* (1979) 35.
20 H. W. Strube and W. Lauterborn, *Z. Angew. Phys., 29* (1970) 349.

*Wear, 153* (1992) 53–64

# Elastic–plastic contact model for bifractal surfaces

B. Bhushan

*Computer Microtribology and Contamination Laboratory, Department of Mechanical Engineering, Ohio State University, Columbus, OH 43210 (USA)*

A. Majumdar

*Department of Mechanical and Aerospace Engineering, Arizona State University, Tempe, AZ 85287 (USA)*

(Received July 28, 1991)

## Abstract

Roughness measurements by atomic force microscopy have shown that the surfaces of magnetic tapes follow two different regimes of fractal structure. For such *bifractal* surfaces, this paper presents an elastic–plastic contact model. The theory is used to predict the real area of contact of a magnetic tape in contact with a flat hard plane. The trends of both the theory and experiments are in agreement. The theoretical predictions show that for contact pressures between 1 kPa and $10^4$ kPa, the fraction of real area of contact in elastic deformation is about 90%. This is in agreement with experimental observations.

## 1. Introduction

The phenomenon of contact between two rough surfaces is of fundamental importance in the study of friction, wear, lubrication, frictional heating, seals and thermal and electrical contact resistance. Unless carefully prepared most surfaces are rough, with roughness appearing random and disordered [1] and ranging from atomic scales [2] to the size of the object. The presence of surface roughness leads to an imperfect contact resulting in the real area of contact being a fraction of the apparent or the nominal area. In all the above applications, the prediction of the real area of contact and the size and spatial distributions of contact spots as a function of the applied load is a basic problem.

Since most surfaces appear random in structure, statistical parameters such as the standard deviations of the surface height $\sigma$, slope $\sigma'$ and curvature $\sigma''$ are conventionally used for characterizing surface roughness. Based on these parameters, several theories have been developed to model the contact mechanics of two rough surfaces. The most widely used one is that proposed by Greenwood and Williamson [3] in which they assumed the model surface to be composed of hemispherical asperities, all having the radius equal to $1/\sigma''$, with their centers distributed normally about the mean plane. Based on this model, several other theories on friction, wear and lubrication have been developed [4]. Recent experiments have shown, however, that the statistical parameters $\sigma$, $\sigma'$ and $\sigma''$ are not unique to a surface and depend on the resolution and the scan length of the roughness-measuring instrument [5–7]. As an example, consider the data in Fig. 1 for a magnetic tape surface, which shows the dependence of these parameters on surface magnification on the instrument resolution [7]. The

0043-1648/92/$5.00

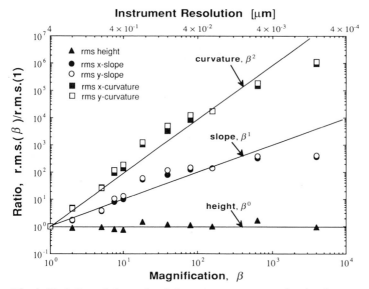

Fig. 1. Variation of the ratio of the root mean square (rms) values at a surface magnification $\beta > 0$ to the corresponding root mean square values at a magnification of unity, with magnification $\beta$. The data for $\beta \leq 10$ were obtained by optical measurements and those for $\beta \geq 10$ were obtained by AFM [7].

strong resolution dependence of $\sigma'$ and $\sigma''$ clearly shows an inadequacy of the conventional statistical methods to characterize surface roughness. This, in turn, is reflected on the resolution dependence of the predictions of the classical theories of contact [6, 7]. Therefore, the assumption of a surface being composed of hemispherical asperities all of a *single* scale, is an over-simplification of a real surface which contains several roughness scales. The question of which range of roughness scales is important for contact mechanics, however, has not yet been answered. Therefore, in all fairness, one must consider all scales of roughness to model contact between two surfaces.

To rectify the problem of instrument-dependent roughness parameters, a new method based on *fractal geometry* has recently been developed [8, 9]. This method is based on the experimental observations which reveal that when a rough surface is repeatedly magnified the roughness at one scale appears very similar to the roughness at other scales. The fractal method uses the concept of non-integer dimensions to characterize this scale-invariant behavior of surface roughness. The advantages of the fractal characterization are, firstly, the roughness parameters are scale-independent, and secondly, the details of roughness at all scales can be easily determined. This is of primary importance in studying any surface phenomenon at the relevant length scales.

Based on the fractal characterization, Majumdar and Bhushan [10] have developed a model of contact which considers the roughness at all scales. The model predicts that the real area of contact $A_r$ and the load $F$ are related by a power law, $A_r \propto F^n$ where the exponent $n$ is a function of the fractal dimension. It was assumed in the model that the fractal characterization parameters remain constant at all length scales. However, recent measurements by atomic force microscopy (AFM) have shown that some surfaces show two fractal regimes at different length scales [7]. To study the contact mechanics of such *bifractal* surfaces, this paper generalizes the original fractal model. The paper first briefly discusses the fractal characterization of surface roughness. Details of the fractal method can be found in papers by Majumdar and Bhushan [9] and Majumdar *et al.* [11]. The contact model of bifractal surfaces is then developed. Finally, the predictions are compared with experiments.

## 2. Fractal characterization

Roughness measurements by instruments of different resolutions have shown that when a surface profile $z(x)$ is repeatedly magnified, more and more roughness keeps appearing as shown in Fig. 2 [1, 6, 12]. Unless artificially textured, the roughness appears disordered and random. Due to the multiscale nature of surface roughness, a profile $z(x)$ can be considered to be composed of a superposition of waves of all wavelengths and random phases. Therefore, to characterize such a profile it is necessary to determine the amplitude of the roughness at each wavelength. This is typically obtained by finding the power spectrum of the profile by the relation

$$P(\omega) = \frac{1}{L} \left| \int_0^L z(x)\, e^{i\omega x}\, dx \right|^2 \tag{1}$$

where $P(\omega)$ is the power of a wave of frequency $\omega$. Here frequency is the reciprocal of the wavelength and has units of inverse length. The integral in eqn. (1) is the Fourier transform of $z(x)$ which provides the average amplitude of waves of frequency $\omega$ whereas $P$ is the square of the amplitude.

Consider a rough surface of fractal dimension $D_s$ for which the vertical cut is a surface profile $z(x)$ of dimension $D = D_s - 1$ [13]. In all generality, the scaling in the $z$-direction will not be the same as in the $x$-direction, implying that the function $z(x)$ is *self-affine* [14]. For a self-affine fractal profile $z(x)$ the power spectrum follows the relation [8, 9]

$$P(\omega) = \frac{G^{2(D-1)}}{\omega^{(5-2D)}} \tag{2}$$

where $G$ is a scaling constant and has units of length. It is important to note that the two parameters, $G$ and $D$, which characterize the power spectrum, are independent of $\omega$ and therefore scale-independent. If the power spectrum of a measured surface profile is found to follow a power law, then when compared with eqn. (2), the dimension $D$ and the scaling constant $G$ can be found. Another method of finding $D$ and $G$ is

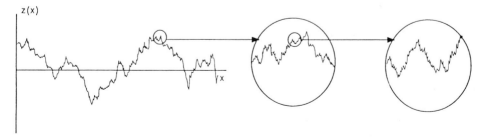

Fig. 2. Qualitative description of surface roughness. Repeated magnifications of a surface profile reveal similar roughness images suggesting a scale-invariant behavior.

56

to determine the structure function $S(\tau)$, defined as $S(\tau) = \langle (z(x) - z(x+\tau))^2 \rangle$ where $\langle \cdots \rangle$ implies spatial averaging. For a fractal surface profile, the structure function $S(\tau)$ can be found as [15]

$$S(\tau) = \langle (z(x) - z(x+\tau))^2 \rangle = \int_{-\infty}^{\infty} P(\omega)(e^{i\omega\tau} - 1)\, d\omega = CG^{2(D-1)}\tau^{(4-2D)} \qquad (3)$$

where the constant $C$ is

$$C = \frac{\Gamma(2D-3)\,\sin\{(2D-3)\pi/2\}}{(2-D)} \qquad (4)$$

Therefore, if the structure function $S(\tau)$ of a measured surface profile is found to follow a power law with the lag $\tau$, then the fractal parameters $G$ and $D$ can be found.

The structure function of a magnetic tape surface is shown in Fig. 3. The roughness was measured by an Atomic Force Microscope at different resolutions [7]. The AFM images of the magnetic tape surface are shown in Fig. 4. Each AFM scan of the surface contained 400 profiles with each profile having 400 digitized points. The structure function was found for each profile and averaged over the 400 profiles. From the data in Fig. 3 it is evident that there are two power-law fractal regimes of roughness which join at a lateral scale of $\tau \approx 0.1$ $\mu$m. It can be observed in Fig. 4 that the diameter of the magnetic particles are typically about 0.1 $\mu$m. Therefore the structure function in region I corresponds to the roughness of single magnetic particles whereas that in region II corresponds to the roughness formed by a collection of particles. Using eqn. (3) to determine the fractal roughness parameters in each region, it was found that in region I $G_1 = 4.68 \times 10^{-7}$ m and $D_1 = 1.14$, whereas in region II, $G_2 = 3.97 \times 10^{-9}$ m and $D_2 = 1.97$. These values satisfy the criterion that at $\tau = 0.1$ $\mu$m, the structure functions of both the regimes must be equal, that is $C_1 G_1^{2(D_1-1)}(10^{-7})^{(4-2D_1)} = C_2 G_2^{2(D_2-1)}(10^{-7})^{(4-2D_2)}$.

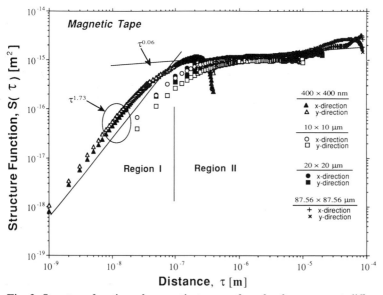

Fig. 3. Structure function of magnetic tape surface for four scans at different resolutions [7].

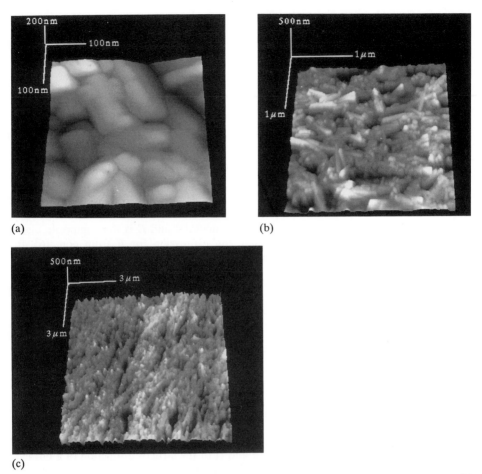

(a)

(b)

(c)

Fig. 4. Images of a magnetic tape surface measured by an atomic force microscope. (a) 400 nm × 400 nm scan; (b) 2.5 $\mu$m × 2.5 $\mu$m scan; (c) 10 $\mu$m × 10 $\mu$m scan. Scan (a) shows that the magnetic particles are about 100 nm in diameter.

## 3. Contact mechanics of bifractal surfaces

The model of contact between two surfaces, having single values of fractal roughness parameters $G$ and $D$ over all length scales, has been developed by Majumdar and Bhushan [10]. The model, however, can not be applied when the fractal parameters change over different length scales as experimentally observed for the magnetic tape in Fig. 3. Therefore, it is necessary to generalize the fractal contact model for bifractal surfaces and eventually multifractal surfaces. This section develops the theory of contact between a bifractal surface and a flat rigid plane. The results are then used to predict the contact mechanics of a magnetic tape and a rigid tape head.

### 3.1. Elastic–plastic regime
The first step in developing the contact theory is to predict the regimes of contact spot sizes which would either be in elastic or plastic deformation. A contact spot is

in plastic contact when the actual deformation of an asperity $\delta$ is larger than the critical deformation $\delta_c$ for the inception of plasticity. For the power spectrum of eqn. (2), it has been shown that for an asperity of lateral length scale $l$, the vertical height $\delta$ is given as [10]

$$\delta = G^{(D-1)}l^{(2-D)} \tag{5}$$

The radius of curvature $R$ for an asperity of lateral scale $l$ is [10]

$$R = \frac{l^D}{\pi^2 G^{(D-1)}} \tag{6}$$

The critical deformation for plasticity has been shown to be [3]

$$\delta_c = \left(\frac{\pi H}{2E}\right)^2 R \tag{7}$$

where $H$ is the surface hardness of the softer material and $E$ is the composite elastic modulus of the equivalent surface. Using the expression for $R$ from eqn. (6), the critical deformation can be written as

$$\delta_c = \left(\frac{\phi}{2}\right)^2 \frac{l^D}{G^{D-1}} \tag{8}$$

where $\phi$ is $H/E$. The relations for $\delta$ and $\delta_c$ in eqns. (5) and (8), respectively, can now be used to determine the range of length scale $l$ where the contact spots will deform plastically or elastically. The critical length scale $l_c$ can be shown to be

$$l_c = \frac{G}{(\phi/2)^{1/(D-1)}} \tag{9}$$

All spots with lateral length scales smaller than $l_c$ deform plastically whereas all spots larger than $l_c$ deform elastically.

For a bifractal surface, each fractal regime must be treated separately. Let the lateral length scale demarcating regions I and II of the structure function of a bifractal surface be $l_{12}$. The lateral length scale of a contact spot is $l$ and the critical spots scales for regions I and II are $l_{c1}$ and $l_{c2}$, respectively, which are obtained by using the corresponding values of $G$ and $D$ in eqn. (9). Now consider the four possible cases which are graphically depicted in Fig. 5.

Case 1 ($l_{c1} < l_{12}$): all contact spots satisfying $l < l_{c1}$ deform plastically whereas those falling in the category $l_{c1} < l < l_{12}$ deform elastically.

Case 2 ($l_{c1} > l_{12}$): all contact spots in region I deform plastically.

Case 3 ($l_{c2} < l_{12}$): all contact spots in region II deform elastically.

Case 4 ($l_{c2} > l_{12}$): all spots with lateral scales falling in the category $l_{12} < l < l_{c2}$ deform plastically whereas those in the category $l > l_{c2}$ deform elastically.

### 3.1.1. Application to magnetic tape–head interface

The contact between the magnetic tape and head surfaces can be studied as the contact between a flat rigid plane and an equivalent surface [3]. Roughness measurements of a magnetic tape and head surfaces have shown that the magnetic tape is much rougher than the magnetic head over several decades of length scales [7]. Therefore, it is safe to assume that values of $G$ and $D$ for the equivalent surface are the same as those of the magnetic tape surface [11]. From the structure function in Fig. 3, it is evident that $l_{12} = 0.1$ $\mu$m.

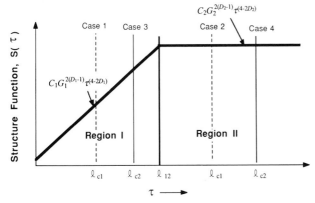

Fig. 5. Schematic diagram of the structure function of a bifractal surface with different combinations of critical length scales.

The material properties for the magnetic tape A considered in Figs. 3 and 4 are $H=0.25$ GPa and $E=1.75$ GPa whereas those for a magnetic head are $H=6.9$ GPa and $E=122$ GPa [4]. The properties of the equivalent surface are then $H=0.25$ GPa and $E=1.94$ GPa. Using these values and those of $G$ and $D$ for regions I and II, the critical length scales in these regions can be calculated to be $l_{c1}=1780$ μm and $l_{c2}=0.087$ μm. Since these values satisfy cases 2 and 3 discussed above, it can be concluded that all contact spots with lateral length scales in region I deform plastically and those in region II deform elastically.

### 3.2. Size distribution of contact spots

The physics of interfacial forces such as adhesion and deformation that are responsible for friction and static contact are known to be highly size-dependent [16–18]. To predict the cumulative effect of interfacial interactions from the study of an individual contact spot, one must know the statistical size distribution of contact spots. In the study of geomorphology of the earth, Mandelbrot [19] found that the cumulative size distribution of islands on the earth's surface follows the power-law $N(l) \propto l^{-d}$, where $N$ is the total number of islands of characteristic diameter or size larger than $l$ and $D$ is the fractal dimension of the coastline of the islands or the surface profile generated by a vertical cut. This cumulative size distribution can be normalized as $N(l)=(l_L/l)^D$ where $l_L$ is the lateral length of the largest island. This ensures that when $l=l_L$, $N=1$ verifying that there can be only one largest island.

For a bifractal surface, the power-law cumulative size distribution must be generalized. It is proposed that the cumulative size distributions $N_1$ and $N_2$ for regions I and II, respectively, of a bifractal surface are given as

Case A $(l_L<l_{12})$:

$$N_1(l) = \left(\frac{l_L}{l}\right)^{D_1} \quad \text{for } l<l_{12} \tag{10}$$

Case B $(l_L>l_{12})$:

$$N_1(l) = \left(\frac{l_L}{l_{12}}\right)^{D_2} \left(\frac{l_{12}}{l}\right)^{D_1} \quad \text{for } l<l_{12} \tag{11}$$

$$N_2(l) = \left(\frac{l_L}{l}\right)^{D_2} \quad \text{for } l_{12}<l<l_L$$

It is evident in eqn. (10) that when the largest contact spot falls in region I of the structure function the size distribution is unaffected by region II. When $l_L$ falls in region II, $N_2$ is unaffected by the contact spots in region I and therefore satisfies the condition that when $l=l_L$, $N_2=1$, indicating that there can be only one largest spot. However, the cumulative distribution in region I is affected by that in region II. Consider the specific case that $l=l_{12}$, then both $N_1$ and $N_2$ yield the same result. In addition, when $l_L=l_{12}$, it is evident that $N_1$ in eqn. (11) reduces to that in eqn. (10).

To predict the cumulative interactions of all the contact spots, it is necessary to determine the frequency distribution $n(l)$, which is defined such that the number of contact spots of size between $l$ and $l+dl$ is equal to $n(l)dl$. The frequency distribution can be determined by differentiating the cumulative distribution to be
Case A ($l_L<l_{12}$):

$$n_1(l)=D_1\left(\frac{l_L^{D_1}}{l^{D_1+1}}\right) \qquad \text{for } l<l_{12} \tag{12}$$

Case B ($l_L>l_{12}$):

$$n_1(l)=D_1\left(\frac{l_L}{l_{12}}\right)^{D_2}\left(\frac{l_{12}^{D_1}}{l^{D_1+1}}\right) \qquad \text{for } l<l_{12}$$

$$n_2(l)=D_2\left(\frac{l_L^{D_2}}{l^{D_2+1}}\right) \qquad \text{for } l_{12}<l<l_L \tag{13}$$

## 3.3. Real area of contact

The real area of contact can be found by adding up the areas of all the contact spots formed during contact of two rough surfaces. For a contact spot of lateral scale $l$, the area is $l^2$ and the number of such spots is equal to $n(l)dl$. Using the frequency distribution of contact spots found in eqns. (12) and (13), the real area of contact, $A_r$, for both cases are
Case A ($l_L<l_{12}$):

$$A_r=\int_0^{l_L}l^2 n_1(l)\,dl=\frac{D_1}{2-D_1}l_L^2 \tag{14}$$

Case B ($l_L>l_{12}$):

$$A_r=\int_0^{l_{12}}l^2 n_1(l)\,dl+\int_{l_{12}}^{l_L}l^2 n_2(l)\,dl=\frac{D_1}{2-D_1}\left(\frac{l_L}{l_{12}}\right)^{D_2}l_{12}^2+\frac{D_2}{2-D_2}l_L^2\left[1-\left(\frac{l_{12}}{l_L}\right)^{(2-D_2)}\right] \tag{15}$$

In eqn. (15) the first integral corresponds to the total area contribution from region I whereas the second integral corresponds to that from region II. These equations establish the relation between the real area of contact and the largest contact spot $l_L$. In the next section, the relation between the load and $l_L$ will be established. This will result in the desired relation between the real area of contact and the compressive load.

## 3.4. Surface load

The total compressive load during contact can be found by adding up the forces of each contact spot in conjunction with the frequency distributions of eqns. (12) and

(13). If the contact spot of lateral length $l$ is in plastic deformation, then the force $f_p$ is given as

$$f_p = Hl^2 \tag{16}$$

where $H$ is the hardness of the softer surface. When the spot is in elastic deformation, the load is given by Hertzian theory as

$$f_e = \tfrac{4}{3} E R^{1/2} \delta^{3/2} = \tfrac{4}{3} \pi^{1/2} E G^{(D-1)} l^{(3-D)} \tag{17}$$

To obtain the final form in eqn. (17) it was assumed that $\delta = l^2/\pi R$ and that $R$ is given in terms of $l$ in eqn. (6).

The various length scales of contact spots characteristic of bifractal surfaces are the critical scales for regions I and II, $l_{c1}$ and $l_{c2}$ respectively, the scale $l_{12}$ demarcating regions I and II and the scale of the largest contact spot $l_L$. From the discussion so far, it is clear that various combinations of these length scales can produce different situations as described in cases 1 to 4 and cases A and B. To determine the surface load for all combinations is a very tedious process. Therefore, only an individual case of a contact between a magnetic tape and head surfaces will be considered here. However, the methodology shown is general and can be applied to other cases.

For the contact of the magnetic tape and head surfaces it was found that $l_{12} = 0.1$ μm and that all spots in region I deform plastically whereas all spots in region II deform elastically. This corresponds to cases 2 and 3. It is also assumed that the size of the largest spot $l_L$ is larger than $l_{12}$ corresponding to case B. The total load $F$ is then obtained as

$$F = \int_0^{l_{12}} f_p(l) n_1(l) \, dl + \int_{l_{12}}^{l_L} f_e(l) n_2(l) \, dl \tag{18}$$

where the first integral corresponds to the total plastic load, $F_p$, arising from contact spots in region I and the second integral is the total elastic load, $F_e$, from contact spots in region II. Using the expressions developed for $f_p$, $f_e$, $n_1$ and $n_2$, the load is found to be

$$F = \frac{D_1}{2-D_1} \left(\frac{l_L}{l_{12}}\right)^{D_2} H l_{12}^2 + \frac{\tfrac{4}{3}\pi^{1/2} D_2}{2D_2 - 3} E G_2^{(D_2-1)} l_L^{(3-D_2)} \left[\left(\frac{l_L}{l_{12}}\right)^{(2D_2-3)} - 1\right] \tag{19}$$

This establishes the relation between to the total load $F$ and the largest spot $l_L$. With the use of eqn. (15) the load–area relation can now be determined.

## 4. Results and discussion

Figure 6 shows a comparison between the experimental data and the theoretical predictions. The experiments were conducted by contacting magnetic tape A with a plane glass piece at various pressures [20]. Since the elastic modulus and the surface hardness of glass is much higher than those of the magnetic tape, the material properties of the equivalent surface would nearly be the same as that of magnetic tape. In addition, since the roughness of the glass surface was much less than that of the tape, the roughness of the equivalent surface would be that of the tape. Using the values of $D_1 = 1.14$, $D_2 = 1.97$, $G_2 = 3.97$ nm, $H = 0.25$ GPa and $E = 1.75$ GPa for the contact between a magnetic tape and glass, eqns. (15) and (19) were used to determine the

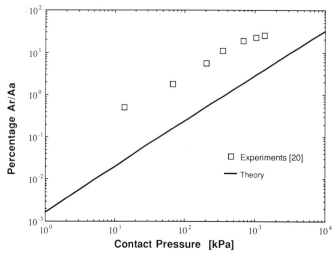

Fig. 6. Comparison of theory and experiments for the real area of contact as a function of contact pressure for a magnetic tape in contact with a hard surface.

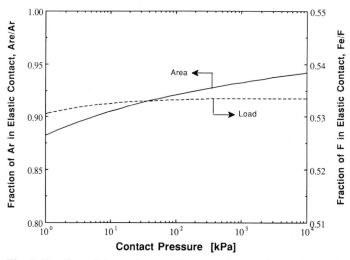

Fig. 7. Fraction of the real area of contact $A_r$ and the total load $F$ in elastic deformation.

real area of contact and the load, respectively. It is evident that although the trends of the experiments and the theory are the same, there is a consistent disagreement by an order of magnitude. In the experimental investigations, Bhushan [20] used an optical interference technique to measure the real area of contact. It was found that the measurements could over-estimate the contact area by as much as one-half to one order of magnitude [21]. Due to the consistency in the disagreement, it is possible that there could be errors in the measurement of mechanical properties, such as the surface microhardness and the elastic modulus.

For a given contact pressure, that is load divided by apparent area, Fig. 7 shows the fraction of real area of contact and the load in *elastic* deformation. The ratio of elastic contact area to the total contact area, $A_{re}/A_r$, is about 90% and increases slightly with load. This high fraction of elastic contact area is in agreement with the observations of Bhushan [20] who used optical interferometry to find that the real area of contact was reversible with load. The ratio of the load in elastic deformation to the total load, $F_e/F$, is about 53.5% and remains nearly constant. Therefore, although the contact area in plastic deformation is only about 10%, it is responsible for about 46.5% of the total compressive load. The reason for the ratio $F_e/F$ to remain constant can be found in the power law relations of $F_p$ and $F_e$ with $l_L$. Equation (19) suggests that $F_p \alpha l_L^2$ and if $l_L \gg l_{12}$, then $F_e \alpha l_L^{D_2}$. Since $D_2$ is close to 2 it is evident that both the elastic and the plastic loads, and therefore the total load $F$, behave as $l_L^2$. Therefore, the ratio $F_e/F$ must remain constant with $l_L$.

## 5. Conclusions

Roughness measurements and analysis of a magnetic tape at nanometer and micrometer scales have shown that there exist two regimes of roughness below and higher than 100 nm. The surface is called *bifractal* since each roughness regime can be characterized by a different set of fractal parameters.

Based on experimental evidence for the scale dependence of the r.m.s. slope and curvature of the surface, it is concluded that the predictions of the Greenwood–Williamson model would be scale-dependent. To study the contact mechanics of a rough surface characterized by a single set of fractal roughness parameters, a new model was recently developed. This paper generalizes the fractal model for bifractal surfaces. The theory is used to predict the real area of contact of a magnetic tape in contact with a flat hard plane. Comparison with experiments show that the measured real area of contact is higher than the predictions by an order of magnitude. It is felt that the disagreement could be due to errors in the measurement of mechanical properties and the real area of contact. Nevertheless, it is observed that the trends of both the theory and experiments are in agreement. The theoretical predictions show that for contact pressures between 1 kPa to $10^4$ kPa, the fraction of real area of contact in elastic deformation is about 90%. This is in agreement with experimental observations by optical interferometry. In addition, the fraction of the total load in elastic deformation is about 53.5% suggesting that the 10% of the contact area in plastic deformation accounts for about 46.5% of the total load.

## Acknowledgments

One of the authors, A.M., gratefully acknowledges the support of the National Science Foundation through Grant CTS-9010311.

## References

1 T. R. Thomas, *Rough Surfaces*, Longman, New York, 1982.
2 E. D. Williams and N. C. Bartelt, Thermodynamics of surface morphology, *Science, 251* (1991) 393–400.
3 J. A. Greenwood and J. B. P. Williamson, Contact of nominally flat surfaces, *Proc. R. Soc. London, A 295* (1966) 300–319.

4  B. Bhushan, *Tribology and Mechanics of Magnetic Storage Devices,* Springer, New York, 1990.
5  B. Bhushan, J. C. Wyant and J. Meiling, A new three-dimensional non-contact digital optical profiler, *Wear, 122* (1988) 301–312.
6  B. Bhushan and G. Blackman, Atomic force microscopy of magnetic rigid disks and sliders and its applications to tribology, *ASME J. Tribology,* in the press.
7  P. I. Oden, A. Majumdar, B. Bhushan, A. Padmanabhan and J. Graham, AFM imaging, roughness analysis and contact mechanics of magnetic tape and head surfaces, submitted for publication.
8  A. Majumdar and C. L. Tien, Fractal characterization and simulation of rough surfaces, *Wear, 136* (1990) 313–327.
9  A. Majumdar and B. Bhushan, Role of fractal geometry in roughness characterization and contact mechanics of surfaces, *ASME J. Tribology, 112* (1990) 205–216.
10  A. Majumdar and B. Bhushan, Fractal model of elastic–plastic contact between rough surfaces, *ASME J. Tribology, 113* (1991) 1–11.
11  A. Majumdar, B. Bhushan and C. L. Tien, Role of fractal geometry in tribology, *Adv. Inform. Storage Syst., 1* (1991) 231–266.
12  A. Majumdar, Fractal surfaces and their applications to surface phenomena, *Ph.D. Thesis,* Mechanical Engineering, University of California, Berkeley, 1989.
13  B. B. Mandelbrot, *The Fractal Geometry of Nature,* Freeman, New York, 1982.
14  R. F. Voss, Fractals in nature: from characterization to simulation, in H. O. Pietgen and D. Saupe (eds.), *The Science of Fractal Images,* Springer, New York, 1988, pp. 21–70.
15  M. V. Berry, Diffractals, *J. Phys. A, 12* (1978) 781–797.
16  U. Landman, W. D. Luedtke, N. A. Burnham and R. J. Colton, Atomistic mechanisms and dynamics of adhesion, nanoindentation and fracture, *Science, 248* (1990) 454–461.
17  C. M. Mate, G. M. McClelland, R. Erlandsson and S. Chiang, Atomic-scale friction of a tungsten tip on a graphite surface, *Phys. Rev. Lett., 59* (1987) 1942–1945.
18  J. Ferrante and J. R. Smith, Theory of the bimetallic interface, *Phys. Rev. B, 31* (1985) 3427–3424.
19  B. B. Mandelbrot, Stochastic models for the earth's relief, the shape and the fractal dimension of the coastlines, and the number–area rule for islands, *Proc. Nat. Acad. of Sci. U.S.A., 72* (1975) 3825–3828.
20  B. Bhushan, The real area of contact in polymeric magnetic media — II: Experimental data and analysis, *ASLE Trans., 28* (1985) 181–197.
21  B. Bhushan, The real area of contact in polymeric magnetic media — I: Critical assessment of experimental techniques, *ASLE Trans., 28* (1985) 75–86.

*Wear, 153* (1992) 65–78

# Tribological studies of various magnetic heads and thin-film rigid disks

Per Hedenqvist, Mikael Olsson and Sture Hogmark

*Materials Science Division, Department of Technology, Uppsala University, Box 534, S-751 21 Uppsala (Sweden)*

Bharat Bhushan

*Computer Microtribology and Contamination Laboratory, Department of Mechanical Engineering, Ohio State University, Columbus, OH 43210 (USA)*

(Received April 29, 1991; revised and accepted July 15, 1991)

## Abstract

Tribological characterization of three different magnetic heads (Mn–Zn ferrite, $CaTiO_3$ and $Al_2O_3$–TiC) and two different magnetic storage thin-film rigid disks have been made. The abrasive wear characteristics of the two disks (only differing in protective overcoat; diamond-like carbon and yttria-stabilized zirconia, respectively) have been investigated using a precision dimple grinder in order to grind small and well defined wear scars on the disks. The scratch response of the magnetic heads and the rigid disks have been studied using a single tip scratch test equipment *in situ* in the scanning electron microscope. Finally, the friction characteristics of the six possible magnetic head/rigid storage disk couples have been tested using *in situ* sliding tests in a scanning electron microscope.

The results from the abrasive test show that one of the disks (with a diamond-like carbon overcoat) only displays abrasive wear, while the other disk (with a zirconia overcoat) besides abrasive wear also displays extensive spalling of the magnetic coating. The scratch tests show that for all three magnetic heads the friction coefficient increases rapidly with increasing normal force until a constant value, independent of the normal force applied, is reached. For the two disks, the friction coefficient increases with increasing normal force within the entire normal force interval investigated (0–0.5 N). The *in situ* friction tests show that, for a given head material, sliding against the disk with the zirconia overcoat yields lower friction than sliding against the disk with the diamond-like carbon overcoat. It was also found that, for a given disk material, the $Al_2O_3$–TiC head yields the highest friction. All heads, with the possible exception of the $Al_2O_3$–TiC head, were found to be virtually unaffected by sliding against the disks. Further, it was found that scratching of the disks occasionally occurs for the following head/disk combinations: $CaTiO_3$/diamond-like carbon overcoat, $Al_2O_3$–TiC/diamond-like carbon overcoat and $Al_2O_3$–TiC/zirconia overcoat.

## 1. Introduction

In a hard disk drive the head slider is designed to fly above the disk surface when the surface velocity is high enough to produce a hydrodynamic air film capable of supporting the load on the head rails [1]. During start-up and stopping the head rails make contact with the disk, which can lead to wear. Although this is not an immediate problem, over a period of thousands of starts and stops, wear debris could cause interference with the head lift-off.

The overall dimensions of a 3380-type head slider typically are about 4 mm long, 3 mm wide and 1.3 mm high. Two rails (0.30–0.64 mm wide) on the head slider make contact with the disk while the drive is not in use. The trailing end of the head slider contains the read–write transducer while the leading end is relieved to facilitate "lift-off". This relieved area is usually identified as the taper, with a taper angle of about 10–15 mrad. The head slider is gimbal mounted, allowing uniform load distribution on the rails. Modern head sliders are generally made of hard ceramic materials; usually Mn–Zn ferrite, $Al_2O_3$–TiC or $CaTiO_3$.

The substrate used for thin-film hard disks is Al–Mg (96–4) alloy with a thickness of about 1.3 mm. In the case of metal film disks, the Al–Mg substrate is generally plated with Ni–P to a thickness of 10–20 $\mu$m for increased hardness and smoothness. In the case of oxide film disks the aluminium surface is anodized. Most disk substrates are deliberately textured to 4–8 nm root mean square roughness for low stiction and friction. The aluminium alloy surface is then either electroless plated or sputtered with cobalt alloys or $\gamma$-$Fe_2O_3$ to obtain a magnetic coating of about 50–150 nm. An overcoat of sputtered or spin-coated $SiO_2$, sputtered diamond-like carbon or $ZrO_2$–$Y_2O_3$ of thickness 10–30 nm is normally applied over the magnetic layer to reduce friction and wear. Most thin-film disks also use an additional overcoat of perfluoropolyether of thickness 0.5–4 nm. The diameter of modern thin-film disks is either 95 or 130 mm.

Typically, the computer manufacturers perform various types of wear tests on candidate materials which can be used for the head slider and the disk surface [2]. The results are ranked by surface condition or by the amount of material removed after running for a given length of time. Examination of the sliding surface is done after the wear or surface damage has occurred. However, there is still little evidence indicating how the wear or damage was initiated and if precautions can be taken to reduce initiation.

The main goals of this study were to conduct friction and wear tests to better understand the failure mechanisms of various head/disk interfaces.

## 2. Experimental details

### 2.1. Materials

Three different magnetic heads (Mn–Zn ferrite, $CaTiO_3$ and $Al_2O_3$–TiC) and two different rigid thin-film disks were investigated in the present work. The two disks have exactly the same composition, except for the protective layers that consist of either diamond-like carbon or yttria-stabilized zirconia. A sectional view of the rigid disks is given in Fig. 1. The hardness of all heads and disks was estimated using a conventional Vickers' microhardness indenter and a load of 100 g.

### 2.2. Test equipments and parameters

Abrasive wear testing of the two disks was performed using a commercial precision dimple grinder (Gatan Model 656 Precision Dimple Grinder). Normally, its main applications are pre-thinning of transmission electron microscopy (TEM) specimens prior to ion beam milling, exposure of near-surface concentration gradients (e.g. for Auger depth profile analysis) and coating thickness measurements. In the present study though, this equipment is used for grinding accurately sized wear scars on the

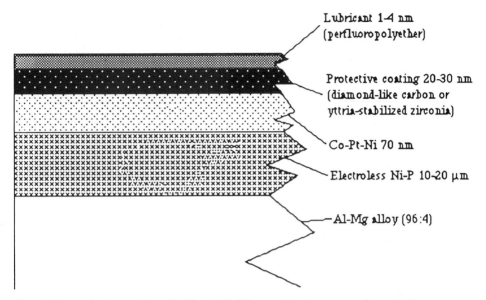

Lubricant 1-4 nm
(perfluoropolyether)

Protective coating 20-30 nm
(diamond-like carbon or
yttria-stabilized zirconia)

Co-Pt-Ni 70 nm

Electroless Ni-P 10-20 μm

Al-Mg alloy (96:4)

Fig. 1. Schematic view of the thin-film rigid disks used in the present investigation.

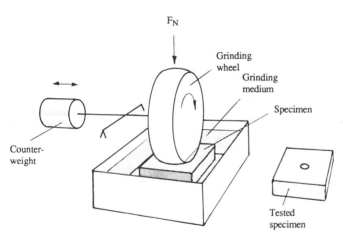

$F_N$

Grinding
wheel

Grinding
medium

Specimen

Counter-
weight

Tested
specimen

Fig. 2. Schematic view of the precision dimple grinder used for the wear tests. A grinding wheel, which is cut out from the centre of a sphere, rotates around a horizontal axis. By adjusting the position of a counterweight, the normal force ($F_N$) between the grinding wheel and the specimen can be adjusted to any value up to 0.5 N. During grinding, the specimen is submerged in a grinding medium.

surfaces of the magnetic storage disks. The general construction of the dimple grinder is shown in Fig. 2. More details on this abrasive test can be found elsewhere [3]. In the present study, a grinding wheel of delrin polymer, a peripheral velocity of 0.25 m s$^{-1}$ and an normal force of 0.1 N were used. A water-based 1 μm diamond suspension was used as grinding medium. Abrasive testing was performed using several sliding distances, ranging from 0.5 up to 200 m. After the test, the wear scars were examined by light optical microscopy (LOM), scanning electron microscopy

Fig. 3. The *in situ* scratch test equipment: (a) overview and (b) detail, showing the diamond stylus (at A) and the mounted specimen (at B).

(SEM) and energy dispersive X-ray spectroscopy (EDX) in order to identify the dominant wear mechanisms.

The single tip scratching experiments (the test equipment is shown in Fig. 3) were performed *in situ* using SEM, which made it possible to continuously monitor the scratching event [4]. A diamond stylus with a spherically rounded tip (radius = 25 $\mu$m) was used for scratching. Since both the normal force ($F_N$) and the tangential force are continuously registered during the course of the test, the friction coefficient ($\mu$) is easily calculated. In the case of the magnetic heads, the scratching was performed on the back side, *i.e.* on the unpolished (as-received) side. After the test, the resulting scratches were examined in the SEM.

The friction experiments were performed using the same test equipment as in the scratching experiments. However, the test equipment was modified for the friction test series by replacing the diamond stylus used for scratching with a holder for the magnetic heads. Friction testing could then be performed by sliding the magnetic heads against the disks. The normal force was varied between 0 and 2 N and the sliding speed was kept constant at 50 $\mu$m s$^{-1}$ throughout the test. After the test, the resulting surfaces were examined in the SEM.

In the abrasive test, only the two disks were examined, while in the scratch and friction tests, all materials or combinations of materials were tested.

## 3. Results

### 3.1. Hardness

The resulting hardness values of all tested specimens are given in Table 1. As can be seen, the heads are 3–10 times harder than the disks, with the $Al_2O_3$–TiC head being 3 times harder than the $CaTiO_3$ head which in turn is about 1.5 times harder than the Mn–Zn ferrite head. This is in accordance with earlier work [5]. Further, it is found that the disk with the diamond-like carbon overcoat is somewhat harder than the disk with the zirconia overcoat. The hardness values of the disks are the composite hardness values, *i.e.* hardness values that are functions not only of the hardness of all materials included in the disks but also of the thickness of the various coatings. In particular, the hardness of the protective coatings is much higher than the present composite hardness values but the coatings are much too thin to significantly influence the disk hardness values.

TABLE 1

Hardness values ($L = 100$ g) of the tested specimens

| Specimen | Hardness ($H_V$) |
|---|---|
| *Heads* | |
| Mn–Zn ferrite | $700 \pm 50$ |
| CaTiO$_3$ | $1050 \pm 50$ |
| Al$_2$O$_3$–TiC | $2800 \pm 500$ |
| *Disks* | |
| Yttria-stabilized zirconia overcoat | $210 \pm 10$ |
| Diamond-like carbon overcoat | $230 \pm 10$ |

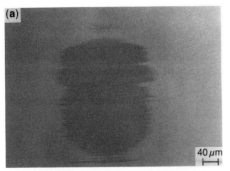 

Fig. 4. Macroscopic appearance of wear scars obtained by the precision dimple grinder (sliding distance 200 m) on (a) the disk with the diamond-like carbon overcoat and (b) the disk with the zirconia overcoat.

### 3.2. Abrasive testing

Figure 4 shows characteristic examples of the macroscopic appearance of the resulting wear scars on the two magnetic disks. While the wear scar on the disk with the diamond-like carbon overcoat has a rectangular shape, the wear scar on the disk with the zirconia overcoat is more circular.

More detailed studies of the periphery of the wear scars revealed that the two disks also exhibit different wear characteristics on a microscopic level. While the disk with the diamond-like carbon overcoat displays pure abrasive wear, see Fig. 5(a), the disk with the zirconia overcoat shows both abrasive wear and spalling, see Fig. 5(b). EDX analysis of the spalled areas showed that the spalling occurs in the magnetic coating/Ni–P coating interface. The spalling tendency is strongly affected by the micro-topography of the substrate, *i.e.* by grooves remaining from the manufacturing procedure. In particular, it can be seen that splinter-like flakes, parallel to the grooves in the substrate, show a high tendency to spall off. Figure 5(b) also shows that extensive buckling of the magnetic coating occurs prior to the spalling event. From Fig. 6 it can be seen that even individual scratches can result in spalling failure, *i.e.* detachment of small coating fragments. This seems to occur preferentially between two neighbouring substrate grooves.

The somewhat poor adhesion of the magnetic coating to the Ni–P coating on the disk with the zirconia overcoat is also evident from microindentations made on this specimen, see Fig. 7. In contrast, the disk with the diamond-like carbon overcoat did

Fig. 5. Periphery of the wear scar on (a) the disk with the diamond-like carbon overcoat and (b) the disk with the zirconia overcoat. Note the extensive spalling tendency of the magnetic coating in (b).

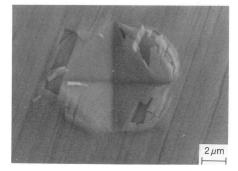

Fig. 6. A single scratch with associated spallings.

Fig. 7. A microindentation on the disk with the zirconia overcoat showing interfacial spalling in the magnetic coating/Ni–P coating interface (10 g load).

not show any spalling tendency at all, neither during abrasion testing nor during microindentation.

### 3.3. Scratch testing
#### 3.3.1. Friction
In Figs. 8(a)–(c) the steady-state value of the coefficient of friction during scratching has been plotted *vs.* $F_N$ for all three heads investigated. It can be seen that $\mu$ increases rapidly with increasing $F_N$ in all three cases, until a constant value ($\mu_c$) is reached. The Mn–Zn ferrite head displays the highest $\mu_c$ ($\approx 0.33$), while the constant values for the $CaTiO_3$ and $Al_2O_3$–TiC heads are more or less equal ($\approx 0.25$).

It was found (see Fig. 9) that the steady-state values of $\mu$ for both disks increased with increasing $F_N$. Generally, $\mu$ is lower for scratching in the disk with the zirconia overcoat and in addition the scatter in $\mu$ in this case is significantly lower than in the case of the disk with the diamond-like carbon overcoat.

#### 3.3.2. Scratch appearance
The appearance of the scratches in the Mn–Zn ferrite is seemingly independent of $F_N$; all scratches display a plasticized, smeared-out interior, with a tendency to

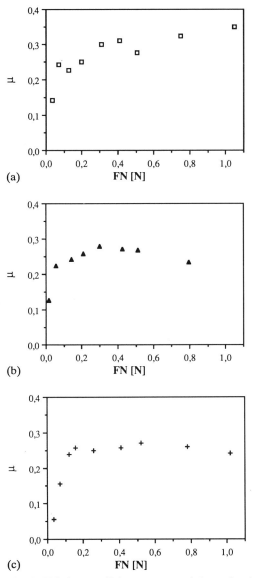

Fig. 8. Friction coefficient *vs.* normal force for (a) the Mn–Zn ferrite head, (b) the CaTiO$_3$ head and (c) the Al$_2$O$_3$–TiC head.

ridge formation, see Fig. 10(a). The rather irregular morphology of the scratch reflects the relatively coarse surface topography of the specimen. For higher normal forces ($F_N > 0.3$ N), tensile cracks can be found in the bottom of the scratch (see Fig. 10(a)).

On the comparatively well polished and very fine-grained CaTiO$_3$ head, the scratches at low loads are virtually featureless; no ridges are formed and no cracks can be found. The only remaining trace of the traversing stylus is a shallow, plastic groove. At higher normal forces ($F_N > 0.4$ N), minor cracking and microchipping occur

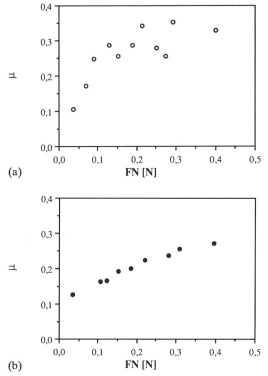

Fig. 9. Friction coefficient *vs.* normal force for (a) the disk with the diamond-like carbon protective overcoat and (b) the disk with the zirconia protective overcoat.

along the scratch rims, see Fig. 10(b). In addition, at these higher loads, some signs of ridge formation can be detected.

The unworn, comparatively fine-grained and rough surface of the $Al_2O_3$–TiC head is plastically compressed and somewhat smeared-out during the scratching process, even at low normal forces. At higher normal forces ($F_N > 0.6$ N), this effect becomes more pronounced and there are also some signs of ridge formation and detachment of individual grains along the scratch rim, see Fig. 10(c).

No significant difference between the two disk specimens can be found. Plastic deformation of the whole composite occurs even at the lowest normal force used ($F_N = 0.03$ N) and increases in severity with increasing $F_N$. At higher normal forces ($F_N > 0.2$ N), the amount of plastic deformation in the scratching direction can be gauged from the displacement of the grinding grooves in the substrate, see Fig. 11(a). Small amounts of material are "extruded" along the rim of the scratch (Fig. 11(b)) and may be removed as small fragments. Contrary to the results from the abrasive testing of the disks, no spallings (*i.e.* adhesive failures) were detected in this test.

### 3.4. Friction testing
#### 3.4.1. Friction

In Figs. 12(a)–(c) the friction coefficient corresponding to a steady-state sliding situation is plotted *vs.* $F_N$ for all materials combinations tested. For the Mn–Zn ferrite head (see Fig. 12(a)), sliding against the disk with the diamond-like carbon overcoat

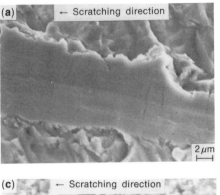

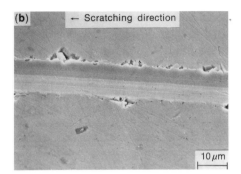

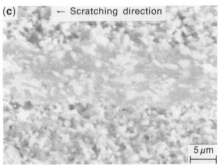

Fig. 10. Characteristics of scratches in the magnetic heads. (a) Tensile cracks in the bottom of a scratch in the Mn–Zn ferrite head. (b) Microchipping along the rim of a scratch in the $CaTiO_3$ head. (c) Slight tendency to ridge formation and detachment of grains along the rim of a scratch in the $Al_2O_3$–TiC head.

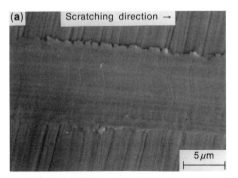

Fig. 11. Characteristics of scratches in the rigid disks. (a) Displacement of grinding grooves in the disk, due to plastic deformation during the scratch event (from the disk with the zirconia overcoat). (b) Detail of the "extruded" material (from the disk with the diamond-like carbon overcoat).

yields an initial decrease of $\mu$ with increasing $F_N$, followed by a more unpredictable dependence on $F_N$ for $F_N > 0.3$ N. However, an approximate mean value of $\mu$ is 0.20 for these loads. For sliding against the disk with the zirconia overcoat, $\mu$ is more or less independent of $F_N$, with a mean value of approximately 0.18.

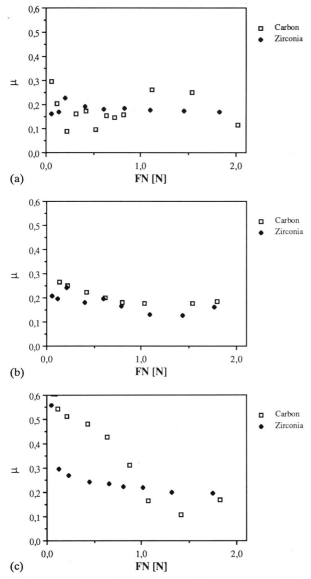

Fig. 12. Friction coefficient *vs.* normal force for (a) the Mn–Zn ferrite head sliding against the two disks, (b) the CaTiO$_3$ head sliding against the two disks and (c) the Al$_2$O$_3$–TiC head sliding against the two disks.

For the CaTiO$_3$ head (see Fig. 12(b)), $\mu$ first decreases with increasing $F_N$ and then levels out to a more constant value ($\approx 0.18$ for sliding against the disk with the diamond-like carbon overcoat, $\approx 0.14$ for sliding against the disk with the zirconia overcoat).

The Al$_2$O$_3$–TiC head (Fig. 12(c)) behaves somewhat differently; when sliding against the disk with the diamond-like carbon overcoat, $\mu$ is found to decrease (with an almost constant slope) with increasing $F_N$. When sliding against the disk with the zirconia overcoat, a rapid, initial decrease of $\mu$ with increasing $F_N$ is followed by a much more moderate decrease, tending towards a $\mu$ of 0.20–0.22 at the highest loads (1.8 N).

When comparing these results, it is seen that for a given head material sliding against the disk with the zirconia overcoat yields the lowest friction and that for a given disk material the $CaTiO_3$ head yields the lowest friction, closely followed by the Mn–Zn ferrite head. The $Al_2O_3$–TiC head always yields the highest friction.

### 3.4.2. Surface examination

The Mn–Zn ferrite heads proved to be very little affected by the friction testing and no damages or wear marks could be detected, see Fig. 13(a). On the disks, only some slight discolorations showed that any head/disk contact had taken place (Fig. 13(b)).

The $CaTiO_3$ heads also seemed unaffected by sliding against the disks (see Fig. 14(a)) and the appearance of the head surfaces was not found to be influenced by against which disk sliding took place. The disk with the zirconia overcoat also seemed unaffected by the test, while scratches could sometimes be observed on the disks with the diamond-like carbon overcoat (Fig. 14(b)).

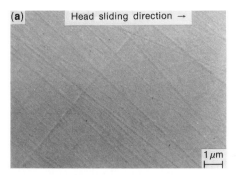
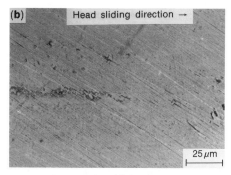

Fig. 13. Characteristics of Mn–Zn ferrite head/rigid disk friction couples. (a) Surface on a Mn–Zn ferrite head tested against the disk with the zirconia overcoat. Only grooves from polishing can be discerned. (b) Discolorations on the surface of a rigid disk with zirconia overcoat.

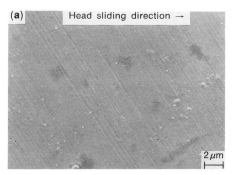
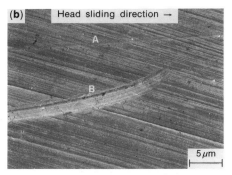

Fig. 14. Characteristics of $CaTiO_3$/rigid disk friction couples. (a) Unaffected magnetic head after sliding against the disk with the diamond-like carbon overcoat. (b) Two different scratches (at A and B, respectively) in the disk with the diamond-like carbon overcoat.

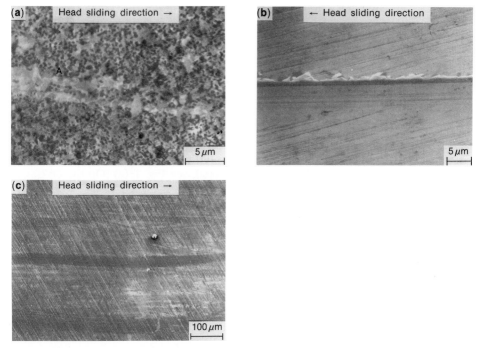

Fig. 15. Characteristics of $Al_2O_3$–TiC/rigid disk friction couples. (a) The $Al_2O_3$–TiC head after sliding against the disk with the diamond-like carbon overcoat. Note the scratch (at A). (b) A scratch in the disk with the zirconia overcoat. (c) Dark "sliding track" on the disk with the diamond-like carbon overcoat.

The $Al_2O_3$–TiC heads were also more or less unaffected by the sliding, but here and there scratches could be found (for sliding against both disks), see Fig. 15(a). This is somewhat surprising, since the $Al_2O_3$–TiC heads are significantly harder than the other heads investigated. Scratches could also be found in both disks (Fig. 15(b)) and in addition large, dark areas, corresponding to a sliding contact between head and disk but not showing any significant signs of wear, could be observed on the disk with the diamond-like carbon overcoat (Fig. 15(c)).

## 4. Summarizing remarks

Abrasion is a major wear mechanism in magnetic storage systems [6] and the hard protective overcoats are deposited onto the disks in order to protect against abrasion. Due to their thinness (<50 nm), however, the overcoats can only be expected to protect against abrasion by relatively small abrading particles. If for some reason large particles are created by wear of the magnetic heads, this wear debris can pose as a serious threat to the performance of the system by penetration of the protective coating. Thus, a major demand on the magnetic heads is that they must have a low tendency to produce wear debris. Further, the use of as hard (and thus abrasion-resistant) overcoats as possible on the disks should be encouraged, in accordance with the results of refs. 1, 7, 8.

Since the composition of the two disks investigated is identical, with the exception of the protective overcoats, it can be deduced that the difference in composite hardness originates from different coating hardnesses and/or thicknesses. Thus it is believed that the diamond-like carbon overcoat is harder and/or thicker than the zirconia overcoat. However, the extreme thinness of the overcoats prevents the determination of the absolute coating hardnesses and thicknesses. Note, however, that Yamashita *et al.* [9] have reported that the wear performance of $ZrO_2$–$Y_2O_3$ overcoat is superior to that of hard carbon, which indicates that a hard coating is not necessarily more wear-resistant.

Since the disks are significantly softer than the magnetic heads, the former are the abrasion-sensitive components. This is the reason why the abrasive test was run only on the two disks.

The different shape of the wear scars during the abrasive test (*cf.* Fig. 4) is attributed partly to a difference in the adhesive strength of the magnetic coating/Ni–P coating interface (*cf.* the following paragraph) and partly to the orientation of the test wheel with respect to the polishing grooves in the disks.

A possible explanation for the spallings in the magnetic coating/Ni–P coating interface on the disk with the zirconia overcoat is that the two different protective coatings interact differently with the diamond grit, thus transmitting different forces to the magnetic coating and thereby also to the magnetic coating/Ni–P coating interface. However, $\mu$ for single tip scratching of the disk with the zirconia protective overcoat is lower than $\mu$ for the disk with the diamond-like carbon overcoat (*cf.* Fig. 9). This also means that the forces transmitted to the magnetic coating/Ni–P coating interface are lower for the disk with the zirconia protective overcoat and, consequently, that the reason for the spallings must be another. Since no other differences are known, we deduce that the deposition processes of the two protective coatings influence the magnetic coating/Ni–P coating interface differently (*e.g.* by diffusion), yielding poorer adhesion characteristics of this interface in the case of disk with the zirconia protective overcoat.

Since no microchipping or detachment of grains was found during scratching of the Mn–Zn ferrite head, it can be concluded that the cohesive strength of this material is better than that of the other heads.

In the sliding friction test, the wear performance of the two friction couples that included the Mn–Zn ferrite head was better than that of the others couples, since no scratches could be found on the disks in this case.

In the scratch test, the initial increase of $\mu$ for the three heads and the disk with the diamond-like carbon overcoat is interpreted as an indication of the existence of a surface film (adsorbates or, in the case of the disks, possibly the lubricating film) which is rapidly broken through.

The continuous increase of the friction coefficient with increasing normal force for the disks is suspected to reflect the increase in the ploughing component ($\mu_p$) of $\mu$ ($\mu = \mu_p + \mu_a$, where $\mu_a$ is the constant adhesive component) due to the increase in penetration depth of the spherical stylus tip which follows from an increased normal force.

It should also be added that the friction coefficients obtained in the scratch test represents a diamond stylus sliding against the tested materials; they should not be taken as measures or predictions of the performance of a real magnetic storage system, incorporating the tested materials.

The results from the friction tests imply that the combinations of a Mn–Zn ferrite or a $CaTiO_3$ head and a disk with a yttria-stabilized zirconia overcoat might be preferred over other head/disk combinations. These materials combinations yield low friction coefficients and also comparatively stable $\mu$ *vs.* $F_N$ plots (a low and stable friction coefficient reduces the risk for surface damages), *cf.* Figs. 12(a)–(b).

Together, the wear and friction data above make it clear that a Mn–Zn ferrite head combined with a disk with a zirconia protective overcoat results in the best wear (no wear debris, no scratching of the disks) and friction (low and stable friction coefficient) characteristics. However, the problem with spalling of the magnetic coating on this disk remains to be solved.

## Acknowledgments

The authors are indebted to Dr Staffan Jacobson of the Materials Science Division, Department of Technology, Uppsala University for valuable discussions during the preparation of this manuscript. Parts of this work have been financially supported by the National Swedish Board for Technical Development (STU).

## References

1  B. Bhushan, *Tribology and Mechanics of Magnetic Storage Devices,* Springer, New York, 1990.
2  H. H. Gatzen, M. J. Smallen and P. T. Tedrow, Head–media wear in 5¼ in. rigid disk drives, in B. Bhushan and N. S. Eiss (eds.), *Tribology and Mechanics of Magnetic Storage Systems, Vol. 4,* STLE, Park Ridge, IL, pp. 116–122.
3  Å. Kassman, S. Jacobson, L. Erickson, P. Hedenqvist, M. Olsson and S. Hogmark, A new test method for the intrinsic abrasion resistance of coatings, *ICMCTF-91, April 22–26, 1991, San Diego, CA.*
4  P. Hedenqvist, M. Olsson, S. Jacobson and S. Söderberg, Failure mode analysis of TiN coated high speed steel: *in situ* scratch adhesion testing in the scanning electron microscope, *Surf. Coatings Technol., 41* (1990) 31–49.
5  B. Bhushan and M. F. Doerner, Role of mechanical properties and surface texture in the real area of contact of magnetic rigid disks, *J. Trib., Trans. ASME, 111* (1989) 452–458.
6  Y. Kawakubo, K. Ishihara, H. Seo and Y. Hirano, Head crash process of magnetic coated disk during contact start/stop operations, *IEEE Trans. Magn., MAG-20* (1984) 933–935.
7  M. Yanagisawa, Tribological properties of spin-coated $SiO_2$ protective film on plated magnetic recording disks, in B. Bhushan and N. S. Eiss (eds.), *Tribology and Mechanics of Magnetic Storage Systems, Vol. 2,* STLE, Park Ridge, IL, pp. 21–26.
8  S. J. Calabrese and B. Bhushan, A study by scanning electron microscopy of magnetic head–disk interface sliding, *Wear, 139* (1990) 367–381.
9  T. Yamashita, G. L. Chen, J. Shir and T. Chen, Sputtered $ZrO_2$ overcoat with superior corrosion protection and mechanical performance in thin-film rigid disk application, *IEEE Trans. Magn., MAG-24* (1988) 2629–2634.
10  M. T. Dugger, Y. W. Chung, B. Bhushan and W. J. Rothschild, Friction wear and interfacial chemistry in thin film magnetic rigid disk files, *J. Trib., Trans. ASME, 112* (1990) 238–245.

# The role of environment in the friction of diamond for magnetic recording head applications

S. Chandrasekar

*School of Industrial Engineering, Purdue University, W. Lafayette, IN 47907 (USA)*

Bharat Bhushan

*Ohio Eminent Scholar Professor, Department of Mechanical Engineering, Ohio State University, Columbus, OH 43210 (USA)*

(Received July 28, 1991)

## Abstract

The coefficient of friction for diamond sliding against diamond and for diamond sliding against a thin-film magnetic disk has been measured at low sliding velocities (millimeters per minute). The experiments were carried out in laboratory air, vacuum ($10^{-8}$ Torr) and hydrogen, helium, nitrogen and oxygen gases at pressures ranging from $10^{-6}$ to $10^{-4}$ Torr. For both the sliding systems, the coefficient of friction was found to be highest in vacuum and lowest in air. Intermediate values were obtained in the presence of the other gases. For diamond sliding against diamond, the coefficient of friction decreased with increasing pressure of the gas in the chamber; this decrease was particularly rapid in the presence of excited hydrogen. Values of the friction coefficient close to that measured in the presence of air were also obtained in the presence of helium and excited hydrogen for diamond sliding against thin-film disk. There was no detectable change in the coefficient of friction for the latter system in air when the humidity was varied between 12% and 80%. The variations in the friction coefficient with different environments are explained in terms of the interactions occurring between the gases and the diamond/disk surface.

## 1. Introduction

Conventional magnetic recording is accomplished by the relative motion of a magnetic disk or tape against a stationary or moving read/write magnetic head. Figure 1 shows a schematic of a typical thin-film rigid disk consisting of a substrate, an undercoat magnetic layer, a hard ceramic overcoat and a thin layer (1–4 nm) of fluorocarbon lubricant. Sometimes there is an additional layer between the magnetic medium and the undercoat to control the magnetic properties of the recording layer. The magnetic head, the slider, is usually made of a ceramic; ceramics that are currently being used include Mn–Zn and Ni–Zn ferrites, alumina–titanium carbide, and calcium titanate. Typically, under steady-state operating conditions, an air bearing of thickness $\approx 0.15$ to 0.4 $\mu$m is formed between the head and the disk, thereby preventing direct contact between the two. The average interface contact pressures between the head and the disk are typically around 7 to 14 kPa (1–2 p.s.i.). Depending on the type of the head–disk system, the head usually starts to fly and leaves the disk-surface at speeds ranging from 2 to 15 m s$^{-1}$. The operating speeds are about 10–60 m s$^{-1}$. Physical contact between head and disk occurs below the flying speed, during start

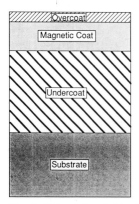

Fig. 1. Schematic of thin-film disk.

and stop and sometimes at isolated asperities during flying. For more details about the description of magnetic recording systems, see refs. 1 and 2.

The storage density of a Winchester-type magnetic disk drive is a strong function of the head-to-disk spacing. For high-density, high-resolution recording, close proximity between the head and the disk is essential. This has necessitated research into systems with extremely small flying gaps ($<0.1$ $\mu$m) between the head and the disk. In the limit one can think of a contact recording system wherein the head and the disk are continuously in contact with one another. The friction between the head and the disk at the contact zones, as well as wear of the magnetic head and disk media, is therefore of great interest. A low coefficient of friction between head-slider materials and the disk surface is highly desirable for a number of reasons. A high coefficient of friction generally results in excessive local heating and contact temperatures, high wear of both head and disk materials and excessive power requirements.

Chandrasekar and Bhushan [3, 4] recently reviewed the frictional behavior of a number of ceramic sliding systems under lightly loaded conditions and furthermore experimentally characterized the frictional behavior of a select group of ceramics in sliding contact against themselves or a thin-film, rigid magnetic disk in air. The ceramics studies were polycrystalline Mn–Zn ferrite, alumina–titanium carbide, calcium titanate, partially stabilized zirconia, silicon nitride and the (111) face of single-crystal diamond. The measurements showed that diamond (111) gave the lowest coefficient of friction ($\mu=0.13$) amongst these ceramics when slid against the magnetic disk under lightly loaded conditions (normal pressure $<0.1$ MPa). Furthermore, the coefficient of friction for diamond against the disk remained low for a longer sliding duration than with the other ceramics. Since a significant increase in the coefficient of friction often coincided with faint microscopically observable wear marks on the disk surface, the observations implied that disk wear was also less for the diamond–disk system.

In order to better understand the frictional characteristics of single-crystal diamond, especially with regard to its use as a slider material in a magnetic recording system, we have carried out studies of the sliding friction of diamond in various gaseous environments and at different humidities in air when in contact with single-crystal diamond and a thin-film, rigid magnetic disk. The experiments were conducted within a vacuum chamber capable of producing vacua of $10^{-8}$ Torr consistently over extended periods of time. The effect of gaseous environments on the friction of diamond when in contact with a magnetic disk is particularly important as hermetically sealed disk drives containing a specific partial pressure of a gas could be devised if such an environment is indeed found to give a low coefficient of friction and wear rate. Type 1a diamond flats were used in all of the experiments and its physical and mechanical properties are given in Table 1.

## 2. Background

In this section we shall briefly review some of the relevant past work on diamond friction; for more details see the review by Tabor [5] and Chandrasekar and Bhushan [3].

The coefficient of friction for diamond sliding on diamond in air is relatively low ($\mu \approx 0.1$) and at low speeds (mm s$^{-1}$), it varies little with sliding speed [6]. It is, however, strongly dependent on the crystallographic direction of sliding, varying by up to a factor of three for {100} faces. On the (001) face, the friction is found to be highest in the $\langle 100 \rangle$ directions and lowest in the $\langle 110 \rangle$ directions. This face shows fourfold symmetry which is also reflected in the variation of the friction coefficient with the direction of sliding. Also, when the stylus has a spherical tip with an (001) tangent plane, the anisotropy of the flat is greatest when the stylus is sliding along a $\langle 100 \rangle$ direction.

The effect of normal load on the coefficient of friction for diamond sliding on diamond has been investigated. Enomoto and Tabor [7] observed an increase in friction with normal load; this increase typically coincided with the onset of damage on the diamond surface which could be detected by cathodoluminescence. Casey and Wilks [6] did not observe any change in the friction coefficient with normal load. Both of these conflicting results have been explained recently by Samuels and Wilks [8] who showed that different load dependences of the friction coefficient are obtained for different crystal and polish orientations of the diamond flat.

When diamond surfaces are rubbed together repeatedly under conditions of high vacuum, the usually low coefficient of friction ($\mu m = 0.1$) increases dramatically to $\approx 1$ after a few hundred cycles of rubbing [9]. This has been attributed to the breakdown of a chemisorbed surface film on the diamond and this breakdown is accompanied by high wear of the diamond. In air, the presence of a lubricating oil is not found to alter the friction coefficient [6].

There has been much speculation as to the origins of friction during the sliding of diamond on diamond. It should be noted here that diamond is a highly elastic solid at room temperature and therefore the question of determining the principal

TABLE 1

Typical physical and mechanical properties of type 1a diamond

| Property | Value |
| --- | --- |
| density | 3.51 g cm$^{-3}$ |
| specific heat | 0.525 J g$^{-1}$ K$^{-1}$ |
| thermal conductivity | 900 W m$^{-1}$ K$^{-1}$ |
| Knoop hardness | 9500 kg mm$^{-2}$ in (110)$\langle 110 \rangle$ |
| Young's modulus | 1000 GPa |
| Poisson's ratio | 0.2 |

sources of frictional energy dissipation is an important one. Above a certain load, depending on the type and size of stylus used in the experiments, extensive cracking of the diamond can occur. While this might be thought to account for the friction, it appears unlikely because diamond has a low fracture surface energy ($\approx 6$ J m$^{-2}$) and this mechanism does not absorb enough energy to account for any significant fraction of the observed friction coefficients. Also, for diamond sliding on diamond, very little ploughing is observed and so the contribution of the ploughing action to the friction coefficient is also expected to be negligible [10]. At present a theory which combines adhesion and surface roughness of the asperities originally proposed by Tabor [5] and extended by Seal [11] is found to give reasonably good agreement with experimental results.

Hayward and Field [10] have carried out some investigations of the effect of low-pressure oxygen and hydrogen (in the molecular state) on the diamond–diamond friction. The studies were carried out with a diamond stylus having a hemispherical tip of radius 90 mm (tip tangent plane being (100)) sliding against the (100) face of a diamond flat. Both these gases were found to reduce the friction coefficient to the value of $\approx 0.1$ from an initially high value in vacuum of $\approx 0.7$. Hayward and Field [10] have attributed this reduction in friction to either the formation of a resistant layer of adsorbed gas atoms on the diamond surface or to the production of a "waxy" debris in the high-friction phase (vacuum) of sliding which perhaps could have acted as a lubricant.

## 3. Experiments and results

### 3.1. Diamond on diamond

The experiments were conducted within a high-vacuum chamber capable of attaining pressures as low as $10^{-8}$ Torr. The experimental apparatus is similar to that described by Chandrasekar and Bhushan [4] with a few modifications. A diamond stylus with a hemispherical tip of radius 200 $\mu$m and of unspecified orientation was mounted on a crossed I-beam fixture which was instrumented with semiconductor strain gauges to measure the normal and frictional forces on the stylus; see ref. 4 for a description of this fixture. The design of the fixture was such as to enable the measurement of frictional forces as small as 0.1 gmf. Normal forces in the range 10–1000 gmf could be applied on the stylus using this fixture. A single-crystal diamond flat, $3 \times 3 \times 1.5$ mm$^3$, with its surface being (111) was polished on a cast iron scaife and brazed on to a sapphire substrate and the assembly mounted on a linear slider. The sapphire substrate could be heated resistively using a tantalum film attached to the substrate. A thermally insulating ceramic piece served to insulate the sapphire substrate from the slider. The diamond flat was slid against the diamond stylus at a speed of 1 mm min$^{-1}$.

Before every sliding experiment, the polished diamond flat (surface being (111)) was heated to 950 °C at $10^{-8}$ Torr for about 10 min and then cooled to room temperature. The vacuum annealing serves to thermally desorb hydrogen gas molecules which are bonded to the diamond surface [12, 13]. The temperature of the diamond surface was determined by observing the tantalum film with a disappearing-filament optical pyrometer. Corrections were made for window transmittance and tantalum emissivity assuming $\epsilon = 0.5$. This latter value is the bulk emissivity of tantalum. A calculation showed that there is a negligible temperature difference between the diamond surface and the tantalum film. Every sliding experiment consisted of 50 cycles or passes of the stylus across the flat over the same track; the track length was kept at 2 mm giving a time of 2 min for the completion of a single cycle at a sliding speed of 1 mm min$^{-1}$. The normal force between the stylus and the flat was kept at 50 gmf, which for the present stylus of 200 $\mu$m tip radius was sufficiently small so as not to cause any surface damage on the flat [7]. The diamond flat was re-polished and vacuum annealed at 950 °C before every sliding experiment.

An ionization gauge with tungsten filaments (Varian model 971-5008) was used to measure the system pressure. Except for the experiment with excited hydrogen, this gauge was mounted remote from the area of the friction experiment within the chamber. Another independent estimate of the system pressure was obtained by measuring the ion pump current. During the experiments with excited hydrogen, the ionization gauge was placed behind the diamond surface with no direct line of sight between the surface and the filament. The gauge now served the purpose of exciting the hydrogen gas admitted into the system; the emission current of the gauge was 3.5 mA. This method of excitation is similar to that used by Pepper [12] in his studies of the transformation of the diamond (110) surface. It could not, however, be determined in our experiments as to whether the excited hydrogen gas was molecular or atomic hydrogen.

The coefficient of friction between the diamond stylus and the flat was measured in the presence of oxygen, hydrogen, and nitrogen gases, excited hydrogen, vacuum and laboratory air at atmospheric pressure. The gases were bled into the chamber at various pressures ranging from $10^{-6}$ to $10^{-4}$ Torr beginning at about two minutes before the start of a sliding experiment; the flow was maintained at this pressure throughout the duration of the experiment. A pressure of $10^{-8}$ Torr was maintained during the experiments in vacuum.

Figures 2 and 3 show the coefficient of friction during the 50 cycles of the sliding experiment in various gaseous environments. The coefficient of friction in vacuum is high ($\mu = 0.8$), see Fig. 2, but it decreases in the presence of the various gases to a value of around 0.08–0.14 (Figs. 2 and 3). The lowest coefficient of friction was measured in air, $\mu \approx 0.09$, while there was not much difference in the friction coefficients measured in the presence of molecular hydrogen, nitrogen and oxygen gases (Fig. 3). The friction coefficient obtained in the presence of excited hydrogen was closer to air, $\mu \approx 0.094$, than to the other gases, see Fig. 3. This could be due to the better adsorbability of excited hydrogen on the diamond (111) surface leading to the formation of a well bonded surface film when compared with the various gases in the ground state [12, 13].

Figure 4 shows the variation in the friction coefficient in the presence of various gases of different pressures. As the pressure of the gas is increased there is a substantial decrease in the value of the friction coefficient; this decrease is steepest below a pressure of $10^{-6}$ Torr. Also the decrease is most rapid with excited hydrogen. It may be noted here that at the pressure of $10^{-6}$ Torr, the time required to form a monolayer of gas molecules at the diamond surface is $\approx 4$ s if we assume a sticking probability per gas molecule collision of 1. This is about 100 times longer than at $10^{-4}$ Torr. Thus one would expect a much thicker layer of gas molecules to be adsorbed at $10^{-4}$ Torr compared with $10^{-6}$ Torr and hence the observed decrease in the friction coefficient is more significant at $10^{-4}$ Torr. The greater decrease in the friction coefficient in the presence of excited hydrogen at $10^{-4}$ Torr compared with the other gases in their ground state, also suggests that this form of hydrogen is more strongly adsorbed and bonded to the diamond surface. In our sliding experiments, we did not detect any "waxy" debris after 50 cycles of sliding. This is most likely due to the fact that the

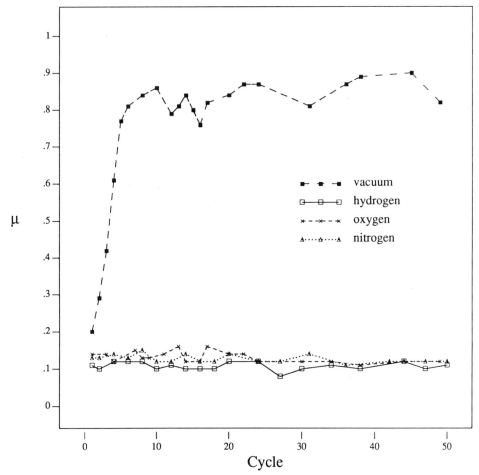

Fig. 2. The coefficient of friction for diamond sliding on diamond in the presence of oxygen, nitrogen and hydrogen gases (pressure = $10^{-4}$ Torr) and in vacuum ($10^{-8}$ Torr).

wear of the diamond surfaces is bound to be negligibly small over this limited duration of sliding, especially at the low normal loads used in the experiments. "Waxy" debris has been observed after many cycles of sliding by Seal [11] and Hayward and Field [10] in their sliding experiments with diamond and this debris is speculated to contain a significant amount of hydrocarbon-like material; it is thus thought of to be a good lubricant.

## 3.2. Diamond on thin-film magnetic disk

Sliding friction experiments were conducted in vacuum and various gaseous environments for a diamond flat (111), $1 \times 1 \times 0.75$ mm$^3$, in contact against a thin-film, rigid magnetic disk material. The diamond flat was glued onto a 3380 type suspension and mounted on the crossed I-beam fixture described in ref. 4. A normal load of 15 gmf was applied between the diamond flat and the surface of the disk material. Since the whole disk could not be accommodated in the vacuum chamber, pieces of the disk $\approx 12.5 \times 12.5$ mm$^2$ in cross-section were cut out and attached to

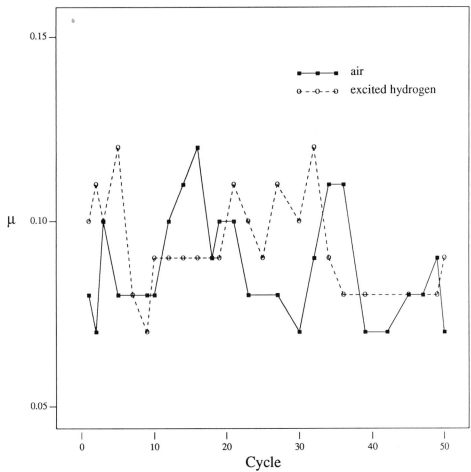

Fig. 3. The coefficient of friction for diamond sliding on diamond in laboratory air (atmospheric pressure) and in excited hydrogen ($10^{-4}$ Torr).

the linear slider in the vacuum chamber. The disk structure consisted of a circumferentially textured Al–Mg alloy substrate with a 10–20 $\mu$m thick electroless plated Ni–P coating, 25–70 nm thick magnetic coating (Co–Pt–Ni), 20–30 nm thick diamond-like carbon coating, and a 0.5–4 nm thick perfluoropolyether lubricant coating. The surface roughness of the finished disk surface was 7.3 nm rms and 48.5 nm peak-to-valley distance. A fresh piece of the disk was used for every sliding experiment. A sliding experiment typically consisted of 25 passes of the diamond flat across the disk surface; the length of each pass was 8 mm and the sliding speed was 4 mm min$^{-1}$. Unlike in the diamond-on-diamond experiments, no vacuum annealing of the diamond flat was carried out for this set of experiments. The diamond flat and suspension were only cleaned ultrasonically in acetone before every sliding experiment.

Table 2 gives the measured coefficient of friction ($\mu$) values for diamond sliding against the disk material in different environments. In the experiments, various gases at pressures of $10^{-4}$ Torr were bled into the vacuum chamber 5 min before the sliding experiment began and the flow was maintained throughout the experiment. The values

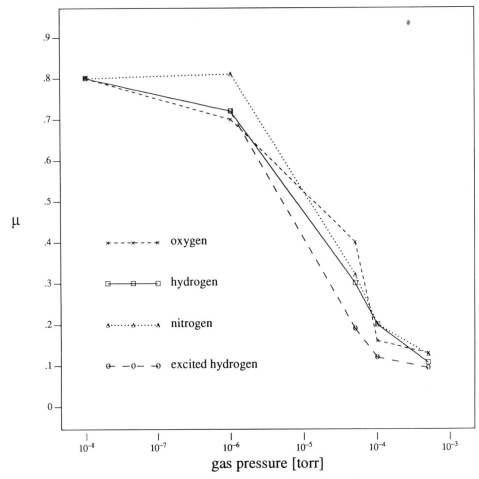

Fig. 4. The coefficient of friction for diamond sliding on diamond in different environments and at various pressures. Each coefficient of friction value plotted in the figure is the average of measurements made over 50 cycles of sliding.

given in the table are averages of measurements made over 25 sliding passes. From Table 2, it is seen that the lowest value for the friction coefficient is obtained from the sliding experiment in laboratory air (relative humidity = 48%), $\mu \approx 0.1$ and the highest value for the friction coefficient in vacuum, $\mu \approx 0.32$. In the presence of molecular hydrogen and helium gases as well as excited hydrogen, the coefficient of friction was $\approx 0.12$ which is somewhat lower than that measured in the presence of oxygen gas ($\mu \approx 0.17$) at $10^{-4}$ Torr. In these experiments, the coefficient of friction value in vacuum was significantly smaller than that observed for diamond sliding on diamond in vacuum. This is most likely due to the fact that there is a thin layer of hydrocarbon lubricant on the disk surface which keeps the friction relatively low even in vacuum.

It has been reported sometimes that humidity changes the friction between a head-slider and a thin-film disk [2]. In order to investigate this effect, air at relative humidities of 12.5, 30, 55 and 79.5% and at atmospheric pressure was continuously flushed through the chamber during a series of sliding experiments. Humidity mea-

TABLE 2

Coefficient of friction of (110) diamond when sliding against magnetic disk material in different environments

| Environment | $\mu$ |
|---|---|
| vacuum ($10^{-7}$ Torr) | $0.32 \pm 0.11$ |
| laboratory air (atmospheric pressure) | $0.1 \pm 0.008$ |
| helium ($10^{-4}$ Torr) | $0.13 \pm 0.01$ |
| hydrogen ($10^{-4}$ Torr) | $0.12 \pm 0.02$ |
| oxygen ($10^{-4}$ Torr) | $0.17 \pm 0.012$ |
| excited hydrogen ($10^{-4}$ Torr) | $0.12 \pm 0.025$ |

sliding speed = 4 mm min$^{-1}$, normal load = 15 gmf

surements were taken with a Vaisala humidity probe and were accurate to within $\pm 1\%$. The coefficient of friction was not observed to change with humidity; its value was within the error bars of the coefficient of friction value measured in laboratory air, see Table 2. On going through the test specimen preparation sequence, it became clear that all of the disk material used in the experiments were stored in a laboratory atmosphere at ambient humidity ($\approx 40$–$50\%$ in our laboratory). Therefore, the surface of the disk material should already contain significant amounts of chemi- and physisorbed water molecules; the presence of these molecules should smear out any changes in $\mu$ occurring due to the change in the relative humidity of the air flowing over the disk surface.

## 4. Discussion

The experimental results have demonstrated the effect of air, oxygen, nitrogen, helium and hydrogen gases in reducing the coefficient of friction of two sliding systems − diamond on diamond, and diamond on thin-film, magnetic disk, when compared with the values of the friction coefficient in vacuum. While the lowest coefficient of friction was observed in laboratory air for both of these sliding systems, hydrogen gas and in particular excited hydrogen caused the most significant decrease in the coefficient of friction between diamond and diamond when the pressures of the two gases were increased from $10^{-6}$ to $10^{-4}$ Torr. This presents indirect but compelling evidence to show that excited hydrogen and to a somewhat lesser extent hydrogen gas adsorbs on the diamond surface and the adsorbed layer prevents direct contact between clean diamond surfaces. Such an adsorbed layer is probably the main reason behind the reduction in friction expecially in the absence of observations of "waxy debris" in our sliding experiments. Hayward and Field [10] also observed a decrease in the friction of diamond on diamond in the presence of low-pressure hydrogen gas which was not excited. If we combine these observations with the spectroscopy results of Pepper [12] and others reviewed therein, the role of adsorbed hydrogen in reducing the friction becomes more clear.

Pepper [12] showed using surface energy loss spectroscopy that the diamond surface undergoes a transformation in its electronic structure when vacuum annealed at $\approx 900$ °C. The transformation is characterized by the appearance of a feature in the bandgap region of the energy loss spectrum and is consistent with the fact that the polished diamond (110) surface is covered with hydrogen which removes the bandgap states and which can be thermally desorbed at 900 °C. This bandgap feature disappears rapidly when the diamond surface is exposed to excited hydrogen at $5 \times 10^{-5}$ Torr. Pepper also observed a reduction in the friction (adhesion) between a clean copper sphere and the diamond surface ((110) and (111)) when the bandgap feature disappears. We have observed, likewise, a reduction in the friction between diamond and diamond when the vacuum annealed surface of a diamond flat was exposed to excited hydrogen.

Hydrogen (also excited hydrogen) and helium gases at $10^{-4}$ Torr were also observed to reduce the friction between diamond and magnetic disk surface more so than oxygen gas but less than laboratory air, see Table 2. Again an adsorption type mechanism may play a role, though this has not been as clearly established as for diamond on diamond. It may be noted that helium has a low molecular interaction due to its low density, monotomic nature and chemical nobility. Even if a slightly adsorbed film of helium were to cover the disk and diamond surfaces, the interaction between the two surfaces could be significantly reduced. In this context it would be interesting to carry out an experiment to see whether the bandgap states on a clean diamond surface (vacuum annealed) are altered by the presence of helium.

With both the sliding systems studied, we have observed the friction coefficient in the presence of various gases to decrease most markedly from its value in vacuum around a pressure of $5 \times 10^{-5}$ Torr, see Fig. 4. As the pressure of the gas is increased still further, the coefficient of friction values are expected to reach the value observed in laboratory air. In the presence of laboratory air at atmospheric pressure, a well adsorbed film is expected to form on the sliding surfaces, thereby resulting in a low value for the friction coefficient. Of course the adsorbability of different constituents of air to the diamond and disk surfaces should be quite different.

The friction measurements for diamond sliding against diamond show that the coefficient of friction in vacuum increased rapidly from an initial value of $\approx 0.2$ to $\approx 0.8$ within five traversals of the diamond flat by the stylus. Such increases have been observed by Bowden and Hanwell [9] also, though after about 500 sliding passes. The contact pressures between the diamond surfaces in their experiments was also higher than in ours. It appears that the reason for this sharp increase in friction with sliding duration is due to the breakdown of surface contaminant films. In the present experiments, at least the diamond flat surface was cleaned by vacuum annealing at 950 °C and therefore little or no contaminant layers are expected to be present at the beginning of the sliding experiment. Hence the coefficient of friction increased within five passes of sliding.

The observations suggest that it may be possible to use single-crystal diamond surfaces treated with excited and maybe even molecular hydrogen as a slider material in magnetic recording systems with ultralow flying heights. The smallest coefficient of friction between diamond and thin-film disk surface measured in our experiments is $\approx 0.1$, which is smaller than values reported for other slider materials in contact with disk surfaces [3]. Furthermore, suitable treatment of the diamond surface and the presence of an appropriate gaseous environment could lead to even lower friction. Another potential application for suitably pre-treated diamonds may be as a bearing material in vacuum. This is because diamond normally cannot be used as a bearing material in vacuum because of its high friction and associated wear. The recent success in the preparation of diamond thin films could accelerate the use of diamond for such applications.

## 5. Conclusions

The coefficient of friction between two sliding single-crystal diamonds and between single-crystal diamond and a magnetic, thin-film disk has been measured in vacuum and in various gaseous environments at low sliding velocities ($<5$ mm min$^{-1}$). While lowest friction was observed in the presence of laboratory air in our experiments, hydrogen gas and in particular excited hydrogen gas at pressures as low as $10^{-4}$ Torr, was found to significantly reduce the friction coefficient of both of the above sliding systems. This suggests that it is this constituent of laboratory air which may contribute to its friction-reducing property. The reduction in friction is most likely to be due to the adsorption of a hydrogen film on the diamond and perhaps also the disk surface leading to a well lubricated sliding interface. The results show that suitably pre-treated diamond surfaces could have potential applications as magnetic head-sliders in recording systems and in bearing surfaces in vacuum.

## Acknowledgments

S. Chandrasekar would like to acknowledge a grant from the National Science Foundation through the Presidential Young Investigator Award which was used in partial support of this research. He would also like to thank the General Electric Co. for supplying some of the diamonds used in the study.

## References

1  C. D. Mee and E. Daniel, *Magnetic Recording I: Technology,* McGraw-Hill, New York, 1987.
2  B. Bhushan, *Tribology and Mechanics of Magnetic Storage Devices,* Springer, New York, 1990.
3  S. Chandrasekar and B. Bhushan, Friction and wear of ceramics for magnetic recording head applications — Part 1: A review, *ASME J. Trib., 112* (1990) 1–16.
4  S. Chandrasekar and B. Bhushan, Friction and wear of ceramics for magnetic recording head applications — Part 2: Friction measurements, *ASME J. Trib., 113* (1991) 313–317.
5  D. Tabor, Adhesion and friction of diamond, in J. E. Field (ed.), *Properties of Diamond,* Academic, London, 1979, Chap. 10, pp. 325–350.
6  M. Casey and J. Wilks, The friction of diamond sliding on polished cube faces of diamond, *J. Phys. D, 6* (1973) 1772–1781.
7  Y. Enomoto and D. Tabor, The frictional anisotropy of diamond, *Proc. R. Soc. London A, 373* (1981) 405–417.
8  B. Samuels and J. Wilks, The friction of diamond sliding on diamond, *J. Mater. Sci., 20* (1988) 213–217.
9  F. P. Bowden and A. E. Hanwell, The friction of clean crystal surfaces, *Proc. R. Soc. London A, 295* (1966) 233–243.
10  I. P. Hayward and J. E. Field, Friction and wear of diamond, in *50 Years of Tribology,* Institute Mechanical Engineers, London, 1987.
11  M. Seal, The friction of diamond, *Philos. Mag. A, 43* (1981) 587–594.
12  S. Pepper, Transformation of the diamond (110) surface, *J. Vac. Sci. Technol., 20* (1982) 213–217.
13  S. Pepper, Effect of electronic structure of the diamond surface on the strength of the diamond–metal interface, *J. Vac. Sci. Technol., 20* (1982) 643–646.

Wear, 153 (1992) 91–105


# A study of parched lubrication


G. Guangteng, P. M. Cann and H. A. Spikes

*Department of Mechanical Engineering, Imperial College of Science and Technology, Exhibition Road, London SW7 2BX (UK)*

(Received August 6, 1991)


## Abstract

The elastohydrodynamic regime of lubrication is now quite well understood, to the extent that theoretically derived equations for lubricant film thickness are used routinely in engineering design. The boundary lubrication regime, which occurs at slow rubbing speeds and in which the surfaces are separated only by a chemically formed layer, is less clearly understood but many of the underlying concepts, such as the formation of a monomolecular adsorbed film or a thicker, reacted, glass-like layer, have been both demonstrated and modelled.

Between these two regimes there remains, however, a territory about which very little is known. This is the regime where a concentrated contact is heavily starved, permitting no conventional elastohydrodynamic film, and yet there remains between the surfaces a film of lubricant whose presence is governed by its rheology rather than its ability to bond to the rubbing surfaces. Such films exist in applications such as gyroscope bearings and probably in many grease-lubricated systems. This regime has been called "parched lubrication" (E. Kingsbury, *Trans. ASME J. Tribol., 107* (1985) 229).

Up until the present it has not been possible to do much more than speculate upon the behaviour of this lubricant regime because such very thin films could not be directly measured. It was possible to deposit lubricant films of known thickness onto surfaces and to measure properties such as friction and wear but it was not possible to relate this to the thickness of such films under operating conditions.

This paper describes an experimental study of parched lubrication which addresses this problem. A recently developed technique for measuring very thin films in concentrated contacts is employed to monitor the occurrence and persistence of thin lubricant films within highly starved, concentrated contacts under a range of conditions. This is combined with IR reflection–absorption spectroscopy to measure the oil film thickness on the out-of-contact surfaces.

The main factors which determine the behaviour and performance of this type of starved film are discussed.


## 1. Background

The regime known as elastohydrodynamic lubrication was first identified by Ertel and Grubin in the 1940s and since then has formed the basis of our understanding of lubricated, concentrated contacts [1]. Conventional hydrodynamic lubrication theory predicts the pressure generated within a lubricant film as it passes between two non-parallel, moving surfaces. Elastohydrodynamics augments hydrodynamics by taking into account two effects of the very high pressures present in non-conforming contacts:

local elastic flattening of the surfaces and the exponential increase in lubricant viscosity that occurs at high pressures [2].

Thus, according to elastohydrodynamics, when two non-conforming bodies such as a ball bearing and raceway are loaded together, a locally flattened contact forms, typically 0.5 mm across. As the two surfaces roll or slide, lubricant is entrained in the converging inlet of this contact. In the region immediately upstream of the flattened contact the hydrodynamic pressures generated within the lubricant become high enough to raise the latter's viscosity by several orders of magnitude. This limits the rate of fluid side flow, with the result that a small but significant proportion of the lubricant is forced to enter the contact to form a separating, elastohydrodynamic film. The film formed is typically 0.1–5 $\mu$m thick. Within the contact the lubricant is under extreme pressure and is a non-Newtonian, glass-like solid. As the lubricant emerges at the rear of the contact it reverts to its original, low pressure, low viscosity state and divides into two thin films on the diverging ball and raceway surfaces.

Elastohydrodynamic (EHD) theory predicts that the separating film thickness will increase with both entrainment speed and bulk lubricant viscosity according to the relationship

$$h \propto (U\eta)^a \tag{1}$$

where $a$ lies between 0.60 and 0.85 depending upon geometry and other operating conditions [2].

The theory of EHD lubrication has been extensively tested experimentally [3–5] with the most unequivocal confirmation coming from direct measurements of film thicknesses in lubricated steel balls on glass or sapphire flat contacts using the technique of optical interferometry [5, 6]. This has demonstrated the validity of eqn. (1) under a wide range of conditions up to a speed limit of about 3 m s$^{-1}$ at which point inlet shear heating effects start to become significant and cause a reduction in film thickness.

The EHD theory outlined above assumes fully flooded inlet conditions and requires that sufficient lubricant be available to fill the converging inlet gap between the two moving surfaces and thence allow the untramelled development of a hydrodynamic pressure.

In many practical applications this is however not the case and the system operates under "starved" conditions. In the late 1960s, starved EHD was studied both theoretically and experimentally. Experimental work was carried out by Wedeven using optical interferometry [7]. Under fully flooded conditions it was noted that a pool of oil formed to fill the inlet and form an air–oil meniscus about one contact diameter out from the immediate contact inlet. However, when the lubricant supply was restricted by wiping most of the oil from the contact track, the meniscus moved inward as the inlet reservoir shrank. This correlated with a reduction in oil film thickness $h$ in the contact and equations relating inlet meniscus distance to film thickness were derived, e.g.

$$\frac{h_{\text{starved}}}{h_{\text{fully flooded}}} = \left(\frac{x/b - 1}{x_0/b - 1}\right)^{0.29} \tag{2}$$

where $x$ and $x_0$ are the distance of the inlet meniscus from the hertzian contact inlet edge in the starved and full-flooded cases respectively [7]. The practical value of such equations is, unfortunately, limited since they require a knowledge of inlet meniscus position, obtainable in optical test equipment but not in real machinery. It is noteworthy that eqn. (2) predicts zero film thickness when the inlet meniscus reaches the contact boundary so that $x/b = 1$. In starvation studies by Wedeven it was found that the film thickness dropped very sharply at this point, to the extent that it could no longer be measured using optical interferometry.

It was a straightforward matter to model this type of starvation numerically, simply by adjusting inlet boundary conditions in the finite difference pressure field across the contact so that hydrodynamic pressure build-up was delayed until close to the contact itself [8].

In 1974 Chiu extended Wedeven's approach by considering how the inlet meniscus was replenished [9]. The aim was to increase the utility of Wedeven's starvation analysis by relating inlet meniscus distance and thence starved film thickness to measurable operating parameters such as rolling speed and lubricant viscosity. Clearly, the lubricant which passes through the contact and remains on the out-of-contact tracks on the rubbing two bodies is not, of itself, sufficient to fill the inlet on a subsequent rotation of the system. Within the inlet, all of the lubricant except that which passes through the contact, will be pushed to the sides to form, in the case of a ball on raceway or flat, two ridges of lubricant on either side of the track. Chiu supposed that some of this latter oil flows back into the track, driven by surface tension, and that the lubricant which thus returns provides the required inlet reservoir. He derived an expression relating the rate of flow-back to lubricant viscosity, rolling speed and surface tension,

$$\frac{\Delta h}{b} = \frac{C_0 T}{2\eta b} t \tag{3}$$

where $\Delta h$ is the increase in film thickness that occurs in the out-of-contact track owing to flow-back in time $t$, $b$ is the radius of the contact, $T$ is the oil–air interface surface tension, $\eta$ is the dynamic viscosity of the lubricant film and $C_0$ is a numerically derived constant, dependent upon the ratio of $b$ to the bulk thickness of the oil coating the two surfaces distant from the contact track, which Chiu termed $h_\infty$.

Chiu also carried out some experimental work using optical interferometry to test the onset of starvation against his model and found good agreement between numerical and experimental data. Unlike Wedeven he did not obtain starvation by restricting the oil supply on the surfaces but instead found that starvation could be produced even in the presence of thick bulk oil films at a combination of high speed for high lubricant viscosity because, under such circumstances, the lubricant could not flow back fast enough into the out-of-contact track to fill the inlet. One limitation of Chiu's mathematical analysis was that it was based upon there being a very thick, out-of-track coating of oil, $h_\infty$ on the two rubbing surfaces. This was appropriate to his experimental conditions but means that his work cannot be directly related to Wedeven's, where starvation was promoted by deliberately reducing the thickness of the oil coating on the bulk surfaces.

The other major contribution to the field of EHD starvation has been made by Kingsbury [10]. After a series of papers on instrument bearing lubrication he proposed, in 1985, a regime known as "parched lubrication" where the degree of starvation is so great that there is effectively no lubricant in the EHD inlet and yet the surfaces are still separated by a fluid-type film. This condition is applicable to some instrument bearings which are run deliberately with a very thin smear of oil but with no bulk free oil on the two surfaces so as to reduce driving torque and provide good spin axis definition.

Kingsbury deposited films of oil 80 and 200 nm thick onto ball bearing surfaces and then showed that bearings could be operated smoothly for considerable periods with no further lubricant supply. He was not able to measure film thickness directly but identified the eventual breakdown of fluid film lubrication by an increase in speed ratio of the bearing. Kingsbury found that the speed ratio remained essentially constant for a period of running up to 4 h in duration, before rising owing, the author suggested, to an increase in contact friction.

Thus, the literature contains two, disparate treatments of starvation of non-conforming contacts. The first, which has been elucidated by Wedeven and Chiu and is reasonably well understood, essentially covers a semi-starved EHD regime where the supply of lubricant to the out-of-contact tracks on the two rubbing surfaces, either by flow-back or other means is enough partially, but not fully, to fill the contact inlet zone. The second form of starvation concerns the fully starved or parched situation where the supply to the out-of-contact track is so small that there is effectively no oil in the inlet except that which passed through the contact on the previous rotation. This condition is still only very poorly understood and little is known about the transition between semi-starved and fully starved lubrication, the lifetime of a parched oil film before it thins to give mixed or boundary lubrication or, indeed, the basic lubrication mechanisms involved in maintaining any lubricant film at all under these conditions.

A major reason for our lack of understanding of the fully starved state is that, because starved film thicknesses are very small, it has not, up to the present, been possible to measure them experimentally. The conventional limit of optical interferometry is approximately one quarter the wavelength of visible light, or 80 nm. Fully flooded EHD film thicknesses are typically between 100 and 5000 nm but once starvation becomes severe the film thickness falls well below the 80 nm measurement limit. This experimental limitation explains why the partially starved regime, where film thicknesses are above 80 nm, is so much more well understood than the parched regime. A second problem in studying extreme levels of starvation is that the supply of lubricant is a critical factor but is very difficult to control in a repeatable fashion. Kingsbury tackled this problem by depositing lubricant from solution and the same approach is adopted in the current study. However, there remains the difficulty of measuring the thickness of deposited lubricant on the surfaces, since there is far too little present to be weighed accurately.

In the current study, two recently developed, advanced experimental techniques, ultrathin film interferometry and Fourier transform IR (FTIR) reflection–absorption spectroscopy, have been used to overcome these problems and thus to carry out a quantitative film thickness study of heavily starved contacts. Ultrathin film interferometry has enabled film thicknesses of lubricant in rolling contacts to be monitored down to a film thickness of 5 nm. FTIR spectroscopy has enabled the film thickness of lubricant films on bulk out-of-contact surfaces to be measured, both before and after a test.

Using these two techniques the aims of the current study were as follows:

(i) to test the parched lubrication concept of Kingsbury and observe the film thickness and lifetime of thin, deposited lubricant films in rolling ball on flat contacts;

(ii) to study the transition between semi-starved and fully starved conditions and to try to bridge the gap between the two approaches.


## 2. Experimental techniques

### 2.1. Ultrathin film interferometry

A novel ultrathin film optical interferometry technique was used to measure EHD film thickness under starved conditions. Unlike conventional interferometry, which has a lower film thickness measurement limit of around 80 nm, the ultrathin film technique can measure films down to as little as 2 nm in rolling contacts. Details of this technique have been reported elsewhere [11] and only a short description will be given here.

A diagram of the rig is shown in Fig. 1. The contact is formed between a 25.4 mm diameter steel ball and the flat surface of a glass disc. The contact is loaded through the ball which is mounted on a shaft, supported on steel rollers and driven via a flexible coupling by an electric motor. The ball drives the disc in nominally pure rolling.

The glass disc is coated on its underside with a chromium semi-reflecting coating, on top of which is a "spacer layer" of transparent silica.

The principle of the technique is shown in Fig. 2. White light is shone into the contact. Some of this light is reflected from the chromium coating but some passes through the silica spacer layer and also through any lubricant film. Constructive interference occurs at a particular wavelength as a result of the path difference between the two reflected beams. By noting which wavelength of white light experiences full constructive interference, the oil film thickness can be determined. The wavelength which has undergone full constructive interference is found by analysing the reflected

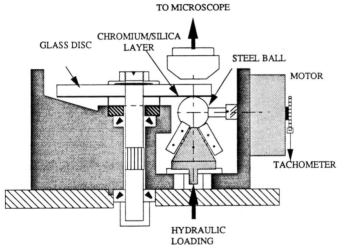

Fig. 1. Schematic diagram of ball on plate test rig.

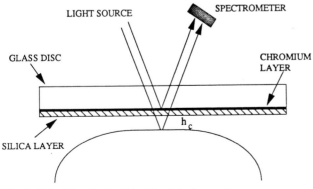

Fig. 2. Principle of ultrathin film interferometry.

96

light using a spectrometer system. The presence of spacer layer ensures a path difference between the two reflected beams even in the absence of an oil film. This makes possible the measurement of very thin oil films, of thickness less than one quarter the wavelength of light.

### 2.2. Fourier transform IR reflection–absorption spectroscopy

The above test method enables very thin films to be measured within rolling contacts. For a full understanding of starvation it is also necessary to know the thickness of the oil layer on the rubbing surfaces outside the contact track. In many starved applications this is likely to be in the range 50–500 nm. Such thin films are very difficult to measure by the standard weighing method since the weight of lubricant is so very small. Typically, a 100 nm film of oil on a 12.7 mm radius steel ball has a mass of 0.0002 g, compared with the ball's mass of 70 g.

An alternative method of measuring film thickness is to observe the optical interference patterns formed by light reflecting off the coated surface. This technique is difficult to apply as a monitoring technique, however, firstly because it requires the film thickness to be already known approximately, to specify the order of the fringes being observed, and secondly because its precision is limited, being based upon the ability of the eye to recognize and distinguish colours.

In the current study, the oil film thickness was measured on the steel ball test surfaces using an FTIR spectrometer in reflection–absorption mode. The spectrometer has a microscope attachment so that an IR spectrum can be taken from a very small area of the surface, 100 $\mu$m across. The strong C–H stretch frequency absorption peak at 2930 cm$^{-1}$, characteristic of all aliphatic, hydrocarbon-based materials, was used as a measure of film thickness. The method was calibrated by depositing lubricant films of different thicknesses onto a steel ball, estimating the thickness of these films by holding the balls under a light and observing the colour of the consequent interference

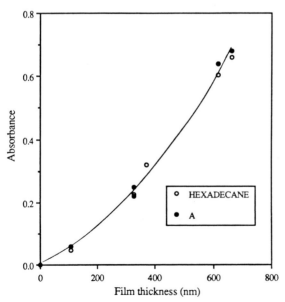

Fig. 3. IR absorbance *vs.* film thickness calibration curve.

fringes and then measuring the extent of IR absorbance at 2930 cm$^{-1}$ using the FTIR microscope. The interference technique could only measure down to 100 nm and the curve was extrapolated to zero for films thinner than that. The spectrometer employed was a Perkin Elmer FTIR instrument with a 3600 data station and Spectra Tech IR Plan microscope. A graph of oil film thickness against IR absorbance obtained for hexadecane and oil A, one of the two synthetic hydrocarbon oils used in the current study, is shown in Fig. 3. As expected the absorbance–film-thickness relationship is not sensitive to details of the lubricant molecular structure of hydrocarbons.

## 3. Materials and test methods

Two additive-free, polyalphaolefin-based, synthetic hydrocarbon test lubricants were tested in this study, one of low and one of high viscosity. The properties of these lubricants are listed in Table 1. The EHD test conditions are summarized in Table 2.

Two lubricant supply methods were used in this study to attain starvation. To examine semi-starved conditions, very small quantities of lubricant were applied to the rotating ball surface using a micropipette. In some cases this quantity was then further reduced by wiping with a paper tissue. It was found that supply using a micropipette gave quite reproducible results although wiping with a tissue was not so repeatable.

In other tests, to obtain very thin films, the method of Kingsbury was employed. The test lubricant was dissolved at fixed concentrations in the range 2%–10% wt./wt. in hexane. The ball was immersed in the solution and then withdrawn by means of its drive shaft. During the withdrawal process the ball was rotated by hand and this was continued until all the solvent had evaporated. The ball was then mounted in

TABLE 1

Properties of the two test lubricants

| | Viscosity (Pas) | | Pressure–viscosity coefficient (GPa$^{-1}$) |
|---|---|---|---|
| | at 25 °C | at 30 °C | |
| Lubricant A (low viscosity) | 0.040 | 0.034 | 12.5 |
| Lubricant B (high viscosity) | 0.93 | 0.645 | 18.0 |

TABLE 2

Experimental test conditions

| | |
|---|---|
| Load (N) | 20 |
| Temperature (°C) | Room temperature (25–28) |
| Rolling speed (m s$^{-1}$) | 0–2 |
| Steel ball | 25.4 mm diameter, M52100 |
| Glass disc | Silica and chromium coated, 10 cm diameter |

the optical EHD test apparatus. This technique was found to give film thicknesses repeatable to within 5%.

Two different test procedures were used to examine respectively the effects of rolling speed and of test time on film thickness.

In one type of test the test rig was assembled and the lubricant applied. The film thickness was then monitored as the rolling speed was raised, as is generally done in conventional optical EHD tests. In some cases the change in film thickness was then noted as the speed was lowered.

In the second type of test, the speed was brought rapidly up to a fixed value and the film thickness monitored at that speed for a considerable time, to determine the stability of any film present.

All tests were carried out in ambient laboratory conditions at a temperature between 25 and 28 °C.

## 4. Results

Figure 4 shows four tests carried out with the low viscosity lubricant A under four limited-supply conditions. Curve A shows the effect of increasing speed after the application of 250 $\mu$l of lubricant, quite a large amount, to the ball surface. Starvation begins at around 0.3 m s$^{-1}$. Curve B shows a continuation of run A after wiping the surplus lubricant off with a tissue. Starvation occurs much earlier, at 0.1 m s$^{-1}$. Curves C and D are curves where respectively 1 and 5 $\mu$l of lubricant were initially deposited onto the ball using a micropipette.

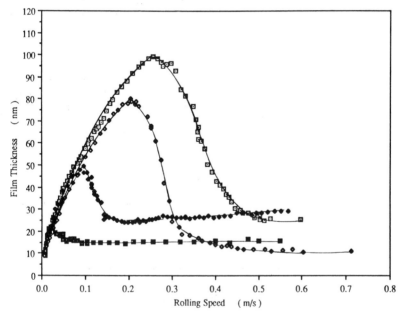

Fig. 4. Effect of rolling speed on film thickness for different bulk coatings of low viscosity oil A at 26.8 °C. □, run A, approximately 250 $\mu$l of oil A on ball; ◆, run B, repeat of test A after wiping ball; ■, run C, 1 $\mu$l of oil A on ball; ◇, run D, 5 $\mu$l of oil A on ball.

Figure 5 shows the same set of results but plotted on log–log axes. This clearly shows the classical linear relationship between log(film thickness) and log(speed) for all the tests, with a sudden drop off in film thickness as starvation occurs. The gradient of the linear portion of Fig. 5 is 0.61.

Of particular interest in Figs. 4 and 5 is evidence that the film thickness reaches a constant level at high speeds.

Figure 6 shows similar film-thickness–speed results but for the more viscous lubricant, B. The results are very similar except that the initial film thickness formed in the fully flooded region is, of course much higher and also the film collapse as starvation occurs seems to take place more precipitately. Each of the curves in Figs. 4–6 took typically 3 h to accrue, so some time effects may be present.

Figure 7 shows how the film thickness responds when the speed is gradually lowered from within the starved regime for an initial 1 $\mu$l micropipetted supply of oil A. The points marked FWD were taken with the speed increasing and BWD with the speed decreasing. The speed–film-thickness relationship is seen to be quite reversible.

Figure 8 shows film-thickness–speed results from tests using solution-deposited films of the low viscosity lubricant. The films were formed from 2%, 4% and 10% wt./wt. solutions to give deposited bulk film thicknesses of 550, 600 and 750 nm respectively. The thickest film appeared initially to give fully flooded behaviour but to starve very early as the speed reached 0.04 m s$^{-1}$. The other two films were starved from the outset and their film thicknesses fell slightly at first but then remained effectively independent of speed throughout the test. Figure 9 shows a log–log plot for the thickest film in Fig. 8. The low speed data superimposes well on the results in Fig. 5. This plot illustrates the effectiveness of the ultrathin film method. All the results in this experiment were below 30 nm and the film thickness levelled off at around 15 nm at high speeds.

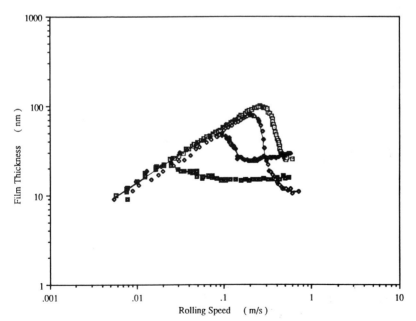

Fig. 5. Log(film thickness) *vs.* log(rolling speed) for different bulk coatings of low viscosity oil A as in Fig. 4.

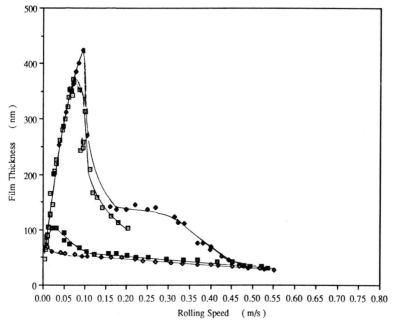

Fig. 6. Effect of rolling speed on film thickness for different bulk coatings of high viscosity oil B at 26.8 °C. For run A, approximately 250 $\mu$l of oil was pipetted onto the ball. This was progressively wiped off with increasing rigour in runs B to D.

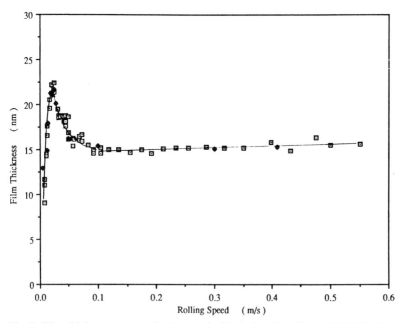

Fig. 7. Film thickness *vs.* speed using 1 $\mu$l of low viscosity oil A at 26.8 °C, showing reversibility with speed: ⊡ FWD, increasing speed; ♦, BWD, decreasing speed.

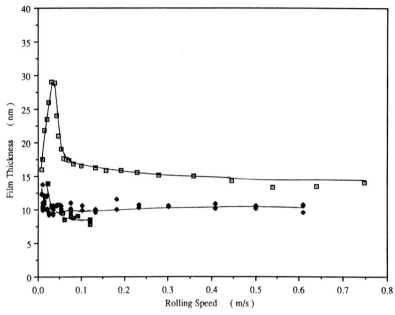

Fig. 8. Film thickness *vs.* speed for solution-deposited layers of low viscosity oil A at 26.8 °C: ▣, 10% solution; ◆, 4% solution; ■, 2% solution.

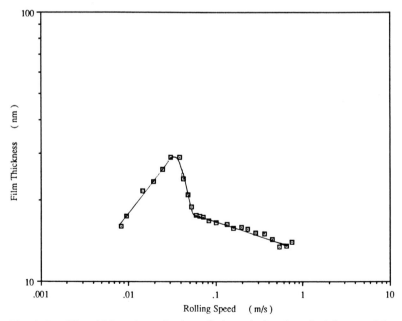

Fig. 9. Log(film thickness) *vs.* log(speed) for solution-deposited layers of low viscosity oil A (10% solution) at 26.8 °C.

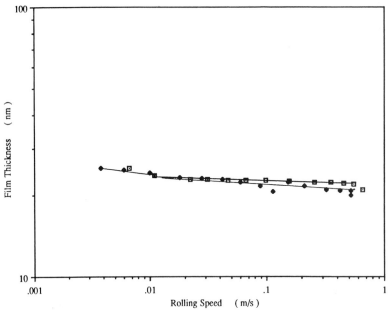

Fig. 10. Film thickness *vs.* speed for solution-deposited layers of high viscosity oil B at 26.8 °C: ⊡, 10% solution; ◆; 4% solution.

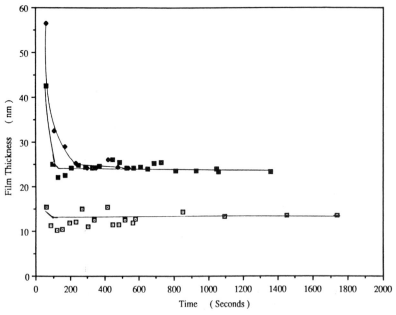

Fig. 11. Film thickness variation with time for solution-deposited films of test oils A and B at a constant speed of 0.01 m s$^{-1}$ and 26.8 °C: ⊡, 4% A; ◆, 10% B; ■, 4% B.

Figure 10 shows film-thickness–speed results for solvent-deposited films of the more viscous oil B. With this lubricant both the 4% and 10% wt./wt. solution-deposited coatings appeared to give fully starved conditions at all speeds and, interestingly, to give a film whose thickness was independent of the bulk oil deposit thickness on the surface. This suggests that flow-back may not be the only factor in determining EHD film formation in these tests.

Figure 11 shows results of three tests where the speed was brought rapidly to 0.1 m s$^{-1}$ and then held at this level for some time. Two tests are for solution-deposited coatings of the more viscous oil. One is for a similar coating of the less viscous lubricant. With the more viscous oil the film thickness was seen to drop very quickly from its bulk coating thickness value to around 25 nm. With the less viscous oil no such effect was noted, presumably because it took place too rapidly to follow, since the first film thickness reading took 40 s to acquire. The less viscous oil also settled to a lower film thickness than the more viscous oil.

## 5. Discussion of results

The results with the thicker films at low to moderate speed accord well with previous optical studies by Wedeven and Chiu. The film thickness initially rises with speed in accordance with fully flooded EHD theory. At a critical speed the film thickness ceases to rise and then falls rapidly as the speed is increased further. This is the semi-starved region where the film thickness correlates with the inlet meniscus. As expected, the speed at which the transition from fully flooded to starved conditions occurs depends both upon the lubricant viscosity and upon the thickness of lubricant coating present on the bulk surfaces outside the contact track. This is almost certainly because flow-back into the track will decrease at both high viscosities and thin bulk oil coatings.

The film thickness does not, however, continue to decrease to zero as the speed increases. Instead, at high speeds, the film thickness levels off to a finite value, generally between 10 and 30 nm. This is not predicted from Chiu and Wedeven's model of starvation and is initially surprising. It is, however, reminiscent of the parched lubrication behaviour described by Kingsbury, although it is induced in Figs. 4 and 6 primarily by high speed rather than by the limited oil availability studied by Kingsbury.

The behaviour of the very thin, solvent-deposited film over time in Fig. 11 is very much in accordance with the parched lubrication model proposed by Kingsbury. As suggested by Kingsbury, when a very thin coating of lubricant is present on the rolling surfaces, a separating film forms between the surfaces that survives for many minutes and even hours. Kingsbury could not measure the thickness of these films but the current study indicates that they are in the range 10–30 nm, depending upon lubricant viscosity and, in some cases, deposited bulk oil thickness. In Kingsbury's study the film appeared eventually to thin to allow the surfaces to come directly into contact. For the 80 nm bulk oil film this took 4 min but for the 200 nm coating, over 2 h. In the current study, once the film had fallen from its original bulk coating thickness there was no further evidence of thinning over 30 min of running, but it should be noted that the films used in this study were thicker than those that Kingsbury employed.

This study shows, for the first time, the essential unity of the semi-starved, inlet meniscus-driven starvation phenomenon and the parched lubrication concept. As the speed is raised or the lubricant supply limited, a bearing system passes from fully flooded conditions, through semi-starved conditions where the film thickness drops, into the parched lubrication regime where a thin but speed-independent film thickness can persist for long periods, perhaps indefinitely.

The observation that a lubricant film of some 10–30 nm continues to separate rolling surfaces even under fully starved conditions is of considerable practical significance. The combined surface roughness of a typical ball-bearing–raceway contact is 50 nm, so parched lubrication can play an important role in protecting these surfaces.

## 6. Mechanisms

The starvation behaviour observed above may usefully be considered in terms of the competing mechanisms of flow of lubricant into and out of the contact tracks on the rolling surfaces.

So long as oil is not deliberately supplied, such as by dip or spray, there are two mechanisms of flow into the track suggested in the literature. Chiu focuses on surface-tension-driven flow and derives eqn. (3) to describe its rate [9]. This equation, which is only valid for very thick out-of-contact oil coatings, predicts flow to be linear with time but independent of rotating speed.

A second possible mechanism of in-flow is due to the centrifugal force pushing the oil radially outward on the glass disc. This can be estimated from an analysis due to Jeffreys [12] who indicates that the flow rate per unit length $Q_L'$ through a film of thickness $h$ under gravity will be given by:

$$Q_L' = \frac{\rho g h^3}{3\eta} \tag{4}$$

where $g$ is the constant of acceleration due to gravity, $\rho$ is the density of the oil and $\eta$ the dynamic viscosity. For a rotating glass disc, where there will be a radial accelerating force outwards, the net flow rate into the whole circumference of the track will, to a rough approximation, be given by:

$$Q' = \frac{2U^2\rho(h_\infty^3 - h_0^3)}{3\eta} \tag{5}$$

where $h_\infty$ is the bulk surface oil coating (neglecting oil ridges), and $h_0$ is the minimum oil film thickness. Interestingly, this flow rate increases with speed owing to the consequent increase in radial acceleration.

There are also two ways that oil can be lost from the contact tracks, by displacement of the inlet meniscus and by side-leakage from the contact itself. In the fully flooded or semi-starved conditions, where there is a reservoir of oil in the inlet, displacement should be the dominant loss mechanism, since all of the inlet pool will be displaced as the contact passes. The extent of the inlet reservoir, and thus the position of the inlet meniscus, will depend upon the rate of flow of oil into the track, so that starvation will occur when the in-flow during a single rotation of the ball and disc is insufficient to fill the inlet to the extent required for full pressure build-up. This is the condition analysed by Chiu and it is critically speed dependent.

As the inlet meniscus approaches the edge of the hertzian contact, either at high speed or owing to a limited bulk oil coating thickness, the loss of oil by displacement will become very small indeed. The dominant oil loss mode is then likely to be side-leakage. Kingsbury suggests that this can be analysed in terms of squeeze flow [13]. Except for an indirect effect via film thickness, this oil loss mode will not depend directly upon rolling speed of the ball or disc since it is a continuous process from within the contact itself, regardless of how fast the ball is travelling. Thus it is possible to envisage how the film thickness will reach a constant, limiting value under extreme starvation at high speeds since, once the speed-dependent displacement of the inlet meniscus has occurred we are left with the balance of the two speed-independent terms: surface-tension-driven flow into the contact track and squeeze flow out of it.

Clearly, all these flow processes are amenable to analysis and modelling and work in this area is proceeding.

## 7. Conclusions

Using an ultrathin film interferometric method it is possible to measure the film thickness in rolling EHD contacts under conditions of severe starvation.

Under fully starved conditions, where there is no measurable inlet meniscus, a film of oil remains to separate the rolling surfaces. This film is typically 10–30 nm thick. The film represents the "parched lubrication" regime defined by Kingsbury.

This type of starvation can be produced by solvent-depositing very thin bulk oil coatings onto the two rubbing surfaces as was done by Kingsbury. However, it can also be produced with moderately thick bulk coatings of oil in systems operating at high speeds.

This type of lubrication is likely to be of great practical significance in the lubrication of high speed bearings, as well as in systems with an intrinsically limited oil supply to the track, such as grease lubricated systems.

## References

1  A. N. Grubin, Contact stresses in toothed gears and worm gears, Book 30, Central Scientific Research Institute for Technology and Mechanical Engineering, Moscow, 1949, DSIR, London, Translation No. 337.
2  B. T. Hamrock and D. Dowson, *Ball Bearing Lubrication: The Elastohydrodynamics of Elliptical Contacts,* Wiley, New York, 1981.
3  A. Dyson, H. Naylor and A. R. Wilson, The measurement of oil film thickness in elasto-hydrodynamic contacts, *Proc. Inst. Mech. Eng., 180 (3B)* (1965–1966) 119.
4  L. B. Silbley and F. K. Orcutt, Elastohydrodynamic lubrication in rolling contact, *ASLE Trans., 4* (1961) 234–249.
5  R. Gohar, Oil film thickness and rolling friction in elastohydrodynamic point contact, *Trans. ASME J. Lubr. Technol., 93* (1971) 371–382.
6  C. A. Foord, W. C. Hamman and A. Cameron, Evaluation of lubricants using optical elastohydrodynamics, *ASLE Trans., 11* (1968) 31–43.
7  L. D. Wedeven, D. Evans and A. Cameron, Optical analysis of ball bearing starvation, *Trans. ASME J. Lubr. Technol., 93* (1971) 349–363.
8  B. J. Hamrock and D. Dowson, Isothermal elastohydrodynamic lubrication of point contacts, part IV — starvation results, *Trans. ASME J. Lubr. Technol., 99* (1977) 15.
9  Y. P. Chiu, An analysis and prediction of lubricant film starvation in following contact systems, *ASLE Trans., 17* (1974) 22.
10 E. Kingsbury, Parched elastohydrodynamic lubrication, *Trans. ASME J. Tribol., 107* (1985) 229.
11 G. J. Johnston, R. Wayte and H. A. Spikes, The measurement and study of very thin lubricant films in concentrated contacts, *STLE Trans. 34* (1991) 187.
12 H. Jeffreys, The draining of a vertical plate, *Proc. Cambridge Philos. Soc., 26* (1929–1930) 204–205.
13 E. Kingsbury, Cross flow in a starved EHD contact, *ASLE Trans., 16* (1973) 276–280.

*Wear, 153* (1992) 107–117

# The behaviour of transverse roughness in sliding elastohydrodynamically lubricated contacts

J. A. Greenwood and K. L. Johnson

*Department of Engineering, University of Cambridge, Trumpington Street, Cambridge, CB2 1PZ (UK)*

(Received August 21, 1991)

## Abstract

Recent calculations have shown that in a sliding elastohydrodynamically lubricated contact, any initial roughness largely disappears and is replaced by (often large) pressure variations. This paper gives an elementary analysis of the process for transverse roughness which provides the conditions under which it occurs, and allows the magnitude of the pressure ripples to be estimated. If the fluid is non-Newtonian, the behaviour will be very different.

## 1. Introduction

Recent advances in computational technique have enabled a number of authors [1–5] to study the behaviour of single transverse ridges or dents, or transverse sinusoidal ripples, on the stationary surface in a sliding elastohydrodynamic contact. Indeed, solutions have been obtained for the more difficult problem of longitudinal waviness [2–5], and the much more difficult transient problem of moving roughness [1, 3, 4], but these do not concern us here. In this paper we consider the extent to which the quantitative behaviour found by computation can be predicted from simple consideration of an infinite sinusoidal surface, and so separate the effect of roughness from that of the bulk elastohydrodynamically lubrication (EHL) contact.

The full numerical solutions show that if we start with a regular sinusoidal surface roughness, transverse to the entraining direction, then in simple sliding with the rough surface stationary, the waviness virtually disappears, to be replaced by sinusoidal pressure ripples (see Fig. 1). This occurs both when the ripples are across a line contact [1, 3], an elliptical contact [2] or a circular contact [3]. A single ridge also disappears, and is replaced by a pressure ripple of much the same size as if the ridge were part of a wavy surface [1, 3]. In contrast, Lubrecht *et al.* [5] show rather limited flattening of sinusoidal roughness across a circular contact; we shall see below why this should be.

It is possible that the basic result, the almost perfect flattening, should have been predicted theoretically, perhaps by consideration of the relative stiffness of film and elastic solid (see ref. 6); here we simply accept it as our starting point. It follows, as Kweh *et al.* [2] point out, that the amplitude of the pressure ripples is what we should expect from elastic contact theory; we shall develop this remark to obtain a criterion for asperity flattening.

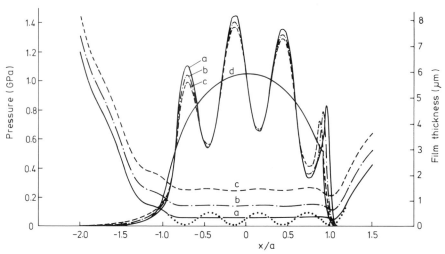

Fig. 1. Longitudinal centre line pressure distributions and film thickness profiles for an elliptical contact (from ref. 2): (a) 140 °C, $\Delta=0.25$ $\mu$m, (b) 80 °C, $\Delta=0.25$ $\mu$m, (c) 50 °C, $\Delta=0.25$ $\mu$m, (d) 140 °C, $\Delta=0$. The undeformed roughness is shown superimposed upon the film profile for 140 °C.

## 2. Analysis: incompressible Newtonian lubricant

We consider the roughness to be sinusoidal ripples, perpendicular to the entraining direction, so that lubrication will be governed by the one-dimensional Reynolds' equation, and we enquire whether the pressure needed to flatten these ripples elastically can indeed be generated. With a finite contact, the pressures can only be found numerically, but if the contact area contains many ripples, then we may use the simple elastic solution for a half-space covered by ripples. It is well known [7] that the elastic deformation of the surface of a half-space due to a pressure

$$p=\bar{p}+p_1 \cos 2\pi x/\lambda \qquad (1a)$$

is

$$v=\frac{\lambda p_1}{\pi}\frac{1-\nu^2}{E} \cos 2\pi x/\lambda \qquad (1b)$$

However, the pressure acts on both bodies forming the contact, and a pressure which eliminates the roughness on one body produces (if the two are the same material) a (negative) roughness of the same amplitude on the other. We are interested not in flattening one surface but in producing a film which is parallel, or almost so; we need therefore the combined deformation, which is

$$v=\frac{2\lambda p_1}{\pi E'} \cos 2\pi x/\lambda \qquad (2)$$

where

$$2/E'=(1-\nu_1^2)/E_1+(1-\nu_2^2)/E_2$$

Thus, an initial sinusoidal roughness of amplitude $\Delta$ can only give a parallel film if there are pressure ripples of amplitude $p_1 = \pi E' \Delta/2\lambda$ superimposed on the smooth surface EHL pressure distribution.

Now, the one-dimensional Reynolds' equation for a lubricant whose viscosity obeys the Barus law $\eta = \eta_0 \exp(\alpha p)$ can be written

$$\frac{h - h^*}{h} = \frac{h^2}{6\eta_0 u_1} \exp(-\alpha p) \frac{\mathrm{d}p}{\mathrm{d}x} \tag{3}$$

To give sinusoidal pressure variations of amplitude $p_1$, the film shape must be

$$\frac{h - h^*}{h} = -\frac{\pi p_1 h^2}{3\eta_0 u_1 \lambda} \exp(-\alpha \bar{p}) \exp(-\alpha p_1 \cos 2\pi x/\lambda) \sin 2\pi x/\lambda \tag{4}$$

Since we are assuming an almost parallel film, i.e. $|(h - h^*)/h| \ll 1$ we have

$$1 - h/h^* \approx \mu \exp(-\alpha p_1 \cos \theta) \sin \theta \tag{5}$$

where

$$\mu = (\pi p_1 h^{*2}/3\eta_0 u_1 \lambda) \exp(-\alpha \bar{p}) \quad \text{and} \quad \theta = 2\pi x/\lambda$$

Figure 2 shows these film thickness variations for a range of values of $\alpha p_1$ (scaled for convenience to keep the maximum amplitude constant). For $\alpha p_1 < 0.5$ the variation is almost sinusoidal (90° out of phase with the pressure ripples), but as $\alpha p_1$ increases the film thickness remains almost constant except for local excursions on either side of the pressure minimum. We shall refer to film thickness variations of this kind as a "Reynolds" ripple.

It can be shown that the maxima and minima are numerically equal, and occur at $\theta = 180° \pm \epsilon$, where

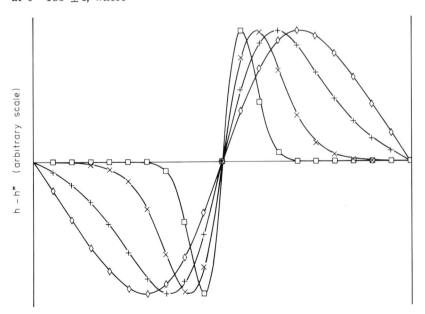

Fig. 2. Film thickness variation for an imcompressible fluid. The pressure minimum is at the mid-point of the graph: $\diamond$ $\alpha p_1 = 0.3$, $+$ $\alpha p_1 = 1$, x $\alpha p_1 = 3$, $\square$ $\alpha p_1 = 10$.

$$\cos \epsilon = \frac{2\alpha p_1}{[1+(2\alpha p_1)^2]^{1/2}+1} \tag{6}$$

(typically $\epsilon$ is 20°–30°), and that the values are approximately (for $\alpha p_1 > 1$)

$$\pm \mu \, \frac{\exp(\alpha p_1 - \frac{1}{2})}{(\alpha p_1 + \frac{1}{4})^{1/2}}$$

Thus, the greatest deviation from a parallel film is $k_1 h^*$, with

$$k_1 \equiv \left[ \frac{h-h^*}{h^*} \right]_{max} \approx \frac{\pi}{3\sqrt{e}} \frac{p_1 \, h^{*2}}{\eta_{min} u_1 \lambda} \frac{1}{(\alpha p_1 + \frac{1}{4})^{1/2}} \tag{7}$$

where $\eta_{min}$ is the viscosity at the pressure minima ($\theta = \pi$). The analysis will be valid provided

(1) the pressure ripples are small enough for the pressure to remain positive everywhere ($p_1 < \bar{p}$), and

(2) $(h/h^* - 1)_{max} \ll 1$.

In practice the second condition is almost redundant. If we estimate $h^*$ from the Kapitza relation $h^* \approx 1.5 \, (\alpha \eta_0 \bar{u})^{2/3} R^{1/3}$ [8] we find

$$k_1 \approx (\alpha p_1)^{1/2} \exp(-\alpha p_{min})(Rh^*/3\lambda^2)^{1/2}$$

which for plausible values of $R, h^*$ is about $\exp(-\alpha p_{min})$ when $\lambda = 0.2$ mm; hence for $\alpha p_{min} > 2$ the film thickness is almost constant. This is confirmed by the various numerical solutions: there is no trace of a Reynolds ripple, except that Goglia *et al.* [1] show what they refer to as a 'microconstriction' at the edges of their hertzian contact - that is, where $p_{min}$ is small. The appearance is the same as our Reynolds ripple.

### 2.1. Effect of compressibility

For a compressible lubricant the term $(h - h^*)$ in the Reynolds equation is replaced by $h - h^* \rho^*/\rho$ where $h^*$ and $\rho^*$ are the values at the pressure maximum. Accordingly,

$$h - h^* = (h - h^*)_0 + h^* (\rho^*/\rho - 1) \tag{8}$$

where $(h - h^*)_0$ is the previous result for an incompressible fluid. It is usual in EHL to take the density variation to be

$$\frac{\rho}{\rho_0} = \frac{1 + \gamma p}{1 + \beta p} \tag{9}$$

with $\gamma = 2.266 \times 10^{-9}$ m$^2$ N$^{-1}$, $\beta = 1.683 \times 10^{-9}$ m$^2$ N$^{-1}$. Then for $p = \bar{p} + p_1 \cos \theta$ we have

$$\frac{\rho^*}{\rho} - 1 = \frac{(\gamma - \beta)p_1}{1 + \beta(\bar{p} + p_1)} \frac{1 - \cos \theta}{1 + \gamma(\bar{p} + p_1 \cos \theta)} \tag{10}$$

Figure 3 shows an example of the film thickness variation for a compressible fluid, with the amplitude of the Reynolds term arbitrarily taken to be one-fifth of the compressibility term. It is clear that because of the local nature of the Reynolds ripple, and the slow variation of the compressibility term, it is possible and convenient to treat the two terms separately.

It is easy to show that for plausible values of $\bar{p}$ and $p_1$ we can put $\cos \theta = -1$ in the denominator in eqn. (10) without serious error (or even drop $p_1$ from the

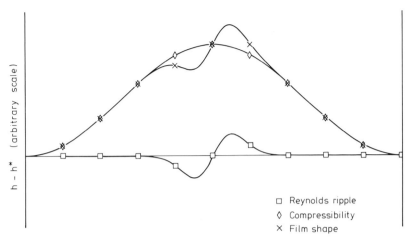

Fig. 3. Combined film thickness due to 'Reynolds' variation and compressibility, $\alpha p_1 = 10$, $k_1 = 0.2k_2$.

denominator completely!) whereupon compressibility leads to a sinusoidal film thickness variation, in phase with the original roughness, with amplitude $k_2 h^*$, where

$$k_2 = \frac{(\gamma - \beta)p_1}{(1 + \beta p_{max})(1 + \gamma p_{min})} \qquad (11)$$

The original idea that the film becomes parallel must now be modified; the amplitude $k_2 h^*$ is left after a change of shape of amplitude $2p_1 \lambda / \pi E'$, so the original amplitude must be

$$\Delta = \frac{2\lambda p_1}{\pi E'} + k_2 h^*$$

$$= p_1 \left[ \frac{2\lambda}{\pi E'} + \frac{(\gamma - \beta)h^*}{(1 + \beta p_{max})(1 + \gamma p_{min})} \right] \qquad (12)$$

This determines $p_1$ (by iteration, starting with $p_{max} = p_{min} = \bar{p}$). We note that for mineral oil and steel at 1 GN m$^{-2}$ the ratio of the two terms is

$$\frac{\text{oil compliance}}{\text{elastic compliance}} \approx 24 \frac{h^*}{\lambda}$$

so that the elastic term will normally be dominant and the roughness will disappear. However, for roughness of very short wavelength this does not hold and the roughness will persist.

## 2.2. Comparison with complete numerical elastohydrodynamic lubrication solutions

The most comprehensive information on the magnitude of the pressure ripples is given by Venner [3], who has a graph showing the increased maximum pressure $\Delta p$ as a function of wavelength. Table 1 gives the values read from his graph, together with our values from eqn. (12).

Agreement is excellent. The slightly smaller effect of pressure $\bar{p}$ at longer wavelengths that we find compared with Venner may be an error in reading his graph, or a real defect of our model due to our assumption of an infinite number of pressure ripples.

TABLE 1

Comparison of amplitudes of pressure ripples with Venner

| λ (mm) | 0.125 | 0.25 | 0.375 | 0.5 | 0.625 | 0.75 |
|---|---|---|---|---|---|---|
| Venner | | | | | | |
| $\Delta p$ ($\bar{p}=1$) | – | 0.67 | 0.44 | 0.32 | 0.27 | 0.23 |
| $\Delta p$ ($\bar{p}=3$) | 1.41 | 0.70 | 0.47 | 0.35 | 0.30 | 0.26 |
| Present theory | | | | | | |
| $p_1$ ($\bar{p}=1$) | – | 0.675 | 0.459 | 0.347 | 0.279 | 0.233 |
| $p_1$ ($\bar{p}=3$) | 1.406 | 0.707 | 0.472 | 0.354 | 0.284 | 0.236 |

$\Delta=0.5$ μm, $E'=226$, all pressures are in G.

TABLE 2

Comparison with ref. 2

| | $h^*$ (μm) | $p_1$ (GN m$^{-2}$) | $k_1h^*$ (μm) | $k_2h^*$ (μm) |
|---|---|---|---|---|
| Case c, 50 °C | 1.34 | 0.379 (0.33) | 0.00014 | 0.0371 (0.04) |
| Case b, 80 °C | 0.70 | 0.408 (0.36) | 0.00035 | 0.0210 (0.01–0.02) |

Values in brackets are estimates from graphs given by Kweh *et al* [2].
$\lambda=0.2$ mm, $\Delta=0.25$ μm, $E'=227$ GN m$^{-2}$, $\bar{p}=1$ GN m$^{-2}$, $u_1=50$ m s$^{-1}$.

TABLE 3

Comparison with Lubrecht *et al.*, ref. 5

| $h^*$ (μm) | $p_1$ (GN m$^{-2}$) | $k_1$ | $k_2$ | $k_1h^*$ (μm) | $k_2h^*$ (μm) |
|---|---|---|---|---|---|
| 0.229 | 0.482 | 0.853 | 0.102 | 0.195 | 0.023 |

$\lambda=0.05$ mm, $\Delta=0.1$ μm, $E'=200$ GN m$^{-2}$, $\bar{p}=0.5$ GN m$^{-2}$, $\alpha=20$ m$^2$ GN$^{-1}$, $\eta_0u_1=0.0833$ N m$^{-1}$.

We find, in agreement with Venner, that for $\lambda=0.125$ mm at 1 GPa the amplitude of the pressure variation exceeds $\bar{p}$ so that the solution must be rejected: the pressure would have to be negative, and cavitation will occur.

The flattening found by Venner is too complete to permit a numerical comparison; all that can be said is that our theory and his calculations agree that the residual variation of film thickness is small. Kweh *et al.* [2] give a case where the variation is just measurable; a comparison is given in Table 2.

It should be noted that Kweh *et al.* consider transverse ripples crossing a circular hertzian contact, so our assumption of an infinite wavy surface is drastic. It is, however, surprising that the pressures for the finite contact should be the smaller ones.

A final comparison may be made with Lubrecht *et al.* [5], who studied the effect of transverse ridges (among other cases) crossing a circular EHL contact. Unlike the other papers cited, they found large film thickness variations across the contact, accompanied by pressures falling to near zero in the valleys.

Our calculations for their case are given in Table 3.

The combination of moderate $\bar{p}_0$ and short wavelength gives a Reynolds ripple larger than the original waviness. Clearly, our analysis is inapplicable, but nonetheless it correctly indicates that flattening does not occur, and predicts the amplitude of the pressure variations with reasonable accuracy.

## 3. Discussion

Most of the authors quoted seem not to have been concerned with the aspects of wavy-surface EHL which interest us - the degree of smoothing, or even the magnitude of the pressure ripples - except in so far as they may lead to surface fatigue. Their primary interest is in the effect of waviness on the minimum film thickness and, in particular, whether this occurs at the rear of the contact as for smooth surfaces. They appear to have answered this question, but in an unhelpful way: both the average film thickness and the minimum film thickness may be either increased or decreased by the waviness - depending entirely on the phase of the waviness with respect to the end of the inlet. Apparent effects of wavelength seem to be due to the consequential, but inadvertent, phase shift, and are of no real interest.

To us, the important consequence is that in heavily loaded contacts the waviness disappears (as does apparently a random roughness), but is replaced by large pressure ripples. (It is demonstrated by Goglia et al. [1], and Venner [3], and tacitly assumed in our theory, that the location of the waviness has no effect on the magnitude of the ripples.)

The magnitude $p_1$ of the pressure ripples is given by eqn. (12)

$$p_1 = \Delta \left[ \frac{2\lambda}{\pi E'} + \frac{(\gamma - \beta)h^*}{(1 + \beta p_{max})(1 + \gamma p_{min})} \right]^{-1}$$

and it appears that this will be valid, and the residual waviness (given by eqn. (11)) will be small, provided the minimum pressure is positive, say for example, $p_1 < 0.9\bar{p}$.

It is, of course, well known that traction in an EHL contact is grossly overestimated by an analysis assuming a Newtonian lubricant. Although the film thickness appears to be correct, the high pressures in the hertzian region raise the viscosity and hence the traction to impossibly high levels even when the Barus relation is replaced by the more moderate Roelands relation. At high speeds the viscosity is reduced by thermal effects, but at moderate speeds the assumption of non-Newtonian behaviour some form of shear thinning is essential.

The overall film thickness is of course established by the behaviour in the inlet, so there is no great inconsistency in calculating it using a Newtonian model, but it is certainly inconsistent to calculate the behaviour of the waviness in the high pressure region without using a model consistent with the observed tractions.

We must consider, therefore, whether the above results remain valid.

## 4. Reynolds–Eyring equation

There is as yet no general agreement on the form of the non-Newtonian constitutive relation, but it seems clear that the Eyring relation

$$\dot{\gamma} = \frac{\tau_0}{\eta} \sinh \frac{\tau}{\tau_0}$$

is reasonably close [9, 10]. Here $\tau_0$ is the "Eyring stress", typically 5 MPa but increasing slightly with pressure; the viscosity $\eta$ of course still depends strongly on pressure, as in the Newtonian models.

Houpert and Hamrock [11] and independently, Conry *et al.* [12] have derived the equivalent to the Reynolds equation for an Eyring fluid. This may be written

$$1 - \frac{h^*}{h} = \left[ S^2 + \left( \frac{\sinh t_p}{t_p t_v} \right)^2 \right]^{1/2} \left( \coth t_p - \frac{1}{t_p} \right) \tag{13}$$

where

$$t_p = \frac{(h/2)(\mathrm{d}p/\mathrm{d}x)}{\tau_0} \qquad t_v = \frac{\eta(u_1 + u_2)}{h\tau_0} \qquad S = \frac{u_2 - u_1}{u_2 + u_1}$$

We note that the shear stresses at the surfaces for a Newtonian fluid are $\tau_0(St_v \pm t_p)$, giving some identification to the terms. Typically $t_v$ (the non-dimensional shear stress based on velocity) is greater than 100, usually much greater, while $t_p$ (the non-dimensional shear stress based on pressure) is of order unity. It follows that for pure rolling ($S = 0$) the equation reduces to

$$1 - \frac{h^*}{h} = \frac{1}{t_p t_v} \left( \cosh t_p - \frac{\sinh t_p}{t_p} \right) \tag{14}$$

$$\approx \frac{1}{6} \frac{t_p}{t_v} = \frac{h^2}{12\eta\bar{u}} \frac{\mathrm{d}p}{\mathrm{d}x} \tag{14a}$$

and we have recovered the normal Reynolds equation. However, unless $S$ is small, the square root term approximates to $|S|$ and the equation reduces to

$$1 - \frac{h^*}{h} = |S| \left( \coth t_p - \frac{1}{t_p} \right) \tag{15}$$

$$\approx \frac{1}{6} |S| t_p = \frac{(|S|h/6)(\mathrm{d}p/\mathrm{d}x)}{\tau_0} \tag{15a}$$

That is, except for pure rolling, the behaviour is very different from that of a Newtonian fluid — being independent of viscosity and speed!

We note also, that just as the ordinary Reynolds equation may be written

$$\left( \frac{h^*}{h} \right)^2 \left( 1 - \frac{h^*}{h} \right) = \frac{h^{*2}}{12\eta\bar{u}} \frac{\mathrm{d}p}{\mathrm{d}x} \tag{16}$$

from which it may be deduced that no solution exists unless $\mathrm{d}p/\mathrm{d}x < (16/9)(\eta\bar{u}/h^{*2})$ (ref. 13, see also ref. 14), so there is a limit on $\mathrm{d}p/\mathrm{d}x$ for the Reynolds–Eyring equation to have a real solution. For pure sliding ($S = 1$) we find that

$$(h^*/2)(\mathrm{d}p/\mathrm{d}x)/\tau_0 \qquad < C < 1 \tag{17}$$

where for all non-small values of $(t_p t_v)$ the limit is close to unity (*e.g.* $t_p t_v = 100$, $C = 0.97501$). This is not a shear stress limitation as such, since the restriction is on $h^* \, \mathrm{d}p/\mathrm{d}x$ not on $h \, \mathrm{d}p/\mathrm{d}x$; the parallel with the limit for a Newtonian fluid (which of course does not have a characteristic shear stress) is appropriate. (Indeed, as $t_p t_v \to 0$, $C \approx \frac{2}{3}(t_p t_v)^{1/2}$ for any $S$, and the Newtonian limit is recovered.)

### 4.1. Behaviour of waviness with an Eyring fluid

We note first that, if the film thickness becomes almost constant, eqn. (12) giving the amplitude of the pressure variations will still be valid. This agrees with the results found by Chang *et al.* [4] for a single asperity; the pressures for an Eyring lubricant are much the same as for a Newtonian lubricant.

If we therefore assume as before that $p = \bar{p} + p_1 \cos 2\pi x / \lambda$, eqn. (27) severely restricts the amplitude of waviness we can study. Taking $p_1 = \pi E' \Delta / 2\lambda$ for simplicity we must have

$$\Delta < \frac{2\lambda^2 \tau_0}{\pi^2 E' h^*}$$

or, using eqn. (12),

$$\Delta < \frac{\lambda \tau_0}{\pi} \left[ \frac{2\lambda}{\pi E' h^*} + \frac{\gamma - \beta}{(1 + \beta p_{max})(1 + \gamma p_{min})} \right]$$

Thus, for the conditions used by Kweh *et al.* [2] (Table 2), the amplitude of the waviness needs to be reduced from 0.25 $\mu$m to 0.15 $\mu$m for any solution to be possible, even though with a Newtonian lubricant the waviness is removed.

Even when a solution is possible, the results with an Eyring fluid are very different. It is a straightforward matter to substitute $p = \bar{p} + p_1 \cos 2\pi x / \lambda$ into eqn. (18) (with $S = 1$) and compare the film thickness variations with those already found. Figure 4 shows the results of varying $\tau_0$ from the realistic value of 5 MN m$^{-2}$ up to 100 MN m$^{-2}$, where the behaviour approaches Newtonian. Compressibility has been ignored. For $\tau_0 < 20$ MN m$^{-2}$ the film thickness variations are 90° behind the pressure. The variations below $h^*$ are greatly increased, but those above $h^*$ are enormously increased; indeed, it is here that the Reynolds–Eyring equation ceases to have a solution if the amplitude of the pressure ripples is increased. It is found that reducing the velocity from 50 m s$^{-1}$ to 0.5 m s$^{-1}$ makes no detectable difference (we have assumed that

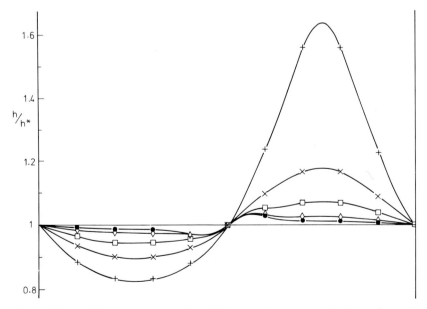

Fig. 4. Effect of Eyring stress on film thickness variation, $\bar{p} = 0.4$ GN m$^{-2}$, $p_1 = 0.25$ GN m$^{-2}$, $\eta_0 = 0.01$ Ns m$^{-2}$, $\alpha = 20$ m$^2$ GN$^{-1}$, $\mu_1 = 0.05$–50 m s$^{-1}$, $h^* = 1$ $\mu$m, $\lambda = 0.2$ mm: $+ \tau_0 = 5$ MPa, $\times \tau_0 = 10$ MPa, $\square \tau_0 = 20$ MPa, $\Diamond \tau_0 = 50$ MPa, $\bullet \tau_0 = 100$ MPa.

$h^*$ does not alter); increasing the mean pressure from 0.4 GN m$^{-2}$ to 1 GN m$^{-2}$ eliminates the local oscillation (the Reynolds ripple) present near the pressure minimum for the higher values of $\tau_0$.

These results agree with those found by Chang *et al.* [4] for a single asperity. They found that conditions which with a Newtonian lubricant led to the almost complete disappearance of the asperity, with an Eyring fluid, leave the total film thickness variation (maximum to minimum) comparable with the initial asperity height, and give a film shape closely resembling that of Fig. 4.

## 5. Conclusion

In an EHL contact with a Newtonian fluid, a transverse sinusoidal roughness will be removed, except for a residual component due to the compressibility of the fluid, in phase with the original roughness; it will be replaced by a sinusoidal pressure ripple whose amplitude $p_1$ can be found from

$$p_1 = \Delta \left[ \frac{2\lambda}{\pi E'} + \frac{(\gamma - \beta)h^*}{(1 + \beta p_{max})(1 + \gamma p_{min})} \right]^{-1}$$

provided that $p_1$ is distinctly less than the mean pressure $\bar{p}$. If the minimum pressure $\bar{p} - p_1$ approaches zero, the analysis fails, and it appears that the roughness will persist. Provided the minimum pressure is not too small so that the minimum viscosity is still high, the only film thickness variation will be that due to compressibility (and so can never lead to metallic contact across the film), the "Reynolds ripples" will be very small.

However, it is widely agreed that the behaviour of lubricants is non-Newtonian in the central region of an EHL contact. If the lubricant is assumed to follow the Eyring law (and presumably any other law which represents shear-thinning), it appears that for small amplitudes of waviness, pressure ripples of much the same magnitude will arise, but will not compress the waviness to produce a parallel film. For larger amplitudes, but amplitudes which would still yield a parallel film with a Newtonian lubricant, the pressure variation ceases to be sinusoidal and our analysis fails.

From the point of view of understanding the mechanisms of film breakdown in the so-called "mixed" regime, it would appear important to consider in more detail the response of a non-Newtonian lubricant to rippled surfaces at EHD pressures. Work to this end is in progress.

## References

1 P. R. Goglia, C. Cusano and T. F. Conry, Effects of irregularities on the EHL of sliding line contacts, part 1, single irregularities, *ASME J. Tribol.*, *106* (1984) 104–112; part 2, wavy surfaces, *ASME J. Tribol.*, *106* (1984) 113–119.
2 C. C. Kweh, H. P. Evans and R. W. Snidle, Micro-EHL of an elliptical contact with transverse and three-dimensional sinusoidal roughness, *ASME J. Tribol.*, *111* (1989) 577–583.
3 C. H. Venner, Multilevel solution of the EHL line and point contact problems, *Ph. D. Thesis*, University of Twente, Enschede.
4 L. Chang, C. Cusano and T. F. Conry, Effects of lubricant rheology and kinematic conditions on micro-EHL, *ASME J. Tribol.*, *111* (1989) 344–351.
5 A. A. Lubrecht, W. E. Ten Napel and R. Bosma, Influence of longitudinal and transverse roughness on the EHL of circular contacts, *ASME J. Tribol.*, *110* (1988) 421–426.

6 K. L. Johnson, J. A. Greenwood and S. Y. Poon, A simple theory of asperity contact in EHL, *Wear, 19* (1977) 91–108.

7 K. L. Johnson, *Contact Mechanics*, Cambridge University Press, Cambridge, 1985.

8 J. F. Archard and E. W. Cowking, Elastohydrodynamic lubrication at point contacts, *Proc. Inst. Mech. Eng., 180* (3B) (1965–1966) 47–56.

9 W. Hirst and A. J. Moore, Non-Newtonian behaviour in EHL, *Proc. R. Soc. London, Ser. A, 337* (1974) 101.

10 K. L. Johnson and J. Tevaarwerk, Shear behaviour of EHD oil films, *Proc. R. Soc. London Ser. A, 356* (1977) 215.

11 L. Houpert and B. J. Hamrock, EHL calculations used as a tool to study scuffing. *In 12th Leeds–Lyon Symp., Lyon,* Butterworths, London, 1986, pp. 146–155.

12 T. F. Conry, S. Wang and C. Cusano, A Reynolds–Eyring equation for EHL in line contacts, *ASME J. Tribol., 109* (1987) 648–658.

13 H. Blok, Inverse problems in hydrodynamic lubrication, in D. Muster and B. Sternlicht (eds.), *Proc. Int. Symp. on Lubrication and Wear, Houston, TX, 1963,* McCutchan, Berkeley, 1965, pp. 1–15.

14 D. Dowson and G. R. Higginson, *Elastohydrodynamic Lubrication*, Pergamon, Oxford, 1966.

# Quantitative analysis of surface topography using scanning electron microscopy

N. K. Myshkin, A. Ya. Grigoriev and O. V. Kholodilov

*Metal–Polymer Research Institute, Byelorussian Academy of Science, Gomel (Byelorussia)*

(Received August 6, 1991)

## Abstract

A supplement to the existing methods of studying topography is proposed, using methods based on analysis of the textural and morphological characteristics that are widely used in image processing theory. A survey of methods of studying roughness, allowing both the images of surfaces and a quantitative estimate of the surface properties to be obtained simultaneously, is presented. A method of evaluating topography using scanning electron microscopy and a personal computer is described.

## 1. General concepts

In studying topography, the need arises for the solution of three basic problems: description of the surface, development of a representative surface evaluation system, and technical realization of the measurements. The last problem is of special importance, since our theoretical concepts are based on quantitative estimates obtained from measurement. Therefore, it is evident that roughness measurements are of primary importance in studying topography. However, the conventional practice in microgeometry is such that we generally proceed in the reverse direction, *i.e.* from a particular theoretical model to the instrumental realization of methods for measuring the microgeometry parameters.

As is well known, the deviation of a real surface from an ideally smooth surface is associated with action on the body of various factors [1]. The heights of the asperities formed fall within a wide range. While, on the basis of the discrete nature of matter, their minimal dimensions may be limited by the dimensions of atomic and molecular formations, the maximal heights (as stated by the authors [2]) are proportional to the length of the profile examined. However, in spite of the fact that there is no universally substantiated criterion for distinguishing asperities on the basis of scale, at the present time there exists the concept of the surface as an ensemble of asperities of four dimensional levels: macrodeviations, waviness, roughness, and subroughness [3]. The basis for this classification is the theorem of superpositioning of deviations due to independent factors [4].

The foregoing concepts form the representation of a surface in such fields as mechanics, machine construction technology, friction theory, heat conduction and so on. On the whole, according to this representation, the surface is examined as the realization of a random field [4–6], the characteristics of which are evaluated on the basis of two-dimensional profilogram samples. In this case the system of topography estimates is based on analysis of the histogramic characteristics of the asperities over some range of their values.

A characteristic feature of this approach is the fact that the mutual influence and interrelationship of the asperities are generally ignored (except for the fact that the surfaces may be classified as isotropic or anisotropic), *i.e.* the spatial organization of the asperities is not taken into account. We can illustrate the ambiguity arising in surface representations in this case. Figures 1(a) and 1(b) show photographs (obtained by scanning electron microscopy (SEM)) of surfaces with different spatial structures. Figures 1(c)–1(f) and Table 1 present the results of a comprehensive study of their microgeometry with the aid of histogramic characteristics and correlation and spectral characteristics. We see that, in spite of the significant difference between the studied objects, practically all the quantitative estimates obtained coincide within the limits of measurement errors, which makes it impossible to determine criteria on the basis of which we can judge the nature of the difference between these surfaces.

The principal reasons why it is not possible to evaluate the topographic properties of surfaces solely with the aid of histogramic estimates were discussed in ref. 7. For example, according to the authors of ref. 7, by superposing histogramic parameters we can achieve quite a good description of practically any phenomenon, including a phenomenon unrelated to the region of the object examined. When we consider that modern instruments yield about 50 different characteristics, all of which may be used subsequently, the drawbacks of this approach become still more evident.

For a more correct representation of the surface it is necessary to be able to characterize it as a three-dimensional object having a definite topology. We can identify at least two levels of concepts which make this possible. The first level is associated with the structural organization of the asperities relative to one another; the second level is associated with the morphological structure of the elementary objects constituting the surface. We shall examine each of these levels.

The structural organization of the asperities can be described using textural characteristics which are widely used in solving various problems in the image analysis field. In spite of the quite clear understanding of what texture is, it is very difficult to define this object formally. This concept can be introduced recursively as follows [8]. On the surface we can find a fragment, the "pattern" of which is repeated regularly within the limits of a region which is large in comparison with the dimensions of the fragment. This pattern is formed by elementary component parts of the fragment, arranged in some non-random order. The elementary part is an approximately homogeneous unit, having approximately the same form over the entire texture region.

In addition to texture characteristics, which can be examined as the "background" spatial characteristic, on the surface we identify an ensemble of specific elements. Such elements may include pores, cracks, individual asperities, transfer particles, segments of non-homogeneities of a different nature, and so on. These elements often have maximal information content in certain studies and their presence explains many processes taking place in the contacting of solid bodies. We should note that the texture and element concepts are interdefinable. The basic internal relationships existing between them can be described as follows. If the changes in local characteristics within the limits of a segment are small, then the element morphology is the dominant characteristic of the geometric properties of the surface. If the characteristics of the elements undergo significant changes, then the texture will be the dominant characteristic of the region.

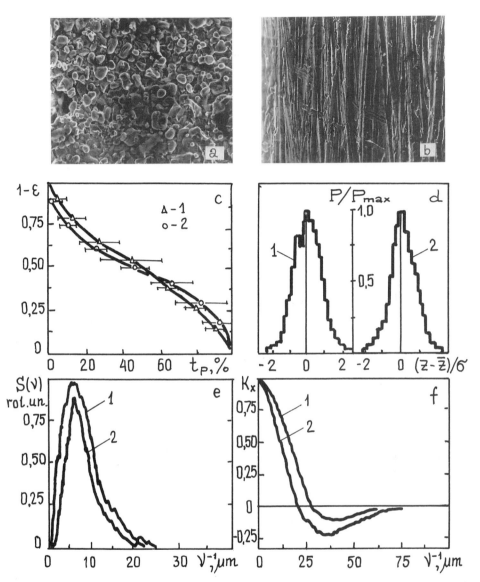

Fig. 1. Results of surface topography study: (a) SEM images of surface modelling isotropic roughness; (b) SEM images of surface modelling anisotropic roughness; (c) bearing area curves; ((d)–(f)) profile autocorrelation functions (index 1 corresponds to the characteristics obtained from surface a; index 2 corresponds to the characteristics obtained from surface (b)).

It is evident that on the surface we can identify several other structures that are associated with the conformation of the surface. We can assume that all these structures form a definite hierarchical sequence. This point of view is finding more and more acceptance at the present time. For example, Gogenepoin and Rogues-Carmes [9] proposed that the microgeometry of surfaces be examined as the realization of a fractal, *i.e.* a structure having a conformation that repeats on various scales and can

TABLE 1

Results of roughness study

| Parameter | Unit of measurement | Specimen 1 | Specimen 2 |
|---|---|---|---|
| $R_a$ | $\mu$m | $3.2 \pm 0.5$ | $2.3 \pm 0.3$ |
| $R_{max}$ | $\mu$m | $19.3 \pm 4.2$ | $15.9 \pm 2.0$ |
| $R_z$ | $\mu$m | $15.0 \pm 3.7$ | $12.2 \pm 1.4$ |
| $H_m$ | $\mu$m | $165.9 \pm 44.4$ | $117.7 \pm 8.7$ |
| $H$ | $\mu$m | $56.7 \pm 18.6$ | $43.2 \pm 7.6$ |
| $R_{SK}$ | – | $-0.1$ | $-0.4$ |
| $R_{KU}$ | – | $0.03$ | $0.04$ |
| $\Delta A$ | deg | $21.9 \pm 1.5$ | $21.0 \pm 1.1$ |
| $A_{SK}$ | – | $-0.4 \pm 0.1$ | $0.2 \pm 0.2$ |
| $A_{KU}$ | – | $-0.8 \pm 0.3$ | $-0.7 \pm 0.3$ |
| $D_e$, $10^4$ | $\mu$m$^{-2}$ | $3.2 \pm 2.0$ | $3.0 \pm 1.0$ |
| $U$ | – | $1.08 \pm 0.02$ | $1.08 \pm 0.01$ |

be determined on the basis of a stochastic interpolation procedure [10]. The basic properties of fractals are determined by the recursive definition of the morphology of the surface formations. As was shown in ref. 11, fractal theory is quite widely applicable, even for the description of surfaces obtained by sand blasting (which are traditionally considered to have a purely random structure). On the whole, the possibility of using fractals reflects surface properties such as the continuity and correlation of the ensembles of its points in space. Thus a surface is a complex, structurally organized geometric object, on which we must identify the characteristic associated both with the scale factors (metric characteristics) and with the concept of the topology of its structure (topological characteristics). However, at the present time an approach has been adopted in which attention is devoted only to the metric characteristics (at least in solving problems associated with friction theory). The inadequacy of this approach has been noted by many authors. Specifically, the need was shown in ref. 12 for a combined analysis of the information obtained by profilometry and microscopy.

The metric and topological characteristics require different techniques to represent the basic information. Thus, for quantitative evaluation of the metric relations it is only necessary to know the values of certain characteristics, for example the heights of the asperities, regardless of their coordinates on the plane. The sampling of these values can also be organized arbitrarily. The most widely used approach is measurement of the roughness along some track with organization of the array of obtained readouts in vector form. However, there is one important aspect concerning interpretation of the estimates. The fact is that a surface is a three-dimensional object, while the analysis of its characteristics is performed in the present case on the basis of two-dimensional profile samples. We can note a whole series of errors that arise in this case. Theories making it possible to perform the corresponding correction have only been developed for surfaces of certain classes [5], and in the general case the procedure for extending the two-dimensional characteristics to an object having three-dimensional properties is non-trivial [13]. For example, a signal that depends on a single spatial variable requires different treatment from a signal that depends on two spatial variables.

In this connection the need arises for the use and development of appropriate instrumental techniques, combining the possibilities of obtaining images of the object and at the same time determining its roughness. Examination of the existing laboratory and engineering methods that meet these requirements makes it possible to emphasize primarily those that use computers.

## 2. Scanning electron microscopy as a measuring system

SEM can be considered as a powerful instrument of morphology analysis, allowing a wide selection of methods for the examination of surface features [14]. It has been shown that it can also be used to measure surface heights at given points [15–17]. In order to use SEM to evaluate roughness statistics, profile measurements and, finally, topographical analysis, additional problems should be solved. We carried out a project of developing an SEM–PC system combining conventional morphology analysis with quantitative analysis of the main topographical parameters.

The SEM images are formed by low energy secondary electrons (SE) whose area of generation is comparable with the electron probe size. The SE emission intensity depends on the local incidence angle of the beam [18];

$$S = S_0 \sec \alpha \tag{1}$$

where $S_0$ is the signal at normal beam incidence, and $\alpha$ is the local slope of surface inclination.

This allows the possibility of determining the slope angle of the asperities of a test specimen by SEM, and using the obtained result for a quantitative evaluation of a number of surface topography characteristics: the specific area, moments of angular asperity distributions, etc. [19]. However, if we consider SEM as a measuring system, it should be noted that a fundamental restriction exists with the SE recording scheme that does not allow intepretation of the SE signal directly and quantitatively. In addition, the signal recorded by SEM is composite in nature. One component is caused by true SE, and the other component is caused by SE excited by BSE (backscattered electrons).

When using the SE signal for quantitative measurements, it is necessary to solve the problem by determining the real angular dependence of the signal recorded by SEM and by finding methods for its processing which take into account the specific character of the detector system used.

A method which uses the peculiarities of image formation by SEM has been proposed elsewhere [20]. It has also been shown that the angular dependence of the signal is given by eqn. (1) and this dependence can be used for quantitative measurements of topographic parameters.

## 3. Statistical parameters obtained by scanning electron microscopy

In recent years, a mathematical approach of the random field theory has been used to describe topography. Knowledge of statistical moments of the spectral density of zero ($m_0$), second ($m_2$) and fourth ($m_4$) orders is helpful in finding characteristics such as height parameter, angular coefficient, and asperity top curvature. Analysis of the SE intensity against the angle of beam incidence indicates that the manner of variations and SE signal amplitude can be useful for the direct estimation of the number of surface extrema $D_s$ (the number of intersections of the signal and the middle line per unit length) and the mean tangent of the microasperity slope $\tan \alpha$. Then the spectral moments are found as follows:

$$m_2 = (\tan \alpha)/\pi \qquad m_4 = 6\pi D_s m_2 \sqrt{3} \qquad m_0 = (\pi m_2)^2/[2l(D_s/1.2)^{1/2} - 1] \qquad (2)$$

There is a relationship between the spectral moments and roughness parameters

$$R_a = (2m_0/\pi)^{1/2} \qquad H_m = (m_2/m_0)^{1/2} \qquad H = 2\pi(m_4/m_0)^{1/2} \qquad (3)$$

The intensity of SE emission depends on the local slope at the point of beam incidence according to eqn. (1).

The tangent of the surface slope at a given point is numerically equal to the modulus of the surface gradient

$$\tan \alpha = q = [(dz/dx)^2 + (dz/dy)^2]^{1/2} \qquad (4)$$

Then expression (1) can be written as follows:

$$S = S_0(1 + q^2)^{1/2} \qquad (5)$$

The gradient probability density has the form [6, 21]

$$P(q) = \Delta^{-1/2}q \exp(-M_2 q^2/4\Delta_1)I_0[q^2(M_2^2 - 4\Delta_1)^{1/2}/4\Delta_1] \qquad (6)$$

By scanning the beam in a raster pattern we can find the value of the signal at each point of the surface being analysed. Averaging the results of measurements over the entire area and transforming the obtained expression to the form $\bar{S}/S_0$, we obtain

$$\bar{S}/S_0 = \int_0^\infty (1 + q^2)^{1/2}P(q) \, dq \qquad (7)$$

Comparing this expression with the results of ref. 22, it is not difficult to see that the right-hand side of eqn. (7) is simply the specific area of a gaussian surface. This implies that $U = \bar{S}/S_0$. We note that when measuring the secondary electron emission (SEE) intensity at each point of a surface that has extrema, the minimal value $S_{min}$ will be equal to $S_0$ since the gradient is equal to zero at the extremum points.

Thus the specific surface area (SSA), taking account of its roughness, can be defined as the ratio of the average value of the array of SEE intensity readouts to the minimal value $U = \bar{S}/S_{min}$.

We shall examine the possibility of evaluating the SSA over a select asperity spacing range. Realization of this possibility enables the surface structure and its degree of development on various scale levels to be determined. Because of the finite dimensions of the primary beam, the value of the SEE intensity is determined by the emission characteristics not at a point but rather over some region bounded by the probe dimensions. Since interaction of the beam electrons takes place over the entire area of the given region, the asperities with characteristic dimensions less than the probe diameter have an influence on the value of the signal. If the topographic characteristics of such asperities are stationary within the limits of the entire surface being analysed, then their influence reduces to the addition of a component to the signal level. This can be taken into account by suitable normalization. Then for a given probe diameter the analysed value of the signal will characterize the slope of the nominal surface of the interaction region [15].

Therefore, the selectivity of SSA evaluation for the lower scale of asperity spacings can be realized by changing the electron beam diameter. Values of SSA obtained by this method are determined by asperities with spacings larger than the beam diameter and less than the size of the area under examination. The SSA for a given spacing scale can be obtained using the following assumptions. Let SSA values have been measured using two different beam diameters $d_1$ and $d_2$ ($d_1 < d_2$). Obviously, $F(d_1) > F(d_2)$ as a real area $F(d_1)$ measured with beam diameter $d_1$ is greater than $F(d_2)$ because of the additional value related to asperities with spacings between $d_1$ and $d_2$. A surface area with spacings higher than $d_2$ can be considered as nominal in this case. Then, the SSA can be found from the equation

$$U(d_1, d_2) = F(d_1)/F(d_2)$$

Multiplying the numerator and denominator on the right-hand side by the scanning area $l^2$ we can obtain

$$U(d_1, d_2) = U(d_1)/U(d_2) \qquad (8)$$

The accuracy of the method realized using SEM was determined on the basis of the characteristics of a model surface. The slopes of this surface were simulated by mounting a smooth surface (glass plate) at various angles relative to the incident beam. From the ensemble signal readouts obtained we determined the SSA, the magnitude of which was compared with the value calculated analytically. The results of the experiments showed that the SSA was determined with an accuracy of about 5%. We studied specimens of rough surfaces obtained by machining: grinding (internal, circular, plane), turning, reaming, face milling, and planing. The choice of machining techniques is associated with their wide use in fabricating machine parts. The parameter $R_a$ of the surfaces studied ranged from 0.20 to 1.60 $\mu$m. To determine the contribution to the SSA of asperities of different sizes, the measurements were made with a variable probe diameter — from 0.07 to 9.0 $\mu$m. The results of these investigations are given in Table 2.

For a fixed probe diameter the scatter of the SSA values of different specimens (regardless of $R_a$) is within the limits of experimental error, therefore we plotted the averaged dependences of the SSA on the lower asperity spacing bound.

It is clear that a decrease in spacings between asperities corresponds to a relative increase in slope angles and SSA (Figs. 2 and 3). When examining this correlation we should remember that there is a superposition of asperities with different size scales on the surface. From this point of view the increase in slope angle with decrease in spacing can be explained by the additional effect of smaller asperities placed on the slopes of larger asperities. Selective estimation of the slope angles obtained at fixed values of spacings between asperities (Fig. 4) has shown that values of the angles are 6°–7° for all the spacings and for all the specimens.

## 4. Surface profiles obtained

Consider a surface with a certain roughness value. Assume that the picture contrast recorded is determined only by the surface topography, and the surface is a set of randomly oriented elementary planes with areas no smaller than the generation areas. Figure 5 shows a unit area of this surface between the coordinate planes. The coordinate system $XYZ$ is fixed to the incident electron beam, i.e. the $y$ axis. The $Y$–$X$ plane is the scanning plane. Let a denote the point of beam incidence at the surface. The signal value at the point of incidence is independent of the scanning direction and

TABLE 2

Effect of machining type on the SSA (numerator) and average slope angle (denominator); the electron beam diameter was in the range 0.07–9.0 $\mu$m

| Treatment | Roughness $R_a$ ($\mu$m) | | | |
| --- | --- | --- | --- | --- |
| | 1.6($\nabla$6) | 0.8($\nabla$7) | 0.4($\nabla$8) | 0.2($\nabla$9) |
| Turning | Chip-type machining | | | |
| | 1.047 | 1.036 | 1.054 | – |
| | 5.40 | 5.43 | 8.55 | |
| Boring | 1.013 | 1.012 | 1.015 | – |
| | 6.59 | 5.05 | 7.68 | |
| Planing | 1.069 | 1.043 | – | – |
| | 7.21 | 8.03 | | |
| Milling | 1.055 | 1.029 | – | – |
| | 8.41 | 5.03 | | |
| Cylindrical grinding | Abrasive machining | | | |
| | – | 1.043 | 1.050 | 1.061 |
| | | 7.11 | 5.05 | 9.32 |
| Internal grinding | 1.047 | 1.035 | 1.026 | 1.034 |
| | 7.30 | 9.15 | 8.08 | 7.28 |
| Plane grinding | 1.047 | 1.038 | 1.038 | 1.036 |
| | 7.03 | 10.80 | 6.47 | 8.75 |

is always determined by the beam incidence angle, which in general for an isotropic surface does not lie in the plane of beam travel. To determine the surface profile for the scanning plane, let us find the slope values of microasperities at this section. If the surface section profile is represented as the realization of a random function

$$Z = f(x) \tag{9}$$

then in the vicinity of the beam incidence point the following expression holds

$$dZ = \tan \psi \, dx \tag{10}$$

where $\psi$ is the beam incidence angle in the scanning plane. From analytical geometry the angles $\alpha$ and $\psi$ are related in the following way

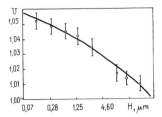

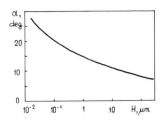

Fig. 2. Averaged dependence of SSA on magnitude of low asperity spacing bound for all the studied surfaces.

Fig. 3. Asperity slope as a function of the profile spacing.

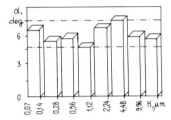

Fig. 4. Profile of irregularities of slope distribution depending on spacing.

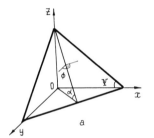

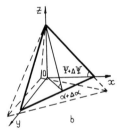

Fig. 5. Diagram for the derivation of eqn. 15: (a) for the surface before rotation; (b) for the surface after rotation.

$$\cos \alpha = \cos \psi \sin \phi \qquad (11)$$

where $\phi$ is the angle between a vector perpendicular to the plane of interest and the $y$ axis. Determine the contrast arising from the specimen rotation about the $y$ axis through an angle

$$C = (S_1 - S_2)/S_1 \qquad (12)$$

where $S_1$ and $S_2$ are the signal values at the $i$th point before and after rotation respectively.

Taking into account that for SE the following equation holds (1), the incremental signal $S_1 - S_2$ may be calculated by differentiating expression (1) with respect to $\psi$ in terms of eqn. (11)

$$dS = S_0 \tan \psi \Delta\psi / \cos \psi \sin \phi \qquad (13)$$

128

Then eqn. (12) results in

$$C = \tan \psi \Delta \psi \qquad (14)$$

Thus, the contrasts at identical points due to specimen rotation about the coordinate axis depend only on the tilt angle $\Delta \psi$ and the profile slope at the section perpendicular to the rotation axis. The elevation at this section may be expressed as

$$Z(x) = \frac{1}{\Delta \psi} \int_0^\infty \tan \psi \, dx = \frac{1}{\Delta \psi} \int_0^\infty [(S_1 - S_2)/S_1] \, dx \qquad (15)$$

For the anisotropic surfaces, a scanning direction can always be chosen such that the surface normally coinciding with the direction of maximum SE emission will lie in the plane of beam travel, that is, when $\alpha$ is equal to $\psi$. Then the height of a surface element may be defined as

$$Z(x) = \int_0^\infty [(S/S_0)^2 - 1]^{1/2} \, dx \qquad (16)$$

For this method we can evaluate the limiting vertical resolution on the basis of the physical aspects of SE formation and the capabilities of the recording equipment. In the case examined we can consider that the vertical resolution is determined by

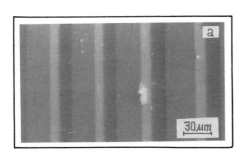
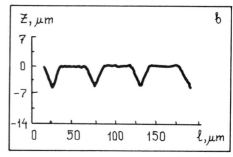

Fig. 6. Reconstruction of the surface profile: (a) SEM image of the surface (horizontal field width of 300 $\mu$m); (b) reconstructed profile.

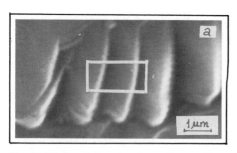
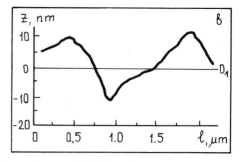

Fig. 7. Study of the structure of crystalline silicon cleavage: (a) SEM image of the surface (horizontal field width of 10 $\mu$m); (b) reconstructed surfface profile, $00_1$ is the electron beam line scan.

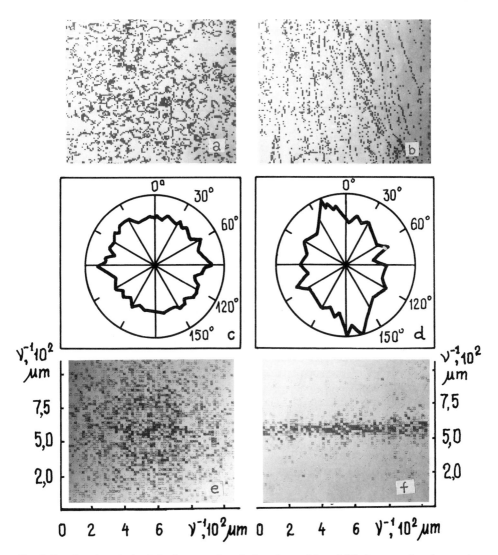

Fig. 8. Results of analysis of the images of studied surfaces: (a) and (b) show results of operation of segmentation and findings of skeletons of the images presented in Fig. 1(a) and 1(b); (c) and (d) are rotational histograms of a number of points of binary images of (a) and (b) for specified directions of summation; (e) and (f) show two-dimensional spectral densities of images (a) and (b) in Fig. 1.

noise fluctuations and the electron probe diameter. Examinations of the characteristics influencing the magnitude of the noise and use of the Zigert–Kotel'nikov "ideal observer" criterion make it possible to obtain the relation connecting the noise in the measuring system with the vertical resolution $R_v$ (without accounting for aberrations in the SEM electron-optical system):

$$R_v = (2W/\pi\gamma)(2e/\beta\Delta t)^{1/2}\tan\{\arccos[W^{-1}\ln(g/p) + 0.5]\} \tag{17}$$

130

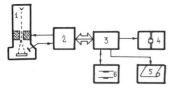

Fig. 9. Block diagram of a measuring SEM microcomputer complex: (1) scanning electron micrograph; (2) linking block; (3) computer; (4) data plotter; (5) matrix printing device; (6) flexible disk.

We can find that for the most widely used tungsten thermocathode with a signal-to-noise ratio of about 10 (which is quite achievable) $R_v$ is of the order of 10 nm.

Several types of specimens were studied to test the validity of the proposed method. Figure 6 presents the results of a surface study of a test object with a triangular cross-section. The fidelity of the reconstruction of the surface profiles by the proposed procedure at low magnifications is supported by the profilometric study. Figure 7 illustrates the potentiality of the method at high magnifications. The figure shows a silicon surface cleavage at a 30 000-fold magnification.

The texture and the morphology, combined under the general definition of "topology", require for their quantitative evaluation a special technique for representation of the information — the images determined by some functional transformation of geometric properties of the surface to values of brightness of a series of points. The existing analytic apparatus of image processing theory [23] makes it possible to identify effectively and analyse the various formations on the surface, perceived as characteristic visually interpretable elements. Thus, Figs. 8(a), (b) show the results of analysis of the images of Figs. 1(a), (b), which involved segmentation of the images and finding the skeletons, making it possible to identify the texture of the surfaces. Further analysis of the binary images obtained by the rotational histogram method makes it possible to determine the dominant orientation of the asperities and the direction of their grouping (Figs. 8(c), (d)).

## 5. Instrumentation and software

The procedure developed was tested on an SEM–microcomputer complex, a block diagram of which is shown in Fig. 9. The computer (3) exchanges information with the scanning electron microscope (1) through a connecting block (2) which includes an analog-to-digital converter to enter images into the computer (8 bytes, 12 $\mu$s cycle), a numerical scanning generator (256–256 points), which controls the probe sweep and SEM display, a digital-to-analog converter to enter the results (8 bytes), a control circuit to synchronize the complex and switch SEM regimes according to the program. The software based on the methods described can realize the estimation of roughness and morphological analysis. The software is composed on the module principle which permits new procedures to be incorporated. The interface is inserted into the XT-slot of the PC and ensures connection of all types of commonly used microscopes.

# 6. Conclusions

The surface is a complex three-dimensional object with a spatial correlation. Geometrical structures related in a hierarchical sequence can be separated in this object. From this point of view studies in topography should be based on the synthesis of the surface from elements determined at different morphological scales. A more adequate characterization of surfaces requires the combined use of concepts of both metric and topological properties. Considering that in studying surfaces and analysing images we must solve problems that are associated with the study of structured objects and, in addition, considering the fact that the images can be examined as a technique of organization of roughness information, it is possible to use the analytic techniques of image processing theory to study surface microgeometry.

SEM–computer systems can be considered as an adequate instrument of surface analysis with capabilities both for morphology and quantitative roughness measurements, as well as surface texture evaluation.

# References

1 I. V. Dunin-Berkovskii and A. N. Kartashova, *Measurement and Analysis of Surface Roughness, Waviness, and Noncircularity,* Mashinostroenie, Moscow, 1978 (in Russian).
2 R. S. Sayles and T. R. Thomas, Surface topography as a non-stationary random process, *Nature (London), 271*(2) (1978) 431–434.
3 N. B. Demkin and E. V. Ryzhov, *Surface Quality and Contact of Machine Parts,* Mashinostroenie, Moscow, 1981 (in Russian).
4 D. V. Linnik and A. P. Khusu, Mathematical-statistical description of ground surfaces, *Inzh. Zb. SSSR, 20* (1954) 46–57 (Russian translation).
5 P. R. Nayak, Random process model of rough surfaces, *ASME J. Lubr. Technol., 93F*(3) (1971) 398–407.
6 N. F. Semenyuk and G. A. Sirenko, Description of the topography of anisotropic rough friction surfaces with the aid of a random-field model (total curvature, principal curvatures and ratio of principal curvatures at tips of microasperities, specific area of gaussian surface and specific volume of clearance), *Sov. J. Friction Wear, 1*(5) (1980) 42–48.
7 P. G. Scott, Surface methodology: a new philosophical approach, *Wear, 109*(2) (1986) 267–274.
8 R. M. Haralick and R. Bosley, Texture features for image classification, *Proc. 3rd ERTS Symp., 1973, NASA SP-351* (NASA Goddard Space Flight Center, Greenbelt, MD), pp. 1929–1969.
9 J. J. Gogenepoin and C. R. Rogues-Carmes, Fractal approach to two-dimensional and three-dimensional surface roughness, *Wear, 109*(2) (1986) 119–126.
10 B. B. Mandelbrot, *Fractals: Form, Chance and Dimension,* Freeman, San Francisco, CA, 1977.
11 J. M. Martin and D. P. Bentz, Fractal-based description of the roughness of blasted steel panels, *J. Coatings Technol., 59* (1986) 35–41.
12 T. R. Thomas, Comparison of scanning electron microscopy and styles raster measurements of wear, *Wear, 109*(2) (1986) 343–350.
13 T. Pavlidis, *Algorithms for Computer Graphics and Image Processing,* Redio i Srysz, Moscow, 1987 (in Russian).
14 A. Yu. Sasov and V. N. Sokolov, Digital processing of SEM-images, *Izv. SSSR, Phiz. Ser., 48*(12) (1984) 2389–2396.
15 J. Lebiedzik, Automatic topographical surface reconstruction in the SEM, *Scanning, 2*(4) (1979) 230–237.
16 O. V. Kholodilov, A. Ya. Grigoryev and N. K. Myshkin, Reconstruction of true topographies of solid surfaces in scanning electron microscope using secondary electrons, *Scanning, 9*(4) (1987) 156–161.

17 A. Ya. Grigoryev, N. K. Myshkin and O. V. Kholodilov, Surface microgeometry analysis methods, *Sov. J. Friction Wear, 10* (1) (1989) 111–124.
18 H. O. Muller, Die Abhangigkeit der SE einiger Metalle vom Einfallswinkel des Primaren Katodenstrahls, *Z. Phys., 104* (1934) 475–481.
19 A. Ya. Grigoryev, N. K. Myshkin, N. F. Semenyuk and O. V. Kholodilov, Evaluating specific area by the secondary electron emission method, *Sov. J. Friction Wear, 9*(5) (1988) 18–22.
20 A. Ya. Grigoryev, Processing of signals recorded by ET-detector based on quantitative analysis of information in SEM, *Scanning, 12* (1990) 87–91.
21 M. S. Longiet-Higgins, Statistical geometry of random surfaces. In *Gidrodynamicheskaya Neustoychivost,* Mir, Moscow, 1964, pp. 124–167 (Russian translation).
22 N. F. Semenyuk and G. A. Sirenko, Description of topography of anisotropic rough friction surfaces using random field model (peak height distribution, average peak curvature, surface gradient), *Sov. J. Friction Wear, 1*(3) (1980) 70–76.
23 N. K. Pratt, *Digital Image Processing,* Mir, Moscow, 1982 (Russian translation).

## Appendix A: Nomenclature

| | |
|---|---|
| $A_{SK}$, $A_{KU}$ | asymmetry and excess of asperity slope angle distribution respectively |
| $C$ | contrast |
| $d$ | probe diameter |
| $D_e$ | surface extreme density |
| $F$ | real area of surface |
| $g$, $p$ | *a priori* probabilities of appearance or absence of signal respectively |
| $H_m$, $H$, | |
| $R_{SK}$, $R_{KU}$ | asymmetry and excess of asperity height distribution respectively |
| $I_0$ | zero-order Bessel function with imaginary argument |
| $K_x$ | autocorrelation function |
| $l$ | length plane |
| $m_0$, $m_2$, $m_4$ | isotropic surface zero-, second- and fourth-order spectral density moments |
| $P$ | event probability |
| $P_{max}$ | maximal event probability |
| $P(q)$ | gradient probability density |
| $q$ | surface gradient |
| $R_h$ | vertical resolution |
| $R_v$ | horizontal resolution of method |
| $R_a$, $R_{max}$, $R_z$ | surface roughness parameters |
| $S$ | intensity of SEE with oblique incidence of primary beam |
| $S_0$ | intensity of SEE with normal incidence of primary electrobeam |
| $S_1$, $S_2$ | values of SEE at some point before and after specimen rotation respectively |
| $S(\nu)$ | spectral density |
| $U$ | specific area of surface |
| $W$ | signal-to-noise ratio |
| $x$, $y$, $z$ | coordinate system in which the surface is described |
| $Z$ | surface section profile height at some point |
| $\bar{Z}$ | mean profile height |

*Greek symbols*

| | |
|---|---|
| $\alpha$ | local angle of surface slope at point of beam incidence |
| $\beta$ | brightness of electron source |
| $\gamma$ | aperture of electron source |

| | |
|---|---|
| $\Delta A$ | average asperity slope angle |
| $\Delta t$ | discreteness of signal readout |
| $\Delta_1, M_2$ | surface invariants |
| $\epsilon$ | relative approach |
| $\sigma$ | mean square deviation |
| $\nu$ | spatial frequency |

# Mechanics and materials in fretting

L. Vincent

*Département Matériaux-Mécanique Physique (CNRS URA 447), Ecole Centrale de Lyon, 36 avenue Guy de Collongue, BP 163, 69131 Ecully Cedex (France)*

Y. Berthier, M. C. Dubourg and M. Godet

*Laboratoire de Mécanique des Contacts (CNRS URA 856), Institut National des Sciences Appliquées de Lyon, 20 avenue Albert Einstein, 69621 Villeurbanne Cedex (France)*

(Received August 4, 1991)

## Abstract

Materials fail through overstressing and overstraining. Overstressing leads to crack initiation and later propagation which can cause failure. Overstraining leads to material transformation, for instance strain hardening, followed by changes in material properties such as toughness loss.

This paper presents an overview of the work done in the last ten years on fretting, and illustrates these types of failure with respect to this particular form of damage. It divides the factors that govern overstressing and overstraining into three groups: the imposed conditions, the material properties and limits, and the material response. It places types of damage relative to each other on fretting maps. A flow chart starting from the imposed conditions and ending with failure, and showing all possible alternatives, is drawn.

The chart is then discussed in the light of fretting wear and fretting fatigue tests. It is shown that it is common during one test to cover both overstressing and overstraining conditions which complicates the interpretation of data. Static fretting fatigue which avoids that complication is therefore recommended.

## 1. Introduction

Fretting is one of the modern plagues of industrial machinery [1, 2]. It is sometimes responsible for premature fatigue failures and often limits component life [3, 4]. It occurs in quasi-static assemblies such as splines [5], cables [6, 7], turbine blade assemblies [8], and in nuclear power plants [9]. It is easy to identify in steel contacts as it produces the well known "red powder".

Fretting is complex. In 1982, Beard [10] suggested that more than 50 parameters played a role in fretting and wrote that the subject was encumbered with misconceptions, half truths and sometimes downright errors. This paper attempts to present an overview of fretting as it appears today; it lists the questions to which satisfactory answers have been brought, and those that must be answered in the coming years.

## 2. Damage, fretting wear and fretting fatigue

Fretting damage is divided into fretting wear and fretting fatigue [1, 2]. Fretting wear starts when particles are detached from the rubbing surfaces or first-bodies. It leads to loss of clearance in many applications but can cause jamming when debris is trapped in the contact. It is common in distributed contacts such as flanged fittings, bearing housings etc. Fretting fatigue starts when cracks are initiated within or at the edge of the contacts. It leads to component failure as cracks propagate. It is found in concentrated contacts such as shaft keys, wire strands etc. Even though the origins of fretting fatigue and fretting wear are different, both forms of damage often coexist in the same contacts.

Some care must be exercised in terminology. It is common to talk about fretting wear when the contact load acts alone, or fretting fatigue when an external load, for instance a cyclic tensile load, is superimposed on the contact load. This can create some confusion as wear and cracks can be found in both types of loading.

## 3. New developments

A lot has been done in tribology, in materials science, in fracture mechanics, and in data presentation during the last ten years to clarify the subject and explain the contradictions referred to by Beard [10]. The new developments presented briefly below are centred around work performed during the last ten years by the Laboratoire de "Mécanique des Contacts" de l'Institut National des Sciences Appliquées (INSA) and by the Laboratoire "Matériaux-Mécanique Physique" de l'Ecole Centrale de Lyon (ECL) [11–14].

### 3.1. Tribology

Recent work [15, 16] has shown that a three-body contact can be broken down into five basic elements (Fig. 1): the two rubbing solids or first-bodies, the interface or third-body bulk, and the two screens that separate that bulk from the first-bodies. The screens and interface bulk form the third-body. These five basic elements are known as sites and are numbered $S_1$ to $S_5$. The difference in velocity between points A and B is thus accommodated along line AB. In each site, the velocity can be accommodated according to four different modes labelled respectively $M_1$ to $M_4$ and which correspond to the elastic, rupture, shear, and rolling modes. The combination of five sites and four modes leads to 20 velocity accommodation mechanisms (VAMs).

For instance, machine elements, test specimens and supports deform elastically ($S_1M_1$ and $S_5M_1$). Elastic deformations also accommodate larger amplitudes when first-body stiffness is reduced by cracks ($S_1M_2$ and $S_5M_2$). Both these VAMs are common in fretting. Third-body sites $S_2$, $S_3$ and $S_4$ are also activated in fretting.

VAMs are useful as they focus on how and where the difference in velocity between rubbing solids is taken up. The concept is general, and is applicable to all contacts from lubrication to "dry wear" which can also be looked upon as a flow problem [17]. A friction problem is only understood when the activated VAMs are identified.

### 3.2. Materials science and damage

Materials fail through overstressing and overstraining. The relation between overstressing and overstraining when damage is present is not limited to classical stress–strain laws. Overstressing leads to crack formation or rupture either instantaneously or after fatigue. Material transformation is noted in the immediate crack lip vicinity; it is only observable by transmission electronic microscopy. Overstraining leads to microstructural transformations. In contact problems, these are called tribological

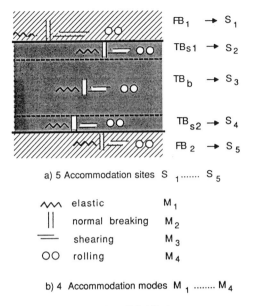

a) 5 Accommodation sites S $_1$ ······· S $_5$

ʌʌʌ  elastic          M $_1$

||    normal breaking  M $_2$

=     shearing         M $_3$

OO    rolling          M $_4$

b) 4 Accommodation modes M $_1$ ········ M $_4$

FB : First-Body ; TB : Third-Body ;
TBb : Third-Body (bulk) ; TBs : third-body screen

Fig. 1. Velocity accommodation mechanisms (VAMs, $S_iM_j$) for three-body contacts.

transformed zones (TTZs). They are known to have mechanical properties significantly different from those of the original materials. TTZs are observable on classical optical microscopes after chemical etching [18]. Some of the difficulties in the interpretation of fretting results discussed above come from the fact that fretting failures can be caused by these two mechanisms.

Thus, two types of macroscopic degradations are found in contacts: in overstressing, crack initiation which is highly localized; in overstraining, the TTZ which covers the friction track. Both overstressing and overstraining are governed by surface and volume effects.

Progress in the understanding of fretting damage is thus impaired by changes in material properties which have not yet been quantified [19, 20]. In low toughness materials, such as some ceramics and glasses, debris or cracks form rapidly as the first-bodies have little residual plasticity, and $A\%$, the percentage elongation to rupture, is low. For higher toughness materials, such as metals or metal alloys with high $A\%$, crack initiation or debris production is not instantaneous. Debris emerge from a very hard modified metallographic structure made out of very stable phases possessing fine grain size distributions ($\approx 250$ Å). The progressive drop in concentration of small tempering carbides ($\epsilon$, $M_2C$) in steels and of the $\beta$ phase in titanium alloys, observed during rubbing tests, are common in low cycle fatigue tests. However, the very small grains found in the newly formed microstructure, along with the high level of cumulated plastic strain in the layers close to the surface, all point to the more complex dynamic recrystallization mechanism.

Dynamic recrystallization starts during the first passes of the wear test and the locally transformed (or consolidated) surface rapidly becomes unable to *accommodate* the deformation imposed by the contact load and it *cracks*. The material "shakes down" [21], and debris spring from the fragile transformed layer.

In fretting, cracks are initiated at the edge of the contact, and the tribological transformed zones are found in the contact zone. This signifies that the contact conditions are not the same in both locations and that during and after transformations the material properties are also different.

### 3.3. Fracture mechanics

Crack *initiation* is predictable as it is governed by overstressing [22–26]. Similar behaviours and results can therefore be expected from both well controlled friction and traction tests. The maximum internal tensile stress $\sigma_{xx}$, or skin stress, which is available for well defined geometries if load and traction are known, can therefore be compared with the tensile fatigue limit stress $\sigma_D$ produced in classical material tests. This amounts to using a Wöhler type approach, with its fatigue limit $\sigma_D$, which takes into account internal effects such as yield stress and toughness variations, and external effects such as environment, frequency etc. If $\sigma_{xx} < \sigma_D$, initiation is avoided. If $\sigma_{xx} > \sigma_D$, cracks are expected and the incubation time, which depends on both material toughness and rate of change of toughness (cyclic strain hardening), is also governed by the difference between these two values. For brittle materials, a similar approach can be used, based on the rupture stress $\sigma_R$ rather than on $\sigma_D$.

In most fatigue and fretting fatigue laboratory tests, the entire test specimen is stressed. Any crack formation therefore decreases the effective section of the specimen and crack initiation normally leads to propagation and failure, as the stress intensity factors (SIFs) $K_I$ rise during the test. The situation is different in industrial contacts where, because of design, the stresses are high in the contact vicinity but drop rapidly away from that zone. Under these conditions, recent work has shown that the SIFs $K_I$ and $K_{II}$ decrease as cracks grow out of the high stress region, and that propagation can stop [27–30]. The same work has also shown that under fretting conditions, cracks are often closed and that propagation, if any, occurs most likely in mode 2. This is important from a design point of view as cracks do not necessarily propagate in practice even though they do in laboratory rigs.

### 3.4. Friction logs and fretting maps

Curves giving the variation of the coefficient of friction against time or number of cycles do not produce evidence which can be used to determine the activated VAMs. Friction logs are much more powerful. In a three-dimensional friction log (Fig. 2), the tangential force $F$ is recorded as a function of the imposed displacement $D$ for each cycle and of the number of cycles. Load, frequency, amplitude, contact geometry, material combination and environment are specified in each log. Figure 2 shows a classical friction log obtained with steel specimens. It is made out of individual force–displacement (FD) cycles, or friction loops, which take on different shapes (Fig. 3): a closed (cc) conservative FD cycle, associated with elastic accommodations ($S_1M_1$); tangential contact stiffness is given by the slope of the FD line; an elliptic (ec) slightly dissipative FD cycle, found in contacts which exhibit either partial slip or interfacial crack friction or both ($S_1M_2$ and $S_3M_?$); a trapezoidal (tc) cycle, characteristic of gross slip; the near horizontal segments are dissipative ($S_3M_?$), the near vertical segments correspond to the elastic displacements ($S_1M_1$) noted above.

Fretting maps were originated by Vingsbo and coworkers [31, 32]. They isolated three fretting regimes: stick, mixed stick and slip, and gross slip. Here [33, 34], two fretting maps (Fig. 4) are drawn from families of friction logs, *i.e.* logs drawn for

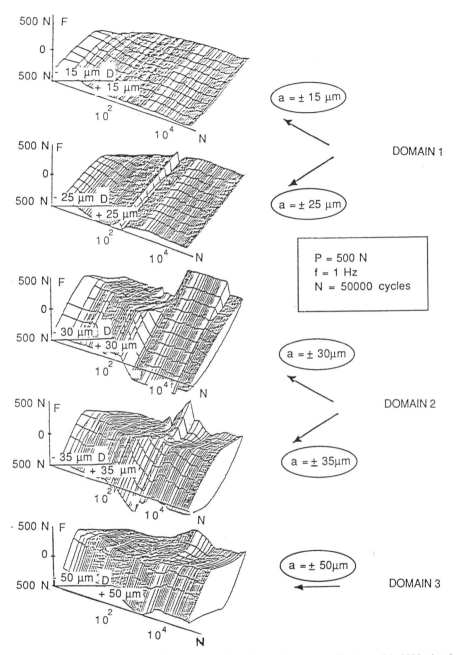

Fig. 2. Three-dimensional friction logs obtained for different amplitudes with 7075 aluminium alloys.

different amplitudes and loads. The first, the running condition fretting map (RCFM) plots loads $P$ *vs.* nominal amplitude for a given frequency and a given roughness. Zones of stick, partial slip and gross sliding are also identified. It is close to the

140

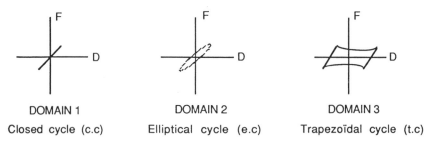

DOMAIN 1                DOMAIN 2                DOMAIN 3

Closed cycle (c.c)      Elliptical cycle (e.c)      Trapezoïdal cycle (t.c)

Fig. 3. Characteristic friction loops.

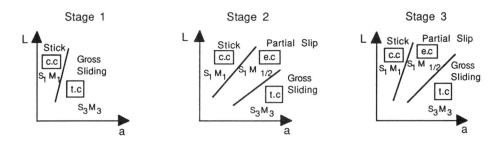

Running Condition Fretting Maps (L : Load, a : Amplitude)

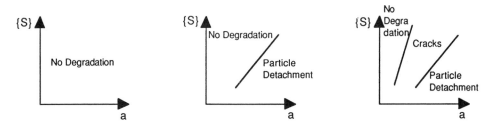

Material Response Fretting Maps (S : Stress, a : Amplitude)

Fig. 4. Running condition and material response fretting maps.

Vingsbo map, except for the fact that it has been drawn for a different number of cycles, which shows that the three zones vary in extent during the test. The second, the material response fretting map (MRFM), plots stress or equivalent stress *vs.* amplitude. Three zones are also identified in these maps: no degradation, cracks and particle detachment zones. The second map is also shown to vary during the test, along with the effective VAMs and the material properties. Running conditions, material response and VAMs are intimately related.

Even if drawn with the same axes, the zones isolated in RCFMs and MRFMs do not superimpose, even though particle detachment is usually associated with gross slip, cracking is usually associated with partial slip, and no degradation is usually associated with no slip. As an example, unlike aluminium alloys which yield large cracks, fatigue-resistant titanium alloy MRFMs do not exhibit cracks under partial slip conditions.

Representative types of RCFMs and MRFMs, drawn schematically in Fig. 4, show that these maps give both guides and trends. The frontiers between zones are not as clear as indicated, since the transition from one zone to the other is gradual; they vary during the test, particularly for the crack domain related to overstressing.

Fretting maps serve today to identify contact kinematic conditions (adhesion, partial slip, gross slip). Partial slip clearly appears as the most detrimental mode for crack initiation. Critical values of slip amplitude were found for which fretting fatigue crack propagation is high and in all likelihood lifetime is minimal [33].

### 3.5. Conclusions

The developments presented above throw a different light on the interpretation of fretting data and their transposition to industrial conditions. Advances in tribology point to the necessity of identifying the velocity accommodation mechanisms. The introduction of both friction logs and friction maps presents data which are very much richer than those given by standard friction curves. The awareness of changes in material properties during testing is necessary to understand changes observed in material behaviour. The extension of fracture mechanics to real contact situations explains behaviours which were not clear earlier.

Unfortunately, all these advances underline the complexity of the entire fretting process and point to the many factors both imposed by the test, and induced by the test running conditions which govern fretting damage. They also point to the difficulty of running a meaningful fretting experiment under both fretting wear and fretting fatigue conditions.

## 4. Governing parameters

Section 3 confirmed that fretting damage is governed by many parameters. This section tries to organize some of them around a flow chart. The parameters identified during experimental campaigns are divided in three groups: imposed running conditions, material properties and limits, and induced running conditions.

### 4.1. Imposed running conditions

The imposed running conditions are those imposed by the test device and the operator.

| Parameters | Units | Observations |
|---|---|---|
| Loads | N | Contact and external |
| Amplitude | $\mu$m | |
| Frequency | Hz | |
| Temperature | °C | |
| Environment | Composition | |

Loads are sometimes expressed in terms of pressure (Pa). The contact load acts within the fretting contact, and the external load takes in all loads, seen by the fretting structure, other than the fretting contact load. Contact loads are usually constant, external loads often vary. Temperature and environment are listed as governing parameters, but their effects are not discussed here.

## 4.2. Material properties and limits

The material properties and limits listed have been shown to play an important role in orienting the test towards one form of damage or another.

| Parameters | Units | Observations |
|---|---|---|
| $K_{ith}$ $(i=1, 2)$ | Pa m$^{1/2}$ | SIF threshold |
| $A\%$ | Non-dimensional | Percentage elongation to fracture |
| $\sigma_D$ | Pa | Wöhler fatigue limit |
| $\sigma_R$ | Pa | Rupture strength |
| $\epsilon_y$ | Non-dimensional | Yield strain |

The Wöhler fatigue limit $\sigma_D$ is taken here in a broad sense as the stress needed for both crack initiation and crack propagation. This is acceptable in classical fatigue tests which exhibit simple stress patterns in which most cracks propagate after initiation. It is not so in all fretting applications as the stress pattern induced by contact loads can be quite complex. All other terms are self explanatory. Some of these parameters, $A\%$ for instance, vary during the test because of cyclic strain hardening. As mentioned in Section 3.3, the rupture strength $\sigma_R$ is considered for brittle materials, which can fail during the first cycle.

## 4.3. Induced running conditions

| Parameters | Units | Observations |
|---|---|---|
| $\sigma_{xx}$ | Pa | Skin stress |
| $\epsilon_{xx}$ | Non-dimensional | Deformation |
| $a_{ci}$ $(i=1, 2)$ | $\mu$m | Critical amplitudes |
| $K_i$ $(i=1, 2)$ | Pa m$^{1/2}$ | Stress intensity factors |

$\sigma_{xx}$ is the internal surface stress (Fig. 4) which is strongly dependent on friction. Critical amplitudes $a_{c1}$ and $a_{c2}$ have no scientific definition to date. They mark the frontiers determined experimentally which separate the different damage domains indicated in the fretting maps. Critical amplitudes are not intrinsic material properties, they depend on test devices, running conditions and particularly on loads and material combinations. Other parameters are self explanatory.

## 5. Fretting chart

Figure 5 indicates how the combination of imposed and induced conditions and material properties interact. A ball on flat geometry is chosen as it is simple to analyse. All conditions, the material combination, roughness, frequency, environment are fixed. Only the fretting amplitude $a$ is varied in this analysis. Load effects are discussed. Two critical amplitudes $a_{c1}$ and $a_{c2}$, where $a_{c2} > a_{c1}$, are identified which define three domains:

| domain 1 | $a < a_{c1}$ | (no slip) |
|---|---|---|
| domain 2 | $a_{c1} < a < a_{c2}$ | (partial slip) |
| domain 3 | $a > a_{c2}$ | (gross slip) |

FRETTING CHART

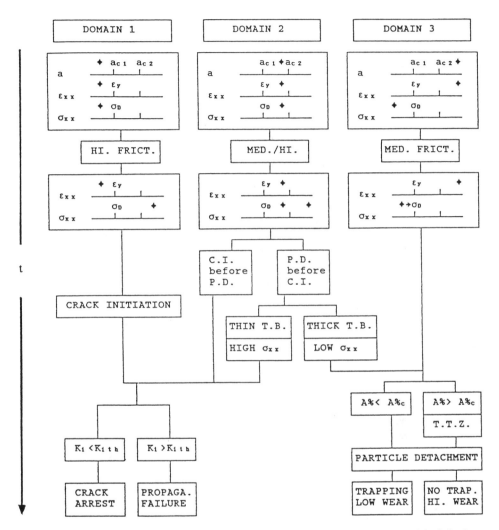

N.B.: C.I. crack initiation, P.D. particle detachment, T.B. third-body
T.T.Z. tribological transformed zone , t : time.

Fig. 5. Fretting chart: crack initiation and propagation, high and low wear.

The amplitude refers to the nominal amplitude imposed on the machine and not to the actual slip at contact. The two are known to differ significantly [11], owing to different forms of velocity accommodation. The critical slip necessary to cause damage often discussed in the literature [35] is the measure of elastic accommodation of the test device, specimen and specimen supports. This is expressed in Fig. 5 by setting the critical amplitude $a_{c1}$ (a machine parameter), opposite the yield strain $\epsilon_y$ (a material parameter), even though the deformation $\epsilon$ is not constant along the contact.

The definitions given above for critical amplitudes $a_{c1}$ and $a_{c2}$ are indicative. They imply that below $a_{c1}$ the relative displacement at contact is close to zero, and that beyond $a_{c2}$ significant slip is observed. Values of around 15 and 50 $\mu$m are commonly observed respectively for $a_{c1}$ and $a_{c2}$; they can be determined from examination of the loops (Fig. 3) in the friction log (Fig. 2). A closed loop is representative of domain 1, a parallelogram of domain 3 and intermediate quasi-elliptical loop of domain 2. Critical amplitudes are of the order of magnitude of tolerances in machines which explains why they vary from one device to another. For low stiffness machines values of up to 100 $\mu$m were noted.

Figure 5 lists the three domains. Yield strain $\epsilon_y$ and fatigue limit $\sigma_D$ are marked respectively on the deformation and the stress lines of each domain. Critical amplitudes $a_{c1}$ and $a_{c2}$ are also noted on the amplitude lines at the top of the figure for each domain. They are kept constant during the test. As noted in Section 3.2, the abscissa of the crack initiation and transformed zones are not the same and, owing to different histories, the material properties are different in both locations. It is therefore not possible to set the stress and the deformation lines by aligning for instance the yield stress $\sigma_y$ (not shown) and the yield strain $\epsilon_y$. The relative positions of lines $\sigma$ and $\epsilon$ vary during the test and of course from one material to another. The black diamonds on the $\epsilon_{xx}$, $\sigma_{xx}$ and $a$ axes locate these parameters with respect to references $\epsilon_y$, $\sigma_D$ and $a_{ci}$.

As expressed in Fig. 5, domains 1, 2 and 3 can be redefined in terms of $\sigma$ and $\epsilon$ instead of $a_{ci}$. In domain 1, $\epsilon_{xx} < \epsilon_y$, in domain 3, $\sigma < \sigma_D$. Different combinations are found in domain 2 which is defined for conditions where $\epsilon_{xx} > \epsilon_y$ and $\sigma_{xx} > \sigma_D$.

The situations observed experimentally in domains 1 and 3 are well differentiated and can be presented relatively simply. Two examples are given. Results noted in domain 2 are not as clear as they combine the tendencies found in the two others. Domains 1 and 3 will therefore be presented first.

### 5.1. Domain 1: crack formation ($\epsilon_{xx} < \epsilon_y$)

(1) Friction is usually low ($f \approx 0.1$) at the start ($\sigma_{xx} < \sigma_D$), pollution screens are rapidly disrupted, and two-body contact is established locally. As relative motion is negligible, adhesion is strong and static friction rises to reach high values ($f \approx 2$) after less than 100 cycles.

(2) At the contact exit, in a ball on flat contact, $\sigma_{xx}$ is given by:

$$\sigma_{xx} = -p_0\{(1 - x^2/a^2)^{1/2} + 2fx/a\}$$

At contact edges, for $x = \pm a$, $\sigma_{xx}$ varies between $+2fp_0$ and $-2fp_0$. As $p_0$ is around 1 GPa, and $f$ is of the order of 1 or 2, $\sigma_{xx}$ alternates between $+4$ and $-4$ GPa which is considerable. The material fatigues and cracks are initiated when $\sigma_{xx} > \sigma_D$. This can take up to $10^5$ cycles. If $\sigma_{xx} < \sigma_D$ (case not illustrated in Fig. 5), no cracks are initiated, and the operation can go on without damage. With brittle materials cracks can occur immediately if $\sigma_{xx}$ is larger than the rupture strength $\sigma_R$.

(3) Cracks propagate after initiation if the stress intensity factors $K_i$ ($i = 1, 2$) are larger than their threshold values $K_{ith}$. As $K_i$ varies with crack length and with the stress field near the crack tip, it can either propagate and lead to component rupture or stop.

### 5.2. Domain 3: particle detachment

(1) Friction is also usually low ($f \approx 0.1$) at the start, but pollution screens are rapidly disrupted, and two-body contact is established locally. Relative motion is no

longer negligible, adhesion is less strong than in domain 1 and the dynamic coefficient of friction rises to $f \approx 1$ after less than 100 cycles and levels off.

(2) High rates of deformation ($\epsilon_{xx} \gg \epsilon_y$) are imposed on the material within the contact zone over a thickness of between 10 and 100 $\mu$m. If the percentage elongation to fracture $A\%$ of the material of the contact is small, the contact zone breaks up and debris is produced quasi-instantly. If $A\%$ is high, the material strain hardens, goes through a transformation phase (Section 3.2) and only then produces debris. Phase transformation can postpone debris formation until after 1000 cycles.

(3) The rest of the test is governed by the factors that control particle trapping and elimination from the contact. If the rate of elimination is high and debris circulation avoided, wear is high, component function is lost by increased clearance which leads to shocks, noises and other nuisances. If the rate of elimination is low, satisfactory component life can be expected.

### 5.3. Domain 2: mixed crack formation and particle detachment

Domain 2, where $\epsilon_{xx} > \epsilon_y$ and $\sigma_{xx} > \sigma_D$, is characterized by the competition between crack formation and particle detachment. Both forms of damage are observed. Two cases are identified.

(1) Crack formation precedes particle detachment, with $\sigma_{xx} \gg \sigma_D$ or $\sigma_{xx} > \sigma_R$ and $\epsilon_{xx} > \epsilon_y$. This condition is characteristic of low toughness materials. Cracks form, specimen stiffness drops, the effective amplitude also drops, $\epsilon_{xx}$ can reach or go below $\epsilon_y$. The process is then similar to that described for domain 1 which, depending on the relative values of $K_i$ and $K_{ith}$, leads either to crack propagation and failure or to crack arrest which guarantees satisfactory operating conditions.

(2) Particle detachment precedes crack formation, with $\sigma_{xx} > \sigma_D$ and $\epsilon_{xx} \gg \epsilon_y$. This condition is characteristic of high toughness materials. If the particle bed or third-body (TB) formed is thin, the skin stress $\sigma_{xx}$ stays constant and the SIFs remain high. The process is again similar to that described for domain 1. If the third-body is thick, $\sigma_{xx}$ drops, initiation can be avoided or not. If avoided, the SIFs are still low and the process follows the path described in domain 3.

As noted earlier, critical amplitudes depend on material and test device compliance, friction and running conditions. The critical amplitudes drop for instance as the load increases. The three domains presented here are representative of many materials, including steel, aluminium alloys etc. With fatigue-resistant alloys such as titanium alloys (Ti–6Al–4V) which are less sensitive to crack initiation and propagation, domains 1 and 2 do not always exist under representative running conditions. Either no degradation or particle detachment (domain 3) is observed.

## 6. Fretting test devices

Fretting fatigue simulators differ from fretting wear devices in that external body forces modify the stress pattern imposed by the contact load. Classical simulators are modified traction machines in which the tensile specimen, which is subjected to an ordinary fatigue test cycle, is also loaded laterally by two fixed friction pads. The relative motion between tensile specimen and pads is governed by specimen extension and machine compliance. The idea is very attractive as it is easy to compare Wöhler curves obtained with and without pads and produce a figure which is believed to be characteristic of the life reduction induced by fretting. The device has however been heavily criticized from quite different angles.

(1) The design engineer notes that the life reduction predicted from fretting fatigue tests is much higher than that noted in practice.

(2) The tribologist observes that the test conditions are not controlled. Interfacial slip, which has been shown earlier to determine the type of damage produced, varies with the tensile load variation imposed by the Wöhler test program and with the friction force which cannot be controlled. The test conditions vary from one material to another because the tensile specimen elongation, and thus up to a point the interfacial slip, is a linear function of Young's modulus $E$. They are not representative, and extrapolation to practice is hazardous.

(3) The material experts note that friction pad action overstresses the tensile specimen and that part of the life reduction can be attributed to overloading and not only to friction and surface effects.

These points cannot be brushed aside easily. Indeed, the change in length $u$ at mid-height (where the friction pads act) of a 15 cm steel tensile specimen subjected to a tensile stress of 100 MPa (or an alternating stress of $\pm 50$ MPa) is given by the elementary formula:

$$u = \epsilon_{xx} l$$

where $\epsilon_{xx} = \sigma_{xx}/E$ with $\sigma_{xx} = 100 \times 10^6$ Pa, $E = 20 \times 10^{10}$ Pa, $l = 0.15/2$ m, $u = 37.5 \times 10^{-6}$ m.

The figure is roughly doubled for aluminium. Values of between 10 and 50 $\mu$m are close to those given as representative of critical amplitudes $a_{c1}$ and $a_{c2}$ in Section 4.4. They of course have to be adjusted to take into account the factors of machine and support compliance etc. mentioned earlier which account for the difference between imposed displacement and actual slip. It is, however, safe to say that the conditions imposed in fretting fatigue simulators span over the range of conditions which can orient the test towards either crack initiation and propagation or particle detachment. Unfortunately, these conditions are not specified for each machine.

To avoid this problem, and transpose the methodology which is centred around running condition fretting maps (RCFM) and material response fretting maps (MRFM), it is best to run systems in which the "body" and "contact" loads and amplitude are controlled separately. This can be achieved in "fretting–static fatigue" tests in which body stress is constant ($R = \sigma_{min}/\sigma_{max} = 1$) and the slip amplitude is controlled. Fretting maps are then plotted for different loads and different amplitudes, at different numbers of cycles. If the test conditions are representative of those found in practice, both fretting maps can help designers, first to identify the type of damage expected for given materials operating under given conditions, second to favour one type of damage over another, by varying for instance component stiffness, and third to choose one palliative (coating) or another. For instance, to avoid fatigue failures which are the most dangerous, and which follow crack initiation, the designer should favour the elastic accommodation mechanism ($S_1M_1$) or if this is not possible seek particle detachment ($S_3M_3$). This last mechanism does open up the entire problem of debris trapping which is a study in itself and which is influenced by many parameters [36].

Life predictions can be made from fretting maps when cracking is the failure mechanism. Crack initiation duration and propagation rates in the contact zone are given by the data collected to plot the fretting maps at different times. Propagation to rupture can, outside of the contact zone, be predicted by classical propagation laws and models.

# 7. Conclusion

Materials fail through overstressing and overstraining. Overstressing leads to crack initiation and later propagation which can cause failure. Overstraining which leads to material transformation (strain hardening), followed by changes in material properties (toughness loss) favours particle detachment. Overstressing can be related to the fatigue limit $\sigma_D$, overstraining to the yield strain $\epsilon_y$. In fretting, overstressing acts at the contact edge while overstraining operates within the contact itself.

The factors which govern overstressing and overstraining can be divided into three groups: the imposed conditions, the material properties and limits, and the material response. This presentation situates one type of damage with respect to another on fretting maps. A flow chart starting from imposed conditions and ending with failure, and showing all possible alternatives, was drawn.

The chart was then discussed in the light of fretting wear and fretting fatigue tests. It was shown that it is common during one test to cover both overstressing and overstraining conditions, which complicates the interpretation of data. Static fretting fatigue which avoids that complication is therefore recommended.

The arguments presented show that, to interpret correctly the data provided in fretting tests and rearranged in fretting maps, and to extrapolate them to an industrial problem, it is necessary to carry out the following steps: identify as closely as possible the contact operating conditions (contact and body forces, amplitude, ...) of the industrial components under study; situate them with respect to those tested in the fretting maps; identify failure mechanisms rather than try to obtain a factor supposedly representative of the drop in fatigue limit to be included in component life predictions; include materials on which practical or prototype information is available to verify the correlation between laboratory tests and practice.

# References

1 R. B. Waterhouse, *Fretting Fatigue*, Elsevier Applied Science, London, 1981.
2 R. B. Waterhouse, *Fretting Corrosion*, Pergamon, Oxford, 1972.
3 P. J. E. Forsyth, Occurrence of fretting fatigue failures in practice. In R. B. Waterhouse (ed.), *Fretting Fatigue*, Elsevier Applied Science, London, 1981, pp. 99–125.
4 D. W. Hoeppner, Fretting of aircraft control surfaces, *AGARD Conf. Proc.* No 161, AGARD, Munich, 1974.
5 P. M. Ku and M. L. Valtierra, Spline wear — effects of design and lubrication, *ASME J. Eng. Ind.*, (1975) 1257–1265.
6 B. R. Pearson, P. A. Brook and R. B. Waterhouse, Fretting in aqueous media, particularly of roping steels in seawater, *Wear, 106* (1985) 225–260.
7 G. Lofficial and Y. Berthier, L'usure dans les cables et conduits flexibles, une étude de cas en tribologie, *Eurotrib, September 1985*, Vol. 3, Ecole Centrale de Lyon, pp. 2.2.1.–2.2.5.
8 C. Chamont, Y. Honnorat, Y. Berthier, M. Godet and L. Vincent, Wear problems in small displacements encountered in titanium alloy parts in aircraft turbomachines, *Proc. Sixth World Conf. on Titanium, June 6–9, 1988, Cannes,* in P. Lacombe *et al.* (eds.), Société Française de Métallurgie, Editions de Physique, 91944 Les Ulis, France.
9 D. H. Jones, A. Y. Nehru and J. Skinner, The impact fretting wear of a nuclear reactor component, *Wear, 106* (1985) 139–162.
10 J. Beard, An investigation into the mechanism of fretting fatigue, *Ph.D. Thesis,* University of Salford, 1982.
11 Y. Berthier, L. Vincent and M. Godet, Fretting fatigue and fretting wear, *Tribol. Int., 22* (4) (1989) 235–242.

148

12 L. Vincent, Y. Berthier and M. Godet, Fretting wear and fretting fatigue damage, *Fatigue 1987,* EMAS, Charlottesville, PA, USA, Vol. 1, 1987, pp. 567–574.

13 Y. Berthier, L. Vincent and M. Godet, Velocity accommodation in fretting, *Wear, 125* (1988) 25–38.

14 Ch. Colombié, Y. Berthier, A. Floquet, L. Vincent and M. Godet, Fretting: load-carrying capacity of wear debris, *ASME J. Tribol., 106* (2) (1984) 185–194.

15 Y. Berthier, Experimental evidence for friction and wear modelling, *Wear, 139* (1990) 77–92.

16 Y. Berthier, L. Vincent and M. Godet, Velocity accommodation sites and modes in tribology, in the press.

17 M. Godet and Y. Berthier, Continuity and dry friction: an Osborne Reynolds approach. In D. Dowson, C. M. Taylor, M. Godet and D. Berthe (eds.), *Fluid film lubrication — Osborne Reynolds Centenary,* Elsevier, Amsterdam, 1987, Fig. 16.

18 S. Fayeuille, P. Blanchard and L. Vincent, Fretting wear behaviour of several titanium alloys, *Proc. STLE Annu. Meet., Montreal, May 1990,* in *STLE Trans.,* in the press.

19 D. W. Hoeppner and G. L. Goss, Metallographic analysis of fretting fatigue damage in Ti–6Al–4V–MA and 7075-T6 aluminium, *Wear, 62* (1980) 287–297.

20 Y. Berthier, L. Vincent and M. Godet, Fretting fatigue and fretting wear, *Tribol. Int., 22* (4) (1989) 235–242.

21 K. L. Johnson, *Contact Mechanics,* Cambridge University Press, Cambridge, 1985, pp. 286–294.

22 K. L. Johnson and J. J. O'Connor, Mechanics of fretting, *Proc. Inst. Mech. Eng., 178* (3J) (1964) 7–21.

23 T. C. Chivers and S. C. Gordelier, Fretting fatigue and contact conditions: a rational explanation of palliative behaviour, *Proc. Inst. Mech. Eng., 199* (C4) (1985) 325–337.

24 J. J. O'Connor, The role of elastic stress analysis in the interpretation of fretting fatigue failures. In R. B. Waterhouse (ed.), *Fretting Fatigue,* Elsevier Applied Science, London, 1981, pp. 23–66.

25 K. Endo and H. Goto, Initiation and propagation of fatigue cracks, *Wear, 38* (1976) 311–324.

26 J. K. Lancaster, Crack propagation and particle detachment in the wear of glass under elastic contact conditions. In D. Dowson, C. M. Taylor, M. Godet and D. Berthe (eds.), *Interface Dynamics, Tribology Series 12,* Amsterdam, 1988, pp. 111–119.

27 D. A. Hills, D. Nowell and J. J. O'Connor, On the mechanics of fretting fatigue, *Wear, 125* (1988) 39–52.

28 M. C. Dubourg and B. Villechaise, Unilateral contact analysis of a crack with friction, *Eur. J. Mech. A, 8* (4) (1989) 309–319.

29 M. C. Dubourg, M. Mouwakeh, B. Villechaise and M. Godet, Crack behaviour under cyclic loading. In D. Dowson, C. M. Taylor, M. Godet and D. Berthe (eds.), *Interface Dynamics,* Elsevier, Amsterdam, 1988.

30 M. C. Dubourg and B. Villechaise, Analysis of multiple fatigue cracks, part I (theory) and II (results), *ASME J. Tribol.,* in the press.

31 O. Vingsbo and D. Soderberg, On fretting maps, *Wear, 126* (1988) 131–147.

32 O. Vingsbo, M. Odfalk and N. E. Shen, Fretting maps and fretting behavior of some FCC metal alloys, *Wear Mater.,* (1989) 275–282.

33 V. Pellerin, Etude du comportement en usure induite sous petits débattements d'alliages d'aluminium et de titane, *Thèse,* Ecole Centrale de Lyon, Lyon, 1990.

34 Z. R. Zhou, S. Fayeuille and L. Vincent, Fretting of aluminium alloys, *Wear,* to be published.

35 P. J. Kennedy, L. Stallings and M. B. Peterson, A study of surface damage at low-amplitude slip, *ASLE Trans., 27* (4) (1984) 305–312.

36 M. Godet, The third-body approach: a mechanical view of wear, *Wear, 100* (1984) 437–452.

*Wear, 153* (1992) 149–162

# Wear behaviour of i-carbon coatings*

D. Klaffke, R. Wäsche and H. Czichos

*Federal Institute of Materials Research and Testing (BAM), Berlin 45 (FRG)*

(Received June 18, 1991)

## Abstract

The wear behaviour of i-carbon coatings on steel and ceramic specimens was investigated under conditions of continuous and oscillating sliding. It was found that both the counterbody material and the operating conditions (sliding velocity and temperature) as well as the environmental humidity have a pronounced influence on the tribological behaviour.

The carbon layers show excellent tribological behaviour with low values of friction and wear provided that the frictional specific power input is below a certain level (approximately $P_F < 5$ W mm$^{-2}$). With respect to the environmental humidity, the carbon layers behaved best under conditions of high humidity. Surface studies by electron spectroscopy for chemical analysis indicated that the carbon bonding states of the coatings remain stable during the tribological loading below the critical transition conditions. Studies of the transferred carbon layers indicated that selective tribo-oxidative processes have occurred during the tribological loading.

## 1. Introduction

Plasma-assisted deposition of carbon layers by a chemical vapour deposition (CVD) process leads to thin coatings of high hardness and high corrosion resistance. Whereas the deposition technique is undergoing further improvement, commercially available coatings are already promising interesting tribological behaviour under certain conditions. Since the tribological behaviour of a coating is always dependent on several parameters of the tribosystem, tribotesting with one fixed set of operational parameters is not sufficient to reveal the characteristics of a system. In a kind of "wear mapping" [1], different tests were applied to evaluate the wear behaviour of i-carbon coatings:

(1) sliding wear tests with silicon-infiltrated silicon carbide (SiSiC) against SiSiC + i-carbon coating – variation of sliding speed and temperature;

(2) oscillating sliding tests with SiSiC against SiSiC + i-carbon coating – variation of humidity at room temperature and variation of temperature;

(3) oscillating sliding tests with coated and uncoated steel (100Cr6,H) against coated and uncoated steel (100Cr6,H) – variation of humidity at room temperature.

## 2. Experimental details

### 2.1. Coating process

Coatings of about 5 µm thickness are deposited by a plasma-assisted CVD process at a substrate temperature of about 250 °C. The coatings are doped with metal atoms

---

*Extended version of a paper presented at the 15th meeting of the International Research Group on Wear of Engineering Materials (IRG–OECD), Cambridge, UK, September 17–19, 1990.

(tantalum or tungsten) to a concentration of approximately 10–20 at.%; the doping concentration is higher at the interface and decreases with increasing thickness. The process is described in detail elsewhere [2, 3].

### 2.2. Sliding tests

The sliding tests are performed in a modified pin-on-disk tribometer with a stationary toroid specimen ($R_1 = 6$ mm, $R_2 = 21$ mm) sliding against a rotating disk within a high temperature test specimen chamber. The test parameters are summarized in Table 1. The details of the tribometer are described elsewhere [4].

### 2.3. Oscillating sliding tests

Two different test rigs are used for the oscillating sliding tests. Tests at room temperature are performed on a tribometer developed by BAM [5, 6], where the tribosystem is running in air of controlled relative humidity $U$. Oscillating sliding tests at elevated temperatures are performed on a commercial test rig [7]. The oscillating sliding tests were performed with different test specimen arrangements as given in Table 2. The tests at elevated temperatures were performed with the parameters summarized in Table 3.

## 3. Results and discussion

### 3.1. Sliding wear

Under dry sliding conditions at room temperature and sliding speeds of 0.11, 0.34 and 1 m s$^{-1}$ the wear resistance of the carbon layer is excellent. No wear could be measured on the coated disk after a sliding distance of 1000 m, whereas the wear coefficient of the SiSiC counterbody was $1 \times 10^{-7}$ mm$^3$ N$^{-1}$ m$^{-1}$. The measured coefficient of friction was initially in the region of $f = 0.3$, but increased slightly during the experiment to reach a steady value of $f = 0.5$ at the sliding distance of 1000 m.

On the coating a wear scar could not be quantified (Fig. 1). The wear track could only be seen by its polished surface in reflecting light. However, it was interesting to notice that perpendicular to the wear track some dark crescent-shaped streaks had been formed. The corresponding profilogram of the wear track shows a smooth surface caused by polishing to a depth of 100 nm, which is the average value of the surface roughness.

At a sliding speed of 3.4 m s$^{-1}$ the layer was completely destroyed by "spalling", *i.e.* "delamination" of the coating. As can be seen in Fig. 2, a wear scar was formed

TABLE 1

Parameters for sliding wear tests

| | |
|---|---|
| Type of motion | Continuous sliding |
| Tribocouple | Toroid–disk, $R_1 = 6$mm, $R_2 = 21$ mm |
| Materials | SiC–SiSiC |
| Coating on | Disk |
| Coating type | H (5 $\mu$m, 20 at.% W) |
| Normal force | 3 N |
| Sliding speed | 0.1, 0.34, 1.0 and 3.4 m s$^{-1}$ |
| Total sliding distance | 1000 m |
| Temperature | Room temperature and 250 °C (deposition temperature) |

TABLE 2

Parameters for oscillating sliding wear tests at room temperature

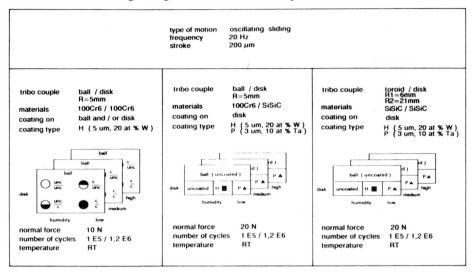

| | type of motion | oscillating sliding |
| | frequency | 20 Hz |
| | stroke | 200 μm |

| tribo couple | ball / disk R=5mm | tribo couple | ball / disk R=5mm | tribo couple | toroid / disk R1=6mm R2=21mm |
| materials | 100Cr6 / 100Cr6 | materials | 100Cr6 / SiSiC | materials | SiSiC / SiSiC |
| coating on | ball and / or disk | coating on | disk | coating on | disk |
| coating type | H ( 5 um, 20 at % W ) | coating type | H ( 5 um, 20 at % W ) P ( 3 um, 10 at % Ta ) | coating type | H ( 5 um, 20 at % W ) P ( 3 um, 10 at % Ta ) |

| normal force | 10 N | normal force | 20 N | normal force | 20 N |
| number of cycles | 1 E5 / 1,2 E6 | number of cycles | 1 E5 / 1,2 E6 | number of cycles | 1 E5 / 1,2 E6 |
| temperature | RT | temperature | RT | temperature | RT |

TABLE 3

Parameters for oscillating sliding wear tests at elevated temperatures

| Tribocouple | Ball–disk $R=5$ mm |
|---|---|
| Materials | 100Cr6–SiSiC |
| Coating on | Disk |
| Coating type | P (3 $\mu$m, 10 at.% Ta) |
| Temperature | Room temperature, 100, 200 and 250 °C |
| Normal force | 20 N |
| Number of cycles | $1 \times 10^5$ |

with an irregular rim created by the spalling of large, irregularly shaped parts of the layer. Considering the relatively high friction coefficient of $f=0.5$, the dark crescent-shaped streaks may be interpreted as microcracks generated in the layer.

The large, irregular broken rims in the wear scar of Fig. 2 show that spalling was the main wear mechanism of the layer when the sliding velocity exceeded a critical value between 1 and 3.4 m s$^{-1}$ under these conditions. The crescent-shaped streaks observed in the wear scar at 0.3 m s$^{-1}$ indicate the latent potential existence of this mechanism even at lower sliding velocities. A transition from low wear to high wear occurs when the specific frictional power input exceeds a critical value, which can be estimated to be in the region of 5 W mm$^{-2}$.

At a test temperature of 250 °C (which is the same as the substrate temperature during the deposition of the layer) another wear mechanism becomes predominant. Figure 3 shows the wear scar at a sliding speed of 0.1 m s$^{-1}$ as observed by scanning electron microscopy (SEM). It can be seen that the layer in the wear track is only partly destroyed by the spalling process. Other parts are still covering the substrate with relatively good adhesion, showing wear scratches. At the border of the wear track an accumulation of black wear particles is found, which are indicative of a graphitization

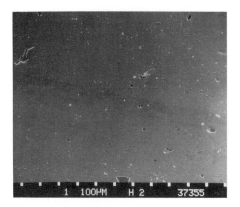

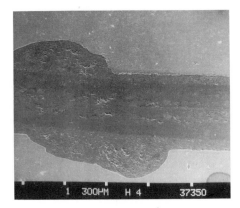

Fig. 1. SEM image of wear scar on i-carbon on SiSiC; $T=25$ °C, $v=0.3$ m s$^{-1}$, $F_N=3$ N, $s=$ 1000 m.

Fig. 2. SEM image of wear scar on i-carbon on SiSiC; $T=25$ °C, $v=3.4$ m s$^{-1}$, $F_N=3$ N, $s=$ 1000 m.

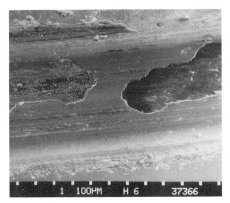

Fig. 3. SEM image of wear scar on i-carbon on SiSiC; $T=250$ °C, $v=0.1$ m s$^{-1}$, $F_N=3$ N, $s=1000$ m.

process due to a tribologically induced phase transformation. At higher sliding speeds the layer inside the wear track was completely destroyed and worn away.

The Vickers hardness (HV 0.05) of the coating is in the range $H_V=2500$–3500 HV for both the room temperature specimen and the specimen after the 250 °C tribotest. This indicates that this "heat treatment" did not lead to a degradation of the layer. Although the observed graphitization process is not yet clear in detail, the relatively high friction coefficient of $f=0.9$ at 250 °C causes a high frictional energy input to the area of contact, subsequently followed by an increase in contact temperature, obviously causing the phase transformation.

### 3.2. Oscillating sliding steel–steel at room temperature

The friction and wear behaviour of coated and uncoated steel (100Cr6) balls against coated and uncoated steel (100Cr6) specimens depends sensitively on the humidity of the surrounding air. The results, given in more detail in ref. 8, can be summarized as follows.

(1) In dry air the wear protection by i-carbon coating is worse than in humid air (see the wear scars and profilograms in Fig. 4).

(2) The coating of one partner is sufficient to increase the wear resistance of the system by nearly two orders of magnitude.

(3) In air of high humidity the wear resistance of the coated–coated couple increases by nearly three orders of magnitude compared with the uncoated–uncoated couple.

(4) The coefficient of friction is much lower than that of the uncoated couple ($f=0.7$) and remains low ($f=0.25$) as long as the coating is not destroyed.

### 3.3. Oscillating sliding steel–ceramic at room temperature

The results of the tests with 100Cr6 balls against i-carbon-coated SiSiC disks can be summarized as follows.

(1) The protection against wear is better in humid air than in dry air (Fig. 5).

(2) The coefficients of wear are higher than in the case of the i-carbon-coated 100Cr6 specimen.

(3) The coefficient of friction is nearly independent of humidity ($f=0.15$), compared with $f=0.7$ (dry air) and $f=0.3$ (humid air) for the uncoated 100Cr6–SiSiC couple [9].

### 3.4. Oscillating sliding ceramic–ceramic at room temperature

Two different types of i-carbon coatings on SiSiC were investigated with uncoated SiSiC as counterbody: type H (20% W, thickness 5 $\mu$m) and type P (10% Ta, thickness 3 $\mu$m). The wear scars and their profilograms after tests in air of different humidity are shown in Fig. 6. In all cases the coating is worn away in the central area and coating material is detectable at the borders of the scars. The wear protection of the coating for this substrate is much smaller than in the case of the steel couple. However, even when the coating is worn away, the system shows a smaller coefficient of wear than the uncoated couple, owing to fresh areas of coated material entering the tribocontact when the size of the wear scar increases. This can be seen from the plot of the square of the linear wear as a function of time ($W_1^2(t)$) in Fig. 7. Since $W_1^2$ is proportional to the volumetric wear, the slope of the $W_1^2(t)$ curve is proportional to the coefficient of wear. While the uncoated system shows nearly constant slopes from the beginning to the end of the test, the system with the coated specimens exhibits an incubation phase of roughly 5 h with very small slopes. The higher wear rate (slope) of the system with type P coating is probably due to the smaller thickness of the P coating. The coefficient of friction is $f=0.5$ in dry air and $f=0.2$ in humid air for the uncoated couple and is only slightly reduced for the couples with i-carbon-coated disks.

### 3.5. Oscillating sliding steel–ceramic at elevated temperatures

Tests at temperatures above room temperature with 100Cr6 balls against i-carbon-coated SiSiC show an increase in wear with increasing temperature [8]. Micrographs of the wear scars on the ball and on the disk at four different temperatures are shown in Fig. 8. As the profilograms reveal, wear is detectable on both bodies, being a little higher for the coated ceramic body at all temperatures. Above 200 °C the coefficient of wear increases drastically. The coefficient of friction is low ($f=0.1$) at room temperature and increases nearly linearly to $f=0.3$ at 250 °C.

154

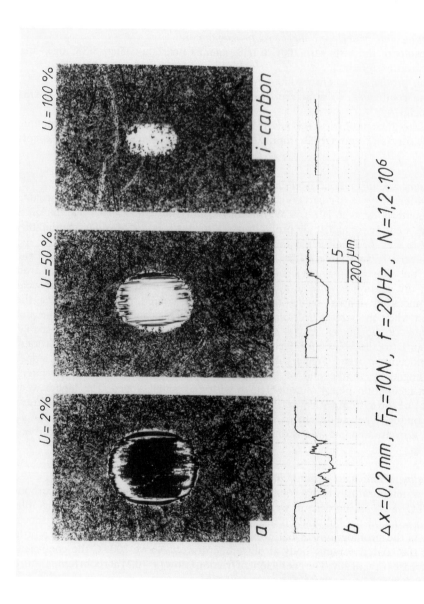

Fig. 4. Optical micrographs of wear scars and profilograms, i-carbon on 100Cr6; $\Delta x = 0.2$ mm, $F_N = 20$ N, $f = 20$ Hz, $N = 1.2 \times 10^6$, steel (100Cr6) ball counterbody.

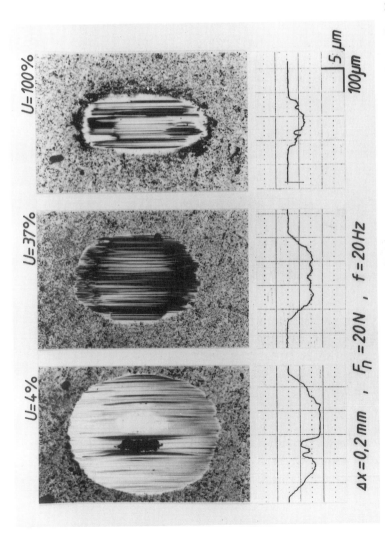

Fig. 5. Optical micrographs of wear scars and profilograms, i-carbon (H) on SiSiC; $\Delta x = 0.2$ mm, $F_N = 20$ N, $f = 20$ Hz, $N = 1 \times 10^5$, steel (100Cr6) ball counterbody.

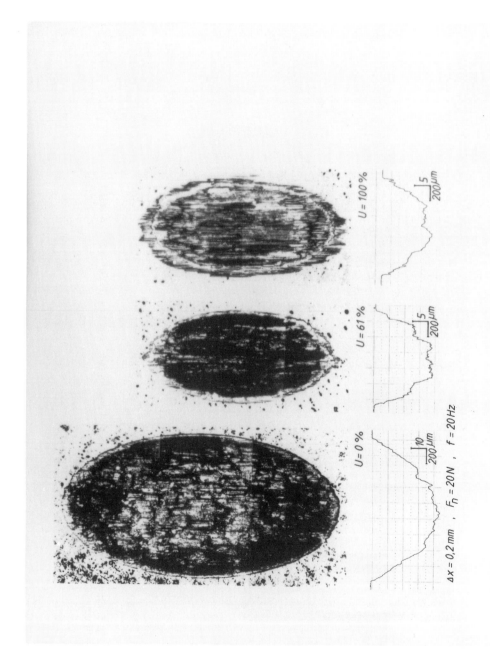

Fig. 6. Optical micrographs of wear scars and profilograms, i-carbon (P) on SiSiC; $\Delta x = 0.2$ mm, $F_N = 20$ N, $f = 20$ Hz, $N = 1.2 \times 10^6$, SiSiC toroid counterbody.

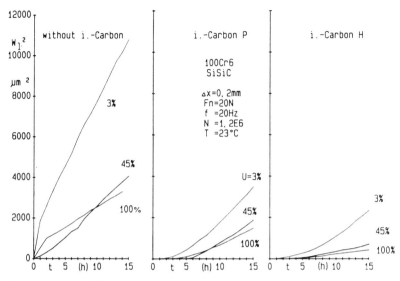

Fig. 7. Square of linear wear as a function of time for tests with steel ball (100Cr6) against uncoated and i-carbon-coated SiSiC in air of different humidities.

### 3.6. Wear mechanisms and surface investigations

Under different test conditions, different mechanisms of wear are found to be predominant. At low sliding speed and room temperature in the case of oscillating sliding, abrasive components are detectable, producing wear scratches probably due to hard wear particles. In tests with steel as counterbody, adhesive transfer of flakes of the coating is important (Fig. 9). At higher sliding speeds and higher temperatures, oxidation and graphitization processes are probably governing the friction and wear behaviour. To prove this assumption, small spot ESCA (electron spectroscopy for chemical analysis) measurements were performed on a wear scar from an oscillating sliding test at room temperature on coating H with a steel ball (100Cr6) as counterbody. (Investigation of the high temperature wear mechanism is still under way and results will be reported later.)

### 3.7. ESCA investigations

The ESCA method gives information about the chemical composition of very thin outermost surface layers (depth of a few atoms). Furthermore, the analysis of the structure of the peaks reveals information concerning the binding state of the elements under investigation; for more details see *e.g.* ref. 10.

To investigate the change in chemical state due to the tribological loading process, small spot ESCA measurements were performed on a wear scar and on the 100Cr6 steel counterbody (ball). To be sure of analysing the i-carbon layer, a wear scar was selected that was not worn through to the substrate. As a reference, the unworn surface of the layer was measured as well. Figure 10 shows the small spot ESCA diagrams of the i-carbon layer inside the wear scar and on the virginal coating. Additionally, an analysis was performed on a wear track produced by sliding wear at

158

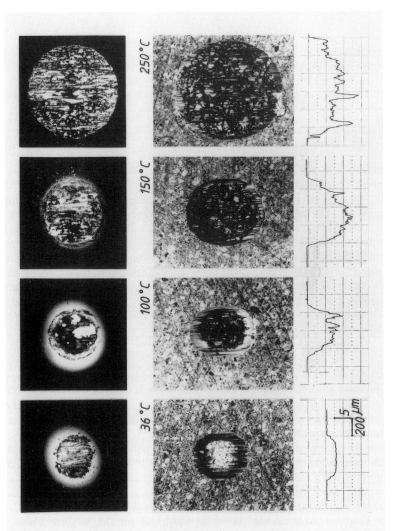

Fig. 8. Optical micrographs of wear scars on steel ball and flat and profilograms, i-carbon (P) on SiSiC, at different temperatures; $\Delta x = 0.2$ mm, $f = 20$ Hz, $F_N = 20$ N, $N = 1 \times 10^5$.

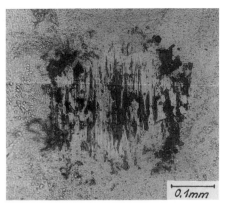

Fig. 9. Optical micrograph of wear scar on steel ball after oscillating sliding test against steel coated with i-carbon (H); $\Delta x = 0.2$ mm, $f = 20$ Hz, $F_N = 20$ N, $N = 1 \times 10^5$.

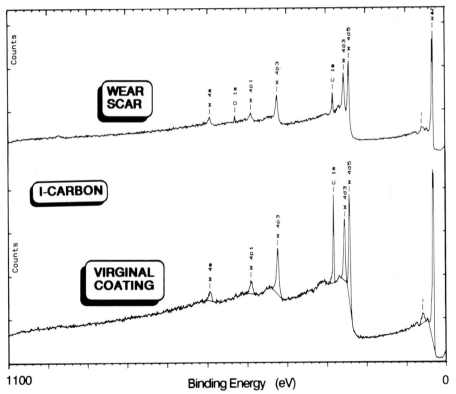

Fig. 10. Small spot ESCA diagrams of i-carbon coating inside (top) and outside (bottom) a wear scar.

a speed of $v = 0.1$ m s$^{-1}$ at room temperature as described in Section 3.1. This analysis showed the same results as that from the wear scar produced by the oscillating sliding motion.

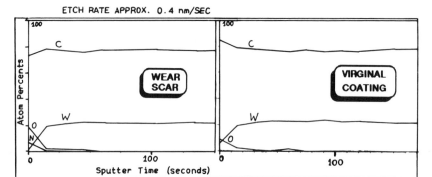

Fig. 11. Depth profiles of different elements of i-carbon coating inside (left) and outside (right) a wear scar.

As can be seen from the diagrams, there is no significant change detectable in the chemical composition between the worn and the unworn surface. The diagrams, which were recorded after a surface-etching process to remove all the contaminants, show only carbon and tungsten as layer-composing elements. A further investigation of the depth profile up to 100 nm (Fig. 11) showed a constant W:C ratio. At the surface a concentration of oxygen is found in both cases, being higher in the wear scar than in the unworn region.

Microscopic investigation of the wear scar on the steel ball revealed the transfer of parts of the i-carbon layer to the ball during the oscillating sliding process. The small spot ESCA results for these transferred parts, which were observed by optical microscopy as irregularly shaped flat parts, showed — as a significant sign of i-carbon transfer — a tungsten content of the same amount as in the original layer.

Analysis of the chemical state of the tungsten atoms showed a binding energy of 35.1 eV for the tungsten $4f_7$ electrons, which is the energy of the W–O bond. The transfer of parts of the layer to the steel ball can possibly explain the relatively low friction coefficients in the i-carbon–100Cr6 steel pairing as described above.

Investigation of the binding energies showed that only for the tungsten atoms could a significant difference in binding state be detected. Analysis of the binding energies of the worn and unworn parts of the layer (Fig. 12) indicated no significant differences either for the carbon binding energies or for the tungsten ones. In the layer, tungsten is bonded to carbon, forming tungsten carbide (WC) with a binding energy of 31.7 eV. These binding states are found in the wear scar as well as in the unworn layer. However, the binding energy of 35.1 eV, which is related to the formation of tungsten oxide ($WO_3$), is also found in both cases. With the information from the depth profile of oxygen (Fig. 11) one can assume that only a thin surface layer of the coating is in the oxidized state.

The observation that there is no WC but only $WO_3$ found in the transferred layer on the ball suggests that a tribo-oxidation process has occurred during the tribological loading. However, this tribo-oxidation process seems to be selective with respect to the WC but not with respect to the C–C bonds.

## 4. Concluding remarks

Under dry sliding conditions metal-doped carbon coatings on SiSiC can reduce the wear of tribocouples considerably. At low sliding speeds (up to 1 m s$^{-1}$) almost

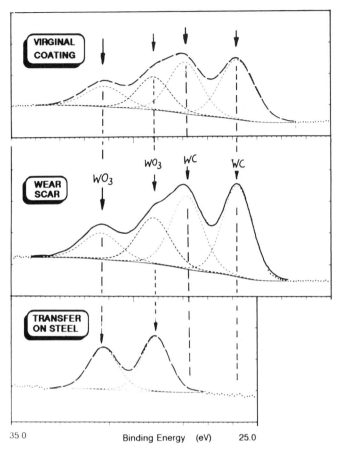

Fig. 12. Small spot ESCA curves of tungsten peaks for virginal surface (top), wear scar (middle) and layer transferred to steel ball (bottom).

no wear is measurable at room temperature. At higher speeds spalling of the layer occurs as a main wear mechanism. At a temperature of 250 °C graphitization of the layer becomes the predominant wear mechanism. The coefficients of friction are relatively high ($f = 0.5$–$0.9$) for SiC as counterbody material.

Under oscillating sliding conditions at room temperature the humidity of the surrounding air influence friction and wear significantly. The coefficient of friction is smaller and the coefficient of wear is much smaller for tests performed in air of high humidity. The wear protection of the layer is more effective if steel is the counterbody material rather than SiSiC. Tantalum and tungsten-doped i-carbon layers show the same tendencies in friction and wear behaviour. At higher temperatures friction and wear increase when the temperature increases.

The small spot ESCA measurements of wear scars obtained in room temperature tests revealed no changes in the composition of the layer and no changes in the chemical state of the carbon bonds. When sliding against steel, transfer of the coating to the uncoated steel ball occurs. The composition of the transferred parts is unchanged; however, tungsten is found in an oxidized state. This may be interpreted as a selective tribo-oxidation process.

162

Under certain conditions of tribotesting, metal-doped carbon layers on steel and on ceramic exhibit low friction and low wear properties. The benefit of these layers appears to be limited to near-room-temperature applications.

## Acknowledgments

The authors are grateful to Mrs. A. Nagel, Mrs. S. Kipry, Mrs. B. Strauss, J. Schwenzien and Professor Yu for microscopical investigations, profilogram measurements and ESCA.

## References

1 O. Vingsbo, M. Odfalk and N.-E. Shen, Fretting maps and fretting behaviour of some f.c.c. metal alloys, *Wear, 138* (1990) 153–167.
2 U. Kopacz and W. D. Münz, Deposition of i-carbon films containing tungsten, *Sixth European Conf. on Chemical Vapour Deposition, Jerusalem, March–April 1987,* Leybold Heraeus, Hanau, 1987, Technical paper no. 11-S25.02.
3 E. Bergmann and G. Vogel, Tribological properties of metal/carbon coatings, *J. Vac. Sci. Technol. A, 4* (1986) 2867–2869.
4 M. Gienau, M. Woydt and K.-H. Habig, Hochtemperaturtribometer für Reibungs- und Verschleissuntersuchungen bis 1000 °C, *Materialprüfung, 29* (7–8) (1987) 197.
5 D. Klaffke, Fretting wear of ceramic–steel; the importance of wear ranking criteria, *Wear, 104* (1985) 337–343.
6 D. Klaffke and K.-H. Habig, Fretting wear tests of silicon carbide, *Wear of Materials,* ASME, New York, 1987, pp. 361–370.
7 D. Klaffke and T. Carstens, Schwingungsverschleissverhalten keramischer Werkstoffe bei hohen Temperaturen, *VDI Fortschr. Ber. Reihe 5, Nr. 203* (1990) 85–96.
8 D. Klaffke and R. Wäsche, Schwingungsverschleiss (Reibkorrosion) von TiN-, TiC- und amorphen Metall-Kohlenstoff-Beschichtungen auf Stahl und Keramik, *Berichtsband des 5. SURTEC-Kongr.,* Hansa, Munich/Vienna, 1989, pp. 447–456.
9 D. Klaffke and R. Wäsche, Tribological behaviour of tungsten doped i-carbon layers deposited on silicon unfiltrated silicon carbide (SiSiC) under sliding and fretting conditions up to 250 °C, *5th Eurotrib, Helsinki, 1989,* Vol. 3, Finnish Society for Tribology, Espoo, 1989, pp. 100–105.
10 H. Hantsche, Grundlagen der Oberflächenanalyseverfahren AES/SAM, ESCA (XPS), SIMS und ISS im Vergleich zur Röntgenmikroanalyse und deren Anwendung in der Materialprüfung, *Mikrosc. Acta, 87* (1983) 97–228.

*Wear, 153* (1992) 163–178

# Sliding friction and wear of plain carbon steels in air and vacuum

S. Venkatesan and D. A. Rigney

*Materials Science and Engineering, The Ohio State University, 116 West 19th Avenue, Columbus, OH 43210-1179 (USA)*

(Received July 30, 1991)

## Abstract

Factors which influence the unlubricated sliding wear of steels are briefly reviewed. Then new results from tests on the sliding of AISI 1045 steel in air and vacuum are described for load and sliding speed combinations near the $T_1$ mild/severe transition of Welsh. Results in air were consistent with those of Welsh and with the wear map of Lim and Ashby. Wear rates in vacuum were less than severe wear rates in air. Significant transfer was not detected. A smooth coating of $Fe_3O_4$ developed on one surface during mild wear.

## 1. Introduction

The sliding behavior of various steels is a vast subject which has received much attention in recent decades. Given the very large number of variables (load, speed, test geometry, composition, microstructure, hardness, environment), it is not surprising that controversies still remain. While there is general recognition that mild and severe wear regimes exist, there is not complete agreement on the factors which control friction and wear in these regimes. Many researchers have associated mild wear with oxide films and severe wear with the absence or destruction of these films. However, oxides may be detrimental in some cases, and other factors have also been associated with mild and severe wear.

In this short paper, it is not possible to provide a complete review of the literature on this subject. Instead, highlights of representative papers are presented to provide a brief overview. Then some new results on the friction and wear of plain carbon steels in air and in vacuum are described.

## 2. Wear maps

Lim and Ashby have reviewed published results on the wear of steels from tests done in air with pin-on-disk testing equipment [1–3]. They have then gathered the data and displayed them on a map in which load and sliding speed are the principal variables. Because different researchers tend to use different combinations of variables, the wear map covers much wider ranges of load, sliding speed and wear rate than the results from any one laboratory. Despite differences in materials, surface condition, equipment and atmosphere used by different investigators, the wear map shows broad patterns of behavior including regimes of mild and severe wear. Thus, it can be used to predict transitions at critical loads or sliding speeds [2, 4]. A related map showing both flash temperature and average surface temperature can be used to determine when thermal effects are important and when they can be neglected [1]. The flash temperature rises rapidly when the sliding speed exceeds about 1 m s$^{-1}$. Maps for environments other than air, *e.g.* vacuum, are not available, but they could be rather different, especially at higher sliding speeds.

## 3. Mild and severe wear

Allowing for the possibility that an oxide layer may not always be responsible for mild wear, the terms mild and severe wear are defined here by the wear rates. For mild wear, the specific wear rate is less than about $10^{-8}$ mm$^3$ mm$^{-1}$ N$^{-1}$; for severe wear, the specific wear rate is greater than about $10^{-6}$ mm$^3$ mm$^{-1}$ N$^{-1}$. The corresponding values of the wear coefficient would be $k < 10^{-5}$ and $k > 10^{-3}$, respectively. Normally, the wear scar is smoother for mild wear than for severe wear.

## 4. Oxygen and oxide films

The importance of oxide films in the dry sliding of steels was recognized early [5–11]. More recently, several authors have emphasized oxide films in their reviews of various aspects of mild and severe wear [12–16].

Bisson *et al.* [7] reported that FeO and Fe$_3$O$_4$ were beneficial and Fe$_2$O$_3$ was "definitely detrimental". However, Iwabuchi *et al.* [17] found that adding a sufficient amount of fine Fe$_2$O$_3$ particles caused mild wear conditions. FeO has been reported to be beneficial [7, 18], but also associated with poor wear resistance [5]. Magnetite (Fe$_3$O$_4$) is commonly associated with mild wear conditions [14, 19]. Sullivan and Hodgson [20] have reported that a mixture of $\alpha$-Fe and Fe$_2$O$_3$ forms protective plateaus. Some of these discrepancies may arise from the fact that many of the diffraction lines for iron and its oxides superimpose [6].

Quinn [13] and many others have assumed that the particular oxide present is the one which would be present at thermodynamic equilibrium, *i.e.* $\alpha$-Fe$_2$O$_3$ at lower temperatures, Fe$_3$O$_4$ at intermediate temperatures and FeO at higher temperatures. Papers on oxidation indicate that kinetic factors are also important and can influence the oxide which nucleates and grows on ferrous materials [21, 22]. For example, Fe$_3$O$_4$ is the only oxide which grows at low temperature if the partial pressure of oxygen is less than 0.01 Torr (1.33 Pa). At higher partial pressures of oxygen, Fe$_2$O$_3$ can grow on the surface of Fe$_3$O$_4$.

The oxidational wear model of Quinn assumes that oxide grows on the surface and that debris is derived from the oxide coating [12, 13]. Others have suggested that the debris particles are oxidized after they are removed from the surface [23, 24], and that a protective coating can be formed by accretion of debris [23].

Sasada [25] has proposed that chemisorption of oxygen plays an important role in mild wear of transition metals. This emphasis is consistent with the approach taken in many earlier papers (*e.g.* [26, 27]). Several authors have reported unusual behavior under high-vacuum conditions [10, 11, 26], when differences in chemisorption become particularly important.

Usually, mild wear behavior is restricted to transition metals [25]. However, adding fine SiC particles to the sliding interface creates mild wear conditions in non-transition metals [28].

It is also recognized that a tribo-coating can be much thicker and/or oxygen can penetrate much further into a material than would be predicted by considering static oxidation at a given temperature [6, 24].

## 5. Other factors

In addition to mechanisms dependent on oxygen and oxides, other factors which have been suggested as responsible for the differences between mild and severe wear include the following: martensite formation [29], different degrees of penetration of contacting asperities [30], work-hardening and solute effects [31], and deformation, transfer and mechanical mixing [32].

## 6. Welsh's work

The work of Welsh [8, 9] on steels was particularly thorough and is quite well known. We have chosen to repeat part of Welsh's work with a medium carbon steel in the vicinity of his $T_1$ mild/severe wear transition, using his results and the wear map of Lim and Ashby [1] as guides. We have used crossed cylinders with the same dimensions used by Welsh. To check for effects of transfer, we have activated some of the specimens so we could use $^{56}$Co as a tracer. Sliding tests were run both in air and in vacuum. An attempt has been made to determine which factors are responsible for the sliding behavior of medium carbon steel for a limited range of load and sliding speed.

## 7. Procedure

Sliding tests were conducted with a 25.4 mm (1 inch) diameter cylinder rotating against a 6.25 mm (0.25 inch) diameter cylinder in the crossed cylinders configuration as in Welsh's work [8, 9]. This is a simple arrangement, but it is awkward when referring repeatedly to the two components. Therefore, in the remainder of this paper, the smaller fixed cylinder is called the pin and the larger rotating cylinder is called the ring.

Details of the experimental arrangement are described in ref. 33. Tests were conducted in air (relative humidity, 60 to 80%) and at reduced pressures [$(1.5-2) \times 10^{-5}$ Torr; $(2-2.6) \times 10^{-3}$ Pa]. The material used for this study was normalized AISI 1045 carbon steel (in wt%, 0.45 C, 0.7 Mn, 0.05 S, 0.04 P) with a hardness 250 VHN (50 g load) and a microstructure of hypoeutectoid ferrite and pearlite (colony size, 50–80 $\mu$m, lamellar spacing 3 $\mu$m). The machined samples were finished by using a series of SiC metallographic papers (120, 240 and 400 grit) and by cleaning ultrasonically, first in acetone and then in methanol.

The normal loads were 0.18, 0.36, 0.56, 0.648, 1.1 and 1.65 kg in air and 0.18, 0.36 and 0.648 kg in vacuum. Sliding speeds ranged from 0.05 to 0.25 m s$^{-1}$ and the sliding distance from 4 to 3200 m (50–40 000 cycles). Wear rates were determined by weight changes measured with a balance which could be read to $\pm 0.1$ mg. These values were confirmed for selected tests by calculations based on wear scar dimensions [33].

Wear surfaces were examined by optical and scanning electron microscopy and by profilometry. Microhardness data were also obtained. Transmission electron microscopy was used to obtain grain size and crystal structure information on selected debris samples.

The role of transfer was investigated by making one member of the sliding pair radioactive. This was achieved by bombarding the steel sample with protons accelerated in a van de Graaff generator to energies between 6 and 6.5 MeV. The resulting $^{56}$Co decays by emitting 0.846 MeV gamma rays which can be detected by using a Ge–Li detector. The activated sample was paired with an unactivated sample for sliding tests.

## 8. Results

### 8.1. Radioactive tracer experiments

Table 1 lists the sliding tests done with activated samples. In most cases, transfer was either absent or too small to be detected. The only case in which transfer was detected was for an activated ring with a load of 0.648 kg, sliding speed of 60 mm s$^{-1}$, 200 cycles (sliding distance about 16 m), in air.

Figure 1 shows a set of spectra for a representative test, in this case for an activated ring sliding in vacuum with a load of 0.648 kg, sliding speed of 0.18 m s$^{-1}$ and 2025 cycles (about 162 m sliding distance). Most of the peaks in the spectra are from background or from various short-lived isotopes created during activation of the sample. They can be ignored. The peak of interest for $^{56}$Co is clearly present for the debris and for the activated ring before and after sliding, but it is absent for the pin. When corrected for the decay of activity according to the half-life of 77.3 days, the combined activity of the ring and debris after the test is equal to that of the ring before the test.

Figure 2 shows the spectrum for the worn pin for the one test in which transfer was detected. The amount of transfer was small.

These results indicate that, for the sliding conditions used in these experiments, transfer had little or no effect on the sliding behavior, at least towards the end of sliding.

TABLE 1.

Sliding tests involving an activated specimen

| Condition | Normal load (kg) | Sliding speed (m s$^{-1}$) | Sliding distance (m) | Sample activated | Transfer detected |
|-----------|------------------|----------------------------|----------------------|------------------|-------------------|
| Air | 1.10 | 0.11 | 20 | Ring | No |
| | 0.648 | 0.08 | 80 | Ring | No |
| | 0.648 | 0.08 | 40 | Pin | No |
| | 0.648 | 0.06 | 16 | Ring | Trace |
| | 0.648 | 0.06 | 8 | Ring | No |
| | 0.56 | 0.035 | 76 | Ring | No |
| Vacuum | 1.10 | 0.10 | 28 | Ring | No |
| | 0.648 | 0.18 | 162 | Ring | No |
| | 0.648 | 0.10 | 60 | Ring | No |
| | 0.648 | 0.06 | 8 | Ring | No |
| | 0.18 | 0.03 | 72 | Ring | No |

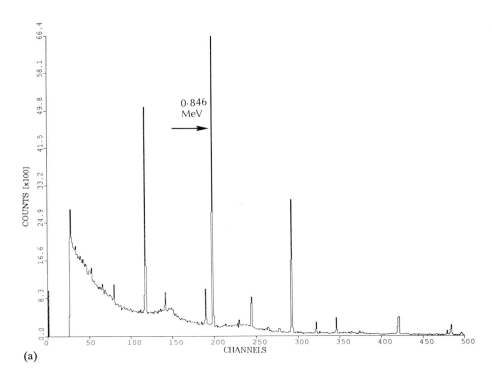

(a)

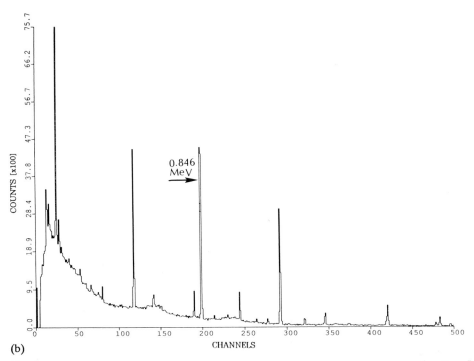

(b)

**Fig. 1.**                                                                 (*continued*)

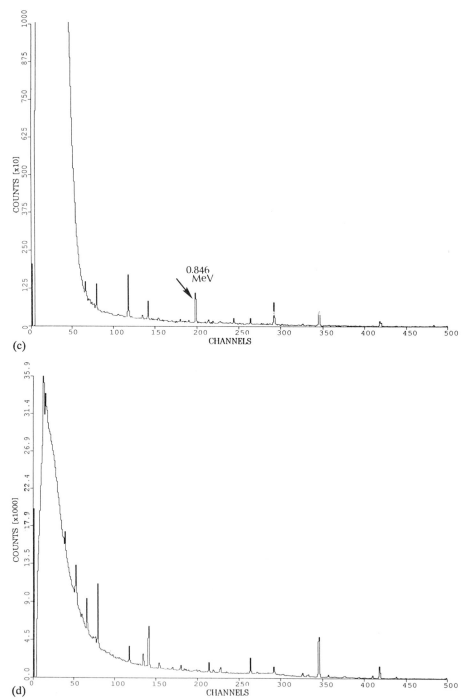

Fig. 1. Spectrum showing counts *vs.* channel number (proportional to energy) for (a) activated ring before wear testing, (b) activated ring after wear testing, (c) debris after wear testing, and (d) pin after wear testing.

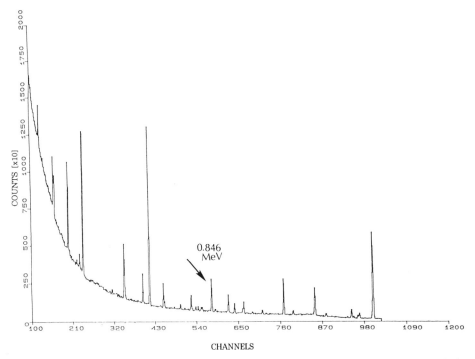

Fig. 2. Spectrum similar to Fig. 1, but for unactivated pin after sliding against activated ring.

## 8.2. Friction

With a low normal load (0.36 kg) in air, there was a brief period of rough sliding followed by smooth sliding and mild wear. The steady-state friction coefficient was about 0.2–0.3. With a higher load (0.648 kg) in both air and vacuum the average friction coefficient was similar but sliding was rough throughout the test. The fluctuations were much larger, some as large as an equivalent friction coefficient of 1.2 for air and 1.8 for vacuum. At lower load (0.36 kg) in vacuum the fluctuations were much smaller.

Occasionally a friction trace for an air test would exhibit smooth sliding after an extended period of rough sliding. Such a distance-dependent transition is expected if the contact area grows sufficiently during sliding. It can be interpreted easily with the aid of a wear map [1].

## 8.3. Wear rates

Wear rates for the different test conditions are given in Table 2. The loads and speeds were selected after reviewing the work of Welsh [8, 9] so we could observe the region around his $T_1$ transition between mild and severe wear for the 1045 steel samples. Intended values for the speeds were 50, 100, 150 and 250 mm s$^{-1}$, but the speed controller had a wide range which made it difficult to set the speed accurately.

In air at loads of 0.648 kg and higher the wear rate was of the order of $10^{-7}$ cm$^3$ cm$^{-1}$, which corresponds to the severe wear regime. There was a general trend for wear rate to increase with both load and sliding speed. At lower loads the wear rates were about $10^{-9}$–$10^{-10}$ cm$^3$ cm$^{-1}$, corresponding to mild wear.

TABLE 2

Wear rate data for sliding tests in air (severe, mild) and vacuum. For test 6 there was a transition from severe to mild wear after about 19 750 cycles

| Condition | Test no. | Normal load (kg) | Sliding speed (m s$^{-1}$) | No. of cycles | Sliding distance (m) | Wear rate (cm$^3$ cm$^{-1}$) | | Specific wear rate (mm$^3$ mm$^{-1}$ N$^{-1}$) | | Wear coefficient, $k$ | |
|---|---|---|---|---|---|---|---|---|---|---|---|
| | | | | | | Ring | Pin | Ring | Pin | Ring | Pin |
| Air (severe) | 1 | 0.648 | 0.12 | 4500 | 360 | $3.5 \times 10^{-7}$ | $1.4 \times 10^{-7}$ | $5.4 \times 10^{-6}$ | $2.2 \times 10^{-6}$ | $1.3 \times 10^{-2}$ | $5.4 \times 10^{-3}$ |
| | 2 | 0.648 | 0.05 | 1500 | 120 | $1.4 \times 10^{-7}$ | $9.2 \times 10^{-8}$ | $2.2 \times 10^{-6}$ | $1.4 \times 10^{-6}$ | $5.4 \times 10^{-3}$ | $3.5 \times 10^{-3}$ |
| | 3 | 0.648 | 0.10 | 20200 | 1610 | $1.4 \times 10^{-7}$ | $1.0 \times 10^{-7}$ | $2.2 \times 10^{-6}$ | $1.5 \times 10^{-6}$ | $5.4 \times 10^{-3}$ | $3.9 \times 10^{-3}$ |
| | 4 | 0.648 | 0.12 | 36120 | 2882 | $1.5 \times 10^{-7}$ | $1.0 \times 10^{-7}$ | $2.3 \times 10^{-6}$ | $1.5 \times 10^{-6}$ | $5.5 \times 10^{-3}$ | $3.9 \times 10^{-3}$ |
| | 5 | 0.648 | 0.50 | 3000 | 240 | $6.6 \times 10^{-8}$ | $5.9 \times 10^{-8}$ | $1.0 \times 10^{-6}$ | $9.1 \times 10^{-7}$ | $2.5 \times 10^{-3}$ | $2.3 \times 10^{-3}$ |
| | 6 | 0.648 | 0.80 | 32525 | 2595 | $1.7 \times 10^{-9}$ | $2.2 \times 10^{-9}$ | $2.6 \times 10^{-8}$ | $3.4 \times 10^{-8}$ | $6.6 \times 10^{-5}$ | $8.4 \times 10^{-5}$ |
| | 7 | 0.648 | 0.12 | 32000 | 2553 | $6.0 \times 10^{-8}$ | $5.3 \times 10^{-8}$ | $9.3 \times 10^{-7}$ | $8.2 \times 10^{-7}$ | $2.3 \times 10^{-3}$ | $2.0 \times 10^{-3}$ |
| | 8 | 1.10 | 0.24 | 3000 | 240 | $4.3 \times 10^{-7}$ | $2.9 \times 10^{-7}$ | $3.9 \times 10^{-6}$ | $2.6 \times 10^{-6}$ | $9.7 \times 10^{-3}$ | $6.6 \times 10^{-3}$ |
| | 9 | 1.10 | 0.24 | 1075 | 85 | $8.3 \times 10^{-7}$ | $2.8 \times 10^{-7}$ | $7.5 \times 10^{-6}$ | $2.5 \times 10^{-6}$ | $1.8 \times 10^{-2}$ | $6.5 \times 10^{-3}$ |
| Air (mild) | 10 | 0.36 | 0.13 | 35000 | 2793 | $2.8 \times 10^{-10}$ | $6.0 \times 10^{-10}$ | $7.8 \times 10^{-9}$ | $1.7 \times 10^{-10}$ | $1.9 \times 10^{-5}$ | $4.1 \times 10^{-5}$ |
| | 11 | 0.56 | 0.12 | 37900 | 3024 | $7.6 \times 10^{-10}$ | $1.2 \times 10^{-9}$ | $1.4 \times 10^{-8}$ | $2.2 \times 10^{-8}$ | $3.4 \times 10^{-5}$ | $5.4 \times 10^{-5}$ |
| | 12 | 0.36 | 0.046 | 3500 | 279 | $1.8 \times 10^{-9}$ | $5.0 \times 10^{-9}$ | $5.0 \times 10^{-8}$ | $1.3 \times 10^{-7}$ | $1.3 \times 10^{-4}$ | $3.5 \times 10^{-4}$ |
| | 13 | 0.18 | 0.06 | 1800 | 144 | $3.6 \times 10^{-9}$ | $2.7 \times 10^{-9}$ | $2.0 \times 10^{-7}$ | $1.5 \times 10^{-7}$ | $5.0 \times 10^{-4}$ | $3.7 \times 10^{-4}$ |
| Vacuum | 14 | 0.648 | 0.05 | 7000 | 559 | $8.0 \times 10^{-8}$ | $9.1 \times 10^{-10}$ | $1.2 \times 10^{-6}$ | $1.4 \times 10^{-8}$ | $3.0 \times 10^{-3}$ | $3.5 \times 10^{-5}$ |
| | 15 | 0.36 | 0.05 | 2500 | 200 | $9.0 \times 10^{-8}$ | 0 | $2.5 \times 10^{-6}$ | 0 | $6.3 \times 10^{-3}$ | 0 |
| | 16 | 0.648 | 0.10 | 8000 | 638 | $4.8 \times 10^{-8}$ | $1.8 \times 10^{-9}$ | $7.3 \times 10^{-7}$ | $2.7 \times 10^{-8}$ | $1.8 \times 10^{-3}$ | $6.9 \times 10^{-5}$ |
| | 17 | 0.648 | 0.064 | 5250 | 419 | $4.7 \times 10^{-7}$ | $4.8 \times 10^{-8}$ | $7.3 \times 10^{-6}$ | $7.3 \times 10^{-7}$ | $1.8 \times 10^{-2}$ | $1.8 \times 10^{-3}$ |

In vacuum the wear rates $(10^{-7}-10^{-8} \ cm^3 \ cm^{-1})$ were between those of mild and severe wear in air. Also, whereas the wear rates of the pin and ring were similar in air, the wear rate of the pin was an order of magnitude less than that of the ring in vacuum.

## 8.4. Microhardness

Microhardness data for worn and unworn material are presented in Table 3 for tests in both air and vacuum. For severe wear tests in air the Vickers hardness number (VHN) on the wear scar was about 450 for the ring and 350 for the pin. For mild wear in air the corresponding values were 350 and 300, respectively. For the case of tests in vacuum, some regions of the wear scars had hardness values similar to those measured after tests in air, while other regions had much higher hardness values. Averages of these high hardness values are the values reported in Table 3 for vacuum tests. Hardness in both environments tended to increase slightly with load but was independent of sliding speed in the range tested.

## 8.5. Wear scars

Profilometer traces and scanning electron microscopy (SEM) images (Fig. 3) provided complementary information about the wear surfaces. For severe wear in air $(0.648 \ kg, 0.12 \ m \ s^{-1})$, the ring surface became uniformly rough with clear evidence of lateral flow (Fig. 3(a)). The pin surface was similar to that of the ring but with small charged particles about 1–5 $\mu$m in diameter (Fig. 3(b)). For mild wear in air $(0.36 \ kg$ and $0.56 \ kg, 0.12 \ m \ s^{-1})$, the ring surface developed rough and smooth regions, with some bright edges indicative of charging (Fig. 3(c)). The pin surface included long grooves about 50 $\mu$m wide and 10 $\mu$m deep. A profilometer trace parallel to the sliding direction was extremely smooth, with variations of less than 1 $\mu$m. After sliding for a long distance in air (38 000 cycles, 3028 m; 0.56 kg, 0.12 m s$^{-1}$), the mild wear surface of the pin developed a coating with elongated pores (Fig. 3(d)). Quantitative stereo-microscopy, as described in ref. 32, yielded values of about 2–2.5 $\mu$m for the thickness of this coating.

TABLE 3

Microhardness data for wear scars

| Condition | Test no. | Test load (kg) | Vickers microhardness, VHN (50 g) | | | |
|---|---|---|---|---|---|---|
| | | | Ring | | Pin | |
| | | | Off track | On track | Off track | On track |
| Air | 1 | 0.648 | 270 | 424 | 240 | 340 |
| (severe) | 5 | 0.648 | 260 | 441 | 240 | 360 |
| | 7 | 0.648 | 260 | 482 | 235 | 310 |
| | 8 | 1.10 | 265 | 510 | 248 | 380 |
| Air (mild) | 12 | 0.36 | 270 | 341 | 240 | 310 |
| Vacuum | 14 | 0.648 | 260 | 1020 | 248 | 875 |
| | 15 | 0.36 | 280 | 750 | 215 | 650 |
| | 16 | 0.648 | 275 | 900 | 230 | 900 |
| | 17 | 0.648 | 270 | 815 | 225 | 650 |

172

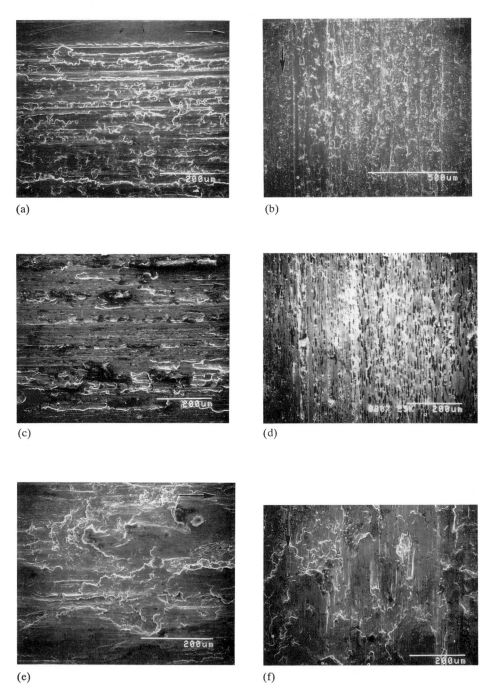

Fig. 3. Secondary electron images of wear scars: (a) ring, severe, air, 0.648 kg, 0.12 m s$^{-1}$; (b) pin, same test as (a); (c) ring, mild, air, 0.56 kg, 0.12 m s$^{-1}$; (d) pin, same test as (c); (e) ring, vacuum, 0.648 kg, 0.07 m s$^{-1}$; (f) pin, same test as (e). The arrow in each case (and in later figures) indicates the sliding direction of the counterface.

In vacuum, with 0.648 kg and 70 mm s$^{-1}$, the ring surface was similar in roughness to the case of severe wear in air, but there were larger overlapping patches indicating extensive plastic flow in the sliding direction (Fig. 3(e)). The pin surface (Fig. 3(f)) was similar to that of the ring.

## 8.6. Debris

Keeping in mind that the conditions selected were near the $T_1$ transition of Welsh, it is interesting to compare the debris generated in air as the load is decreased to approach mild wear conditions. For 1.65 kg and 0.24 m s$^{-1}$, the debris were large (30–60 $\mu$m) and charging was not apparent (Fig. 4(a)). With a reduced load (1.1 kg, 0.24 m s$^{-1}$), there was some charging, as shown Fig. 4(b). This trend continued for 0.648 kg and 0.12 m s$^{-1}$ (Fig. 4(c)). All three samples of debris were strongly ferromagnetic.

At still lower load (0.56 kg and 0.12 m s$^{-1}$), the debris particles were typical of mild wear. Some particles were about 50 $\mu$m long and several $\mu$m thick, but many were 0.1–0.5 $\mu$m and smaller. Charging of the finer particles in the scanning electron microscope was very pronounced. The color of the mild wear debris was darker than for $\alpha$-Fe$_2$O$_3$ but there was a definite red-brown tinge to the debris. Transmission

(a)  (b)

(c)  (d)

Fig. 4. Secondary electron images of debris: (a) severe, air, 1.65 kg, 0.24 m s$^{-1}$; (b) severe, air, 1.1 kg, 0.24 m s$^{-1}$; (c) severe, air, 0.648 kg, 0.12 m s$^{-1}$; (d) vacuum, 0.648 kg, 0.07 m s$^{-1}$.

electron microscopy (TEM) showed that the fine particles consisted of nanocrystalline grains about 2–10 nm in diameter. The electron diffraction pattern for the small particles — which were small enough to transmit electrons without thinning — matched the pattern for $\alpha$-Fe$_2$O$_3$ except that the (024) line ($d = 0.183$ nm) could not be detected. However, the debris collection was strongly ferromagnetic. Electron diffraction patterns for debris obtained at 0.648 kg in air showed lines for $\alpha$-Fe and Fe$_3$O$_4$.

The debris particles generated in vacuum (0.648 kg, 70 mm s$^{-1}$) were larger than those generated in air, as shown in Fig. 4(d). They consisted mostly of $\alpha$-Fe, but some Fe$_3$O$_4$ was also present. The debris sample was strongly ferromagnetic. The grain size was small, 10–100 nm, but larger than in debris from mild wear tests.

*8.7. Sub-surface*

Figure 5 shows two examples of longitudinal cross-sections of ring specimens, the former tested in vacuum and the latter in air. The amount of plastic shear below the surface is strikingly different for the two cases. The deformed region is more than 20 $\mu$m deep in the vacuum case and can not be detected in the particular case shown of severe wear in air.

## 9. Discussion

Transfer of material during sliding is commonly observed for dissimilar metal pairs and it can strongly affect both friction and wear [32]. Transfer during the sliding of steels has also been reported [34–36]. However, for the range of conditions used in the present experiments, the amount of transfer is negligible and has little or no effect on sliding behavior, either in air or in the vacuum environment used for these experiments.

Figure 6 shows that various combinations of increasing load and increasing sliding speed can cause transitions from mild wear to severe wear. This diagram is for tests in air, but data points for tests in vacuum have been included for comparison.

The points marked 1, 2 and 3 in Fig. 6 are revealing. All three are examples of severe wear, but the debris decreases in size and shows less evidence of oxidation in the sequence $1 \rightarrow 2 \rightarrow 3$. At the higher load, the debris is more like that found in vacuum tests, except that the particles are smaller.

All of the debris samples are strongly ferromagnetic, even for the mild wear tests. For the longest test under mild wear conditions, it is clear that there are two kinds

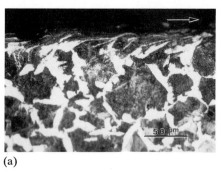 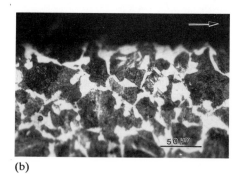

(a)                                        (b)

Fig. 5. Optical microscope images of longitudinal sections of ring specimens: (a) vacuum, 0.648 kg, 0.07 m s$^{-1}$; (b) severe, air, 0.648 kg, 0.12 m s$^{-1}$.

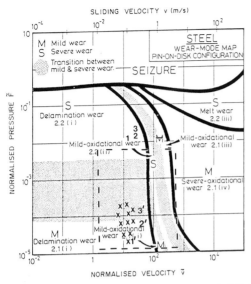

Fig. 6. Wear map for sliding of steels in air [1]. The data from the present work are indicated by the cluster of points and numbers. Points 1–3 were calculated by assuming the initial Hertz contact area; points x and 1′–3′ were calculated by using the final apparent contact area. The data of Welsh are within the boundary surrounding those points.

of particles in the mild wear debris. Electron diffraction shows that the finer ones are $\alpha$-$Fe_2O_3$. The larger ones are similar in size and shape to the elongated pores in the tribo-coating shown in Fig. 3(d). They are probably magnetite.

At low temperatures, the oxidation of iron and of steels proceeds by the formation of $Fe_3O_4$ first, even though $Fe_2O_3$ is thermodynamically favored [21, 22, 37]. This oxide coating depends on grain boundary diffusion for continued growth, so it grows faster if the oxide is fine-grained. It also grows faster on pearlite compared with ferrite regions. The rate depends on the pearlite orientation: it is slower if the lamellae are parallel to the surface. Unless the oxygen partial pressure is too low, $\alpha$-$Fe_2O_3$ can nucleate on the surface of the $Fe_3O_4$. When it does so, it slows the growth of $Fe_3O_4$ [20]. Of course, sliding can modify the oxidation kinetics in a number of ways. For example, it can produce high defect concentrations and fine grain sizes, both of which influence diffusion, it can align pearlite lamellae, it can remove or break up any $\alpha$-$Fe_2O_3$ formed so oxidation can continue, it can mix surface oxides into the subsurface material, etc.

The 2–2.5 $\mu$m thick coating shown in Fig. 3(d) takes some time to develop. It is not detected after short sliding tests of a few hundred or thousand cycles. The coating is considerably thicker than the oxide film present at the start of sliding. The holes which develop in the coating might be exploited as reservoirs when lubricants are used.

The reddish-brown color observed in the mild wear debris is not observed on either the pin or ring wear surface. Perhaps most of the $\alpha$-$Fe_2O_3$ forms by oxidation of the smallest debris, not by growth on the wear surfaces. A simple calculation shows that this could occur very rapidly for particles less than about 0.1 $\mu$m [33].

The Vickers hardness of polycrystalline $Fe_3O_4$ is about 560 and that of $\alpha$-$Fe_2O_3$ is about 755 [38]. The microhardness measured on the surface shown in Fig. 3(d) is about 530 KHN with a 15 g load and 380 KHN with a 50 g load. No cracking was observed in or around these hardness impressions. The depth of the impression is about 1.3 $\mu$m with a 15 g load. These data are consistent with a surface coating of $Fe_3O_4$. Thus, it seems likely that this oxide forms on the wear surface and contributes one component to the debris in mild wear. The other component in the debris, $\alpha$-$Fe_2O_3$, probably forms later.

One of the recurrent subjects in the literature on the tribology of ferrous materials is the so-called "white layer" or "white-etching layer". A review is presented in ref. 29. The layer has variously been described as amorphous material, martensite, oxide or work-hardened material. It is sometimes described as a layer of exceptional hardness. Trilk has recently described very high hardness produced on steel surfaces by sliding in vacuum [4].

We have only encountered very high hardness values on the surfaces of samples tested in vacuum. The sliding speed was insufficient to raise the temperature high enough to produce austenite which would cool rapidly to form martensite. Also, the hardness measured is greater than can be achieved by that mechanism alone [39]. Another possibility is that enough oxide was produced to mix into the near-surface material and raise the hardness by a combination of dispersion-hardening and work-hardening, but that would also be expected in air. Newcomb and Stobbs have suggested an alternative to explain their results on rail steel [31]. They estimated that temperature increases in their case were insufficient to yield normal martensite. With the aid of TEM and ageing experiments, they suggested that plastic deformation led to very high dislocation densities which allowed high supersaturation of carbon. In any case, the high-hardness material produced during our tests in vacuum may be responsible for the lower wear rates in vacuum compared with those found during severe wear in air.

Given the SEM evidence of extensive plastic flow on the wear surfaces after tests in vacuum, it is not surprising that plastic deformation extends well below the surface. However, it is surprising to find no similar deformed material in a longitudinal section after an air test under severe wear conditions (0.648 kg, 0.12 m s$^{-1}$). Wear by microcutting might give that combination of results, but the debris are irregular plates and flakes, not cutting chips. Another possibility is that oxygen embrittled the surface material and facilitated fracture, as previously suggested for some dual phase steels [36] and $Ni_3Al$ [40]. In both cases, oxygen enhanced fracture of either the surface material or the debris. This would be consistent with the observation in the present work that the debris particles are similar in shape but larger when generated in vacuum compared with air (severe wear).

## 10. Summary

(1) Significant transfer was not detected after sliding of medium carbon steel specimens containing radioactive $^{56}$Co. Therefore, transfer is not a principal factor in the unlubricated sliding behavior of these specimens in either air or vacuum for the test conditions used.

(2) Mild and severe wear rates in air differed by about two orders of magnitude. Wear rates in vacuum were less than severe wear rates in air.

(3) Results in air were consistent with those of Welsh and with the wear map presented by Lim and Ashby.

(4) $Fe_3O_4$ was found in all debris samples. A small amount of $\alpha$-$Fe_2O_3$ was found in the debris from mild wear tests. $\alpha$-Fe was found in debris from severe wear tests in air and from tests in vacuum.

(5) Patches of extreme hardness were found on wear surfaces after tests in vacuum. For the low sliding speeds used, their origin is not yet clear.

(6) The smooth coating which developed on the pin when mild wear conditions prevailed for long times is probably $Fe_3O_4$.

## Acknowledgments

The authors are grateful to the Office of Naval Research for support of this research under contract N00014-89-J-1234 (OSURF 721754) and to W. Glaeser and M. Peterson for helpful discussions.

## References

1 S. C. Lim and M. F. Ashby, Overview No. 55, Wear mechanism maps, Acta Metall., 35 (1987) 1–24.
2 S. C. Lim, M. F. Ashby and J. H. Brunton, Wear-rate transitions and their relationship to wear mechanisms, Acta Metall., 35 (1987) 1343–1348.
3 M. F. Ashby and S. C. Lim, Wear-mechanism maps, Scr. Metall., 24 (1990) 805–810.
4 N. Trilk, Wear maps and their application to the unlubricated sliding of steel on steel, M.S. Thesis, Ohio State University, 1990.
5 R. Mailander and K. Dies, Arch. Eisenhuttenw., 16 (1943) 385.
6 J. N. Good and D. Godfrey, Changes found on run-in and scuffed surfaces of steel, chrome plate and cast iron, NASA Tech. Note 1432 (1947).
7 E. F. Bisson, R. L. Johnson and M. A. Swibert, Friction, wear and surface damage as affected by solid films, NASA Tech. Note 3444 (1955).
8 N. C. Welsh, The dry wear of steels: I. The general pattern of behavior, Phil. Trans. R. Soc. A, 257 (1965) 31–49.
9 N. C. Welsh, The dry wear of steels: II. Interpretation and special features, Phil. Trans. R. Soc. A, 257 (1965) 51–70.
10 R. D. Brown and R. A. Burton, An experimental study of the relationship between oxygen partial pressure and friction for 52100 steel, ASME Paper 67-WA/LUB-23 (1967) 1–7.
11 R. Takagi, Effect of oxide film on the friction of 52100 steel in vacuum, ASLE Trans., 13 (1969) 87–98.
12 T. F. J. Quinn, Review of oxidational wear, Part I: The origins of oxidational wear, Tribol. Int., 16 (1983) 257–271.
13 T. F. J. Quinn, Review of oxidational wear, Part II: Recent developments and future trends in oxidational wear research, Tribol. Int., 16 (1983) 305–315.
14 J. L. Sullivan and S. S. Athwal, Mild wear of a low alloy steel at temperatures up to 500 °C, Tribol. Int., 16 (1983) 123–131.
15 K. C. Ludema, A review of scuffing and running-in of lubricated surfaces, with asperities and oxides in perspective, Wear, 100 (1984) 315–331.
16 A. W. Batchelor, G. W. Stachowiak and A. Cameron, The relationship between oxide films and the wear of steels, Wear, 113 (1986) 203–223.
17 A. Iwabuchi, K. Hori and H. Kubosawa, The effect of oxide particles supplied at the interface before sliding on the severe–mild wear transition, Wear, 128 (1988) 123–137.
18 T. H. C. Childs, Fine friction cutting: a useful wear process, Tribol. Int., 16 (1983) 67–84.
19 S. C. Lim and J. H. Brunton, The unlubricated wear of iron, Wear, 113 (1986) 383–393.
20 J. L. Sullivan and S. G. Hodgson, A study of mild oxidational wear for conditions of low load and speed, Wear, 121 (1988) 95–106.

178

21 W. E. Boggs, R. H. Kachik and G. E. Pellissier, The effect of oxygen pressure on the oxidation of zone-refined iron, *J. Electrochem. Soc., 112* (1965) 539–545.

22 D. Caplan, G. I. Sproule, R. J. Hussey and M. J. Graham, Oxidation of Fe–C alloys at 500 °C, *Oxid. Met., 12* (1978) 67–82.

23 J. E. Wilson, F. H. Stott and G. C. Wood, The development of wear protective oxides and their influence on sliding friction, *Proc. R. Soc. London A, 369* (1980) 557–574.

24 W. J. Salesky, R. M. Fisher, R. O. Ritchie and G. Thomas, The nature and origin of sliding wear debris from steels, *Proc. Wear of Materials, 1983,* ASME, NY, 1983, pp. 434–445.

25 T. Sasada, Fundamental analysis of the "adhesive wear" of metals — severe and mild wear, *Proc. JSLE, Int. Tribol. Conf., Tokyo, 1985,* pp. 623–628.

26 D. H. Buckley, M. Swikert and R. L. Johnson, Friction, wear and evaporation rates of materials in vacuum to $10^{-7}$ mm Hg, *ASLE Trans., 5* (1962) 8–23.

27 D. H. Buckley, Influence of chemisorbed films on adhesion and friction of clean iron, *NASA Tech. Note D-4775* (1968).

28 M. Oike, N. Emori and T. Sasada, Effect of fine ceramic particles interposed between sliding surfaces on wear of metals, *Proc. Wear of Materials, 1987,* ASME, New York, 1987, pp. 185–190.

29 T. S. Eyre and A. Baxter, The formation of white layers at rubbing surfaces, *Met. and Mater., 6* (1972) 435–439.

30 K. Hokkirigawa and K. Kato, An experimental and theoretical investigation of ploughing, cutting and wedge formation during abrasive wear, *Tribol. Int., 21* (1988) 51–57.

31 S. B. Newcomb and W. M. Stobbs, *Mater. Sci. Eng., 66* (1984) 195–204.

32 L. H. Chen and D. A. Rigney, Transfer during unlubricated sliding wear of selected metal systems, *Wear, 105* (1985) 47–61.

33 S. Venkatesan, Sliding friction and wear of plain carbon steels in air and in vacuum, *Ph.D. Dissertation,* The Ohio State Univ., Columbus, OH, 1991 (available from University Microfilms, Ann Arbor, MI).

34 J. F. Archard and W. Hirst, An examination of a mild wear process, *Proc. R. Soc. London A, 238* (1956) 515–527.

35 M. Kerridge, Metal transfer and the wear process, *Proc. Phys. Soc. B, 68* (1955) 400–407.

36 M. Sawa and D. A. Rigney, Sliding behavior of dual phase steels in vacuum and in air, *Wear, 119* (1987) 369–390.

37 J. Kruger and H. Y. Yolken, Room temperature oxidation of iron at low pressures, *Corrosion, 20* (1964) 29–35.

38 *CRC Handbook of Chemistry and Physics,* 70th edn., CRC Press, Cleveland, OH, 1989–90.

39 R. A. Grange, C. R. Hribal and L. F. Porter, Hardness of tempered martensite in carbon and low-alloy steels, *Met. Trans. A, 8* (1977) 1775–1785.

40 N. Rao Bonda and D. A. Rigney, Unlubricated sliding wear of nickel aluminides at room temperature and 400 °C, *Mater. Res. Soc. Symp. Proc., 133* (1989) 585–590.

*Wear, 153* (1992) 179–200

# Oxidational wear modelling: I

T. F. J. Quinn

*School of Engineering and Applied Science, United States International University — Europe, Bushey, Herts. WD2 2LN (UK)*

(Received July 30, 1991)

## Abstract

This paper is the first of a series in which increasingly complex oxidational wear models are applied to a tribosystem involving the unlubricated sliding of high chromium ferritic steel pins against austenitic stainless steel discs at speeds between 0.23 and 3.3 m s$^{-1}$.

The most simple oxidational wear model assumes that there is no significant oxidation of the contacting surfaces at the general surface temperature of the pin nor at the general surface temperature of the disc. The model also assumes that a very small number of dominant large plateaux of contact oxidize (at a contact temperature, which is normally much higher than the general surface temperatures of either the pin or the disc) until they reach critical thicknesses which are related to the Archard K factor. The contact temperature is itself related to the division of heat at the plateaux interfaces, a quantity which can be estimated in terms of a surface model in which N circular contacts (each of radius A) are assumed to occur at each of the contacting plateaux of thickness on the pin and on the disc. Since the simple oxidational wear theory also involves both the number N of contacts and the thicknesses of the oxide film on either the pin or the disc, it can be seen that it should be possible to find suitable values of N that will satisfy both the experimentally measured division of heat and the experimental wear rate coefficient, provided that the oxide thicknesses are known.

The main thrust of this paper is to show that, by measuring the critical oxide thicknesses on the pin and on the disc in the scanning electron microscope, it is possible to compute tentative tribological oxidation constants for these particular steels from associated measurements of the wear rate coefficient and the division of heat, using a computer spreadsheet technique which is particularly user friendly. The importance of computer modelling for finding definitive values for the tribological oxidation constants of a tribosystem, and hence for predicting the magnitudes of the contact temperature and the wear rate of a tribo-element undergoing oxidational wear in that system, is also discussed.

## 1. Introduction

There have been several models proposed to explain oxidational wear. Some have equated the volume of wear to the volume of oxide formed on the real areas of contact between sliding metal surfaces, whilst others have related the time to build up critical oxide thicknesses to the Archard K factor. Most models have assumed that there is insignificant oxidation of the real areas of contact at the general surface temperature of the tribo-elements. There is not any general agreement, however, regarding the temperature at which the real areas of contact actually do oxidize. Some workers assume that oxidation of the real areas of contact occurs at the temperature TF that arises while the opposing regions are in actual contact whereas others, notably

0043-1648/92/$5.00

those who specialize in using temperature-measuring devices that view the surface just after it leaves the region of contact, favour some other temperature somewhat less than TF.

The model used in this paper assumes that the real areas of contact can oxidize only at TF. It also assumes that, at any given moment, all the N circular contacts (of radius A) comprising the real area of contact, can only occur on a dominant oxide plateau on each of the opposing surfaces [1]. A further assumption is that a total number 1/K of passes are needed at each contact (over a distance d equal to $2*A$) for the whole of the oxidized plateau to eventually build up to a critical thickness THP on the pin or a critical thickness THD on the disc, at which it becomes unstable and breaks away from its substrate to become part of the wear debris. From the Archard wear law, the $K$ factor is related to the wear rate through the relation

$$WR = K * Ar \tag{1}$$

where WR is the wear rate (measured in terms of volume removed per unit sliding distance) and Ar is the total real area of contact. In the current model, Ar is given by

$$Ar = N * PI * A * A \tag{2}$$

The mass uptake of oxygen per unit area of oxidized material formed at the contact temperature TF during the time for $1/K$ passes to occur at each and every contact can be shown [1] to give rise to the following equation for the wear rate WR:

$$WR = (2 * A * W * AP * EXP\{QP/[R * (TF + 273)]\})$$

$$/(P * U * FO * FO * RH * RH * TH * TH) \tag{3}$$

where W is the load, AP is the Arrhenius constant, QP is the activation energy for oxidation, R is the universal gas constant, TF is the contact temperature in degrees Celsius, P is the hardness of the substrate beneath the oxide plateau, U is the speed of sliding, FO is the fraction of oxide that is oxygen, RH is the density of the oxide and TH is the thickness of the oxide plateau. Since the real area Ar of contact is known to be related to the load W and the hardness P by the relation Ar = W/P, one can write the radius A of contact from eqn. (2) as

$$A = SQRT[W/(P * PI * N)] \tag{4}$$

Hence it is clear that the oxidational wear rate WR is a function of load W, the number N of contacts, the contact temperature TF and the critical oxide plateau thickness TH, as well as several other parameters which should not alter very much in any particular tribosystem. Archard [2] has calculated the contact temperature TF for a sliding system in which there are N metallic contacts between the two sliding surfaces. That analysis for TF was based on an estimate of the division of heat between the two surfaces obtained from calculations in which all the frictional heat $U*FF$ was separately considered to go first into one of the tribo-elements and then into the other. FF is, of course, the frictional force between the elements. The inclusion of an oxide plateau of thickness TH into this analysis means that the theoretical expression for the contact temperature TF now becomes a function of the unknown variables N and TH.

The main thrust of much of the recent work on oxidational wear has been to deduce the limited number of pairs of values of N and TH that will satisfy the experimentally measured division of heat. An even more limited number of these pairs of values are found to be consistent with the experimentally measured mild oxidational wear rate as given by eqn. (3). Until recently, it had generally been assumed that one can take the static oxidation activation energy QP as being appropriate to oxidational wear, whereas one has to use the wear rates themselves to deduce a tribological Arrhenius constant APM. This meant, of course, that one now had three unknowns with only two basic equations, namely the division of heat equation and the oxidational wear equation. A certain amount of intuition was required in order to choose what seemed to be suitable values for TH and TF that were consistent with the average thickness of the oxide (as seen in electron micrographs) and the presence of certain high temperature oxides (as shown by X-ray diffraction of the wear debris). By narrowing the possible values of TF and TH down to just one or two pairs, it had been possible to deduce tribological Arrhenius constant values APM from the wear experiments [1].

There have been suggestions that it is not reasonable to expect the activation energies for tribological oxidation to be the same as the activation energies for static oxidation, and that the static activation energies should not be carried over to the tribosystem undergoing mild oxidational wear. If one accepts that the tribological activation energies should also be deduced from the oxidational wear experiments themselves, this means that one more unknown must now be added to the list of unknown variables — clearly an impossible situation! On the contrary, if one actually measures the plateaux thicknesses accurately for a series of experiments in which the wear rate is strictly proportional to the load W, *i.e.* where the wear rate coefficient remains constant, then the number of unknowns again reduces to three. Furthermore, if one assumes that the QPM values will not change very much between experiments carried out at similar loads in the above-mentioned series, then one can deduce tentative values of both APM and QPM as well as TF and N for that particular tribosystem. This is the basis of the present paper. Subsequent papers will aim at deducing the definitive values for the tribological oxidation constants for any given tribosystem.

## 2. The wear experiments

The details of the experiments have been published elsewhere [3]. Essentially, the experiments were carried out on a specially designed pin-on-disc wear machine, one that was capable of measuring the frictional force, the pin height, the disc temperature and the temperature of the pin at various distances from the sliding interface, on a continuous basis. The pin was made of a high chromium ferritic steel and the disc was made of an austenitic stainless steel. These materials are often used in the exhaust valve system of diesel engines, the ferritic steel being used for the seating while the austenitic stainless steel is used for the valve head. In an attempt to simulate the valve sinkage that sometimes occurs in the seating of this tribosystem, the pins were made of high chromium ferritic steel while the discs were made of austenitic stainless steel.

It is difficult to find any published literature on the static oxidation of these steels. The presence of large amounts of chromium means that their static and tribological oxidation constants are probably very different from those relevant to the low alloy steels used for the early work [1].

Experiments were carried out at pin speeds of 0.23, 1.0, 2.0 and 3.3 m s$^{-1}$ and loads varying from about 8 up to about 90 N. The wear patterns, *i.e.* the "wear rate

182

*vs.* load" curves, are given in Fig. 1. From this graph, one can see that there is a transition somewhat around 65 N for the higher speeds. Above that transition load, there is an increase in the wear rate coefficient. The transition also involved a change in the composition of the wear debris. Below the transition load, the wear debris consisted entirely of the rhombohedral and spinel oxides, thereby indicating mild oxidational wear. Above the transition load, however, there was some austenite or ferrite present as well as the oxides, thereby showing that severe oxidational occurs at these loads. For the 0.23 m s$^{-1}$ experiments, there was no apparent transition. However, the debris always consisted of ferrite, austenite and the rhombohedral oxide, indicating that these experiments were undergoing severe oxidational wear. The terminology of "severe oxidational wear" was first used by Lim and Ashby [4]. It should not be confused with severe metallic wear which is the sort of wear that occurs below the T2 transition of Welsh [5]. It is likely that the transition noted in Fig. 1 is indeed the T3 transition of Welsh [5]. The actual values of the wear rate coefficients are given in Table 1. The thicknesses of the oxide plateaux were measured using a tilted specimen technique in the scanning electron microscope.

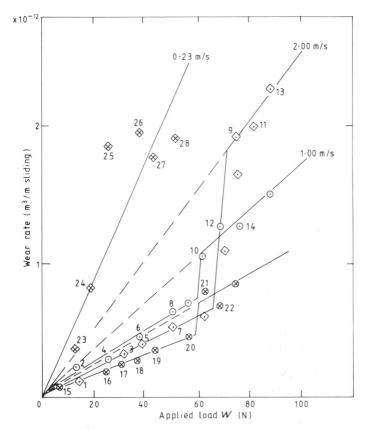

Fig. 1. Wear patterns for high chromium ferritic steel pins sliding on austenitic stainless steel discs at 0.23, 1.00, 2.00 and 3.30 m s$^{-1}$.

TABLE 1

Wear rate coefficients WRC for the high chromium ferritic steel pins

| Speed (m s$^{-1}$) | WRC ($\times 10^{-14}$ m$^3$ m$^{-1}$ N$^{-1}$) | |
| --- | --- | --- |
| | Below transition | Above transition |
| 0.23 | Not applicable | 4.4 |
| 1.00 | 1.3 | 1.7 |
| 2.00 | 1.1 | 2.8 |
| 3.30 | 0.8 | 1.1 |

## 3. Computer analysis of the wear experiments

### 3.1. The use of computer spreadsheets in wear modelling

Previous computer analyses of oxidational wear models have tended to use *FORTRAN* [1], a programming language not readily accessible to the PC user. In this paper, one of the commercially available computer spreadsheet methods has been used (i) in order to deduce the values of the number N of contacts that will provide a theoretical division DTH of heat consistent with the experimentally measured division DE of heat and the oxide plateaux thicknesses THP and THD and (ii) to present the results of many such calculations in a readily understood spreadsheet form. The essence of the spreadsheet is that one can see instantly the effects of changing any of the values of any particular cell in the spreadsheet. It is especially useful for showing when an iterative process has reached the approximation acceptable to the programmer.

As an example, Table 2 shows the spreadsheet program for deducing the number N3 of contacts to satisfy FN = DTH-DE = 0, for the experiment carried out under a load of 31.25 N and at a speed of 2 m s$^{-1}$, *i.e.* experiment 3. (The numbers of the experiments are given near to the appropriate point in Fig. 1.) Rows 1–5 in Table 2(a) have been used for the title and the quantities that remain constant throughout the whole series of experiments. For completeness, these quantities will now be defined: XK is the thermal diffusivity of the pin material, KSP and KSD are the thermal conductivities of the pin and disc materials respectively, KI is the thermal conductivity of the insulator, RA and RT are the outer and inner diameters of the insulating sleeve (as shown in Fig. 6.1 of ref. 1), C is the specific heat of the thermocouple A and R is the universal gas constant. M is a collection of all these terms, for convenience in heat flow calculations which equals SQRT{2*KI/[(KSP*RT*RT)*LN(RA/RT)]}.

The same rows in Table 2(b) relate to quantities that are constant for experiment 3. Once again, for completeness, we shall define them as follows: W3 is the load, U3 is the speed, PP3 is the hardness of the pin material, HT3 is the total heat evolved at the sliding interface, THP3 and THD3 are the measured thicknesses of the oxides on the pin and the disc, TPS3 and TDS3 are the general surface temperatures of the pin and the disc, KOP3 and KOD3 are the thermal conductivities of the oxides on the pin and the disc and DE3 is the experimental division of heat for this experiment.

Column 1 gives the values of FN1 and FN2 for the originally chosen values of N1 = 60 and N2 = 100. These values of FN1 and FN2 are compared with FN3 where N3 = (N1 + N2)/2. All the necessary formula for deducing A, C, TD, TP, DTH and FN are contained in the appropriate cells in the software but do not appear in the printout. The final two items in column 1 are obtained by using conditional statements

# TABLE 2(a)

Spreadsheet programme for deducing the number of contacts (N) to satisfy (DTH-DE) = 0 for Expt 3 (Iterations 1–6)

| GENERAL CONSTANTS | | |
|---|---|---|
| XK = 0.0000008 | KSP = 26.8 | KSD = 15 |
| R = 8.314 | KI = 0.1045 | RA = 0.00795 |
| RT = 0.003175 | C = 0.000011 | M = 29.03172 |

| INTER = | 1 | 2 | 3 | 4 | 5 | 6 |
|---|---|---|---|---|---|---|
| OLD N1 = | 60 | 60 | 60 | 65 | 65 | 65 |
| OLD N2 = | 100 | 80 | 70 | 70 | 67.5 | 66.25 |
| OLD N3 = | 80 | 70 | 65 | 67.5 | 66.25 | 65.625 |
| A1 = 0.000006 | | 0.0000068 | 0.000006 | 0.000006 | 0.000006 | 0.000006 |
| A2 = 0.000005 | | 0.0000059 | 0.000006 | 0.000006 | 0.000006 | 0.000006 |
| A3 = 0.000005 | | 0.0000063 | 0.000006 | 0.000006 | 0.000006 | 0.000006 |
| C1 = 7.794346 | | 7.7943467 | 7.794346 | 7.488566 | 7.488566 | 7.488566 |
| C2 = 6.037475 | | 6.7501023 | 7.216162 | 7.216162 | 7.348580 | 7.417582 |
| C3 = 6.750102 | | 7.2161629 | 7.488566 | 7.348580 | 7.417582 | 7.452820 |
| TD1 = 192.6242 | | 192.62425 | 192.6242 | 280.5026 | 280.5026 | 280.5026 |
| TP1 = 2234.183 | | 2234.1834 | 2234.183 | 2210.928 | 2210.928 | 2210.928 |
| DTH1 = 0.079373 | | 0.0793735 | 0.079373 | 0.112586 | 0.112586 | 0.112586 |
| FN1 = −0.03650 | | −0.036505 | −0.03650 | −0.00329 | −0.00329 | −0.00329 |
| TD2 = 652.5014 | | 479.10918 | 356.0068 | 356.0068 | 319.6309 | 300.4302 |
| TP2 = 5890.804 | | 2154.7689 | 2190.212 | 2190.212 | 2200.283 | 2205.530 |
| DTH2 = 0.099720 | | 0.1819025 | 0.139817 | 0.139817 | 0.126842 | 0.119886 |
| FN2 = −0.01615 | | 0.0660236 | 0.023938 | 0.023938 | 0.010963 | 0.004007 |
| TD3 = 479.1091 | | 356.00680 | 280.5026 | 319.6309 | 300.4302 | 290.5598 |
| TP3 = 0.510907 | | 2190.2126 | 2210.928 | 2200.283 | 2205.530 | 2208.210 |
| DTH3 = 0.998934 | | 0.1398177 | 0.112586 | 0.126842 | 0.119886 | 0.116281 |
| FN3 = 0.883055 | | 0.0239388 | −0.00329 | 0.023938 | 0.004007 | 0.000402 |
| NEW N1 = | 60 | 60 | 65 | 65 | 65 | 65 |
| NEW N2 = | 80 | 70 | 70 | 67.5 | 66.25 | 65.625 |

184

TABLE 2(b)

Iterations 8–15

| W3 = 31.25 | THP3 = 0.000003 | TDS3 = 39 | |
|---|---|---|---|
| U3 = 2 | KOP3 = 5.818942 | TPS3 = 114.7915 | |
| PP3 = 3.5E + 09 | DE3 = 0.115878 | KOD3 = 6.31481 | CONSTANTS FOR EXPERIMENT 3 |
| HT3 = 26.24 | THD3 = 0.000003 | | |

| 8 | 9 | 10 | 11 | 12 | 13 | 14 | 15 |
|---|---|---|---|---|---|---|---|
| 65.3125 | 65.46875 | 65.54687 | 65.54687 | 65.54687 | 65.54687 | 65.55175 | 65.55419 |
| 65.625 | 65.625 | 65.625 | 65.58593 | 65.56640 | 65.55664 | 65.55664 | 65.55664 |
| 65.46875 | 65.54687 | 65.58593 | 65.56640 | 65.55664 | 65.55175 | 65.55419 | 65.55541 |
| 0.000006 | 0.000006 | 0.000006 | 0.000006 | 0.000006 | 0.000006 | 0.000006 | 0.000006 |
| 0.000006 | 0.000006 | 0.000006 | 0.000006 | 0.000006 | 0.000006 | 0.000006 | 0.000006 |
| 0.000006 | 0.000006 | 0.000006 | 0.000006 | 0.000006 | 0.000006 | 0.000006 | 0.000006 |
| 7.470629 | 7.461709 | 7.457261 | 7.457261 | 7.457261 | 7.457261 | 7.456983 | 7.456844 |
| 7.452820 | 7.452820 | 7.452820 | 7.455040 | 7.456150 | 7.456705 | 7.456705 | 7.456705 |
| 7.461709 | 7.457261 | 7.455040 | 7.456150 | 7.456705 | 7.456983 | 7.456844 | 7.456775 |
| 285.5549 | 288.0633 | 289.3130 | 289.3130 | 289.3130 | 289.3130 | 289.3910 | 289.4300 |
| 2209.564 | 2208.886 | 2208.548 | 2208.548 | 2208.548 | 2208.548 | 2208.527 | 2208.516 |
| 0.114445 | 0.115366 | 0.115824 | 0.115824 | 0.115824 | 0.115824 | 0.115852 | 0.115867 |
| −0.00143 | −0.00051 | −0.00005 | −0.00005 | −0.00005 | −0.00005 | −0.00002 | −0.00001 |
| 290.5598 | 290.5598 | 290.5598 | 289.9368 | 289.6250 | 289.4690 | 289.4690 | 289.4690 |
| 2208.210 | 2208.210 | 2208.210 | 2208.379 | 2208.463 | 2208.505 | 2208.505 | 2208.505 |
| 0.116281 | 0.116281 | 0.116281 | 0.116052 | 0.115938 | 0.115881 | 0.115881 | 0.115881 |
| 0.000402 | 0.000402 | 0.000402 | 0.000173 | 0.000059 | 0.000002 | 0.000002 | 0.000002 |
| 288.0633 | 289.3130 | 289.3130 | 289.6250 | 289.4690 | 289.3910 | 289.4300 | 289.4495 |
| 2208.886 | 2208.548 | 2208.548 | 2208.463 | 2208.505 | 2208.527 | 2208.516 | 2208.511 |
| 0.115366 | 0.115824 | 0.115824 | 0.115938 | 0.115881 | 0.115852 | 0.115867 | 0.115874 |
| −0.00051 | −0.00051 | 0.000173 | 0.000059 | 0.000002 | −0.00002 | −0.00001 | −0.00000 |
| 65.46875 | 65.54687 | 65.54687 | 65.54687 | 65.54687 | 65.55175 | 65.55419 | 65.55541 |
| 65.625 | 65.625 | 65.58593 | 65.56640 | 65.55664 | 65.55664 | 65.55664 | 65.55664 |

TABLE 2(c)
Iterations 16–23

| W3 = 31.25 | THP3 = 0.000003 | TDS3 = 39 | |
|---|---|---|---|
| U3 = 2 | KOP3 = 5.818942 | TPS3 = 114.7915 | } CONSTANTS FOR EXPERIMENT 3 |
| PP3 = 3.5E + 09 | DE3 = 0.115878 | KOD3 = 6.31481 | |
| HT3 = 26.24 | THD3 = 0.000003 | | |

| 16 | 17 | 18 | 19 | 20 | 21 | 22 | 23 |
|---|---|---|---|---|---|---|---|
| 65.55541 | 65.55603 | 65.55603 | 65.55618 | 65.55618 | 65.55618 | 65.55620 | 65.55620 |
| 65.55664 | 65.55664 | 65.55633 | 65.55633 | 65.55625 | 65.55622 | 65.55622 | 65.55621 |
| 65.55603 | 65.55633 | 65.55618 | 65.55625 | 65.55622 | 65.55620 | 65.55621 | 65.55620 |
| 0.000006 | 0.000006 | 0.000006 | 0.000006 | 0.000006 | 0.000006 | 0.000006 | 0.000006 |
| 0.000006 | 0.000006 | 0.000006 | 0.000006 | 0.000006 | 0.000006 | 0.000006 | 0.000006 |
| 0.000006 | 0.000006 | 0.000006 | 0.000006 | 0.000006 | 0.000006 | 0.000006 | 0.000006 |
| 7.456775 | 7.456740 | 7.456740 | 7.456731 | 7.456731 | 7.456731 | 7.456730 | 7.456730 |
| 7.456705 | 7.456705 | 7.456723 | 7.456723 | 7.456727 | 7.456729 | 7.456729 | 7.456730 |
| 7.456740 | 7.456723 | 7.456731 | 7.456727 | 7.456729 | 7.456730 | 7.456730 | 7.456730 |
| 289.4495 | 289.4593 | 289.4593 | 289.4617 | 289.4617 | 289.4617 | 289.4620 | 289.4620 |
| 2208.511 | 2208.508 | 2208.508 | 2208.507 | 2208.507 | 2208.507 | 2208.507 | 2208.507 |
| 0.115874 | 0.115877 | 0.115877 | 0.115878 | 0.115878 | 0.115878 | 0.115878 | 0.115878 |
| −0.00000 | −0.00000 | −0.00000 | −0.00000 | −0.00000 | −0.00000 | −0.00000 | −0.00000 |
| 289.4690 | 289.4690 | 289.4641 | 289.4641 | 289.4629 | 289.4623 | 289.4623 | 289.4622 |
| 2208.505 | 2208.505 | 2208.507 | 2208.507 | 2208.507 | 2208.507 | 2208.507 | 2208.507 |
| 0.115881 | 0.115881 | 0.115879 | 0.115879 | 0.115879 | 0.115879 | 0.115879 | 0.115878 |
| 0.000002 | 0.000002 | 0.000000 | 0.000000 | 0.000000 | 0.000000 | 0.000000 | 0.000000 |
| 289.4593 | 289.4641 | 289.4617 | 289.4629 | 289.4623 | 289.4620 | 289.4622 | 289.4621 |
| 2208.508 | 2208.507 | 2208.507 | 2208.507 | 2208.507 | 2208.507 | 2208.507 | 2208.507 |
| 0.115877 | 0.115879 | 0.115878 | 0.115879 | 0.115879 | 0.115878 | 0.115878 | 0.115878 |
| −0.00000 | 0.000000 | −0.00000 | 0.000000 | 0.000000 | −0.00000 | 0.000000 | −0.00000 |
| 65.55603 | 65.55603 | 65.55618 | 65.55618 | 65.55622 | 65.55620 | 65.55620 | 65.55620 |
| 65.55664 | 65.55633 | 65.55633 | 65.55625 | 65.55622 | 65.55622 | 65.55621 | 65.55621 |

TABLE 2(d)
Iterations 24–28

| 24 | 25 | 26 | 27 | 28 | REPEAT OF ITER 28 (9 DECIMALS) | VARIABLES |
|---|---|---|---|---|---|---|
| 65.55620 | 65.55620 | 65.55620 | 65.55620 | 65.55620 | 65.556207299 | OLD N1 |
| 65.55621 | 65.55620 | 65.55620 | 65.55620 | 65.55620 | 65.556207597 | OLD N2 |
| 65.55620 | 65.55620 | 65.55620 | 65.55620 | 65.55620 | 65.556207448 | OLD N3 |
| 0.000006 | 0.000006 | 0.000006 | 0.000006 | 0.000006 | 0.000065843 | A1 |
| 0.000006 | 0.000006 | 0.000006 | 0.000006 | 0.000006 | 0.0000065843 | A2 |
| 0.000006 | 0.000006 | 0.000006 | 0.000006 | 0.000006 | 0.0000065843 | A3 |
| 7.456730 | 7.456730 | 7.456730 | 7.456730 | 7.456730 | 7.4567303563 | C1 |
| 7.456730 | 7.456730 | 7.456730 | 7.456730 | 7.456730 | 7.4567303394 | C2 |
| 7.456730 | 7.456730 | 7.456730 | 7.456730 | 7.456730 | 7.4567303479 | C3 |
| 289.4621 | 289.4621 | 289.4621 | 289.4621 | 289.4621 | 289.46214382 | TD1 |
| 2208.507 | 2208.507 | 2208.507 | 2208.507 | 2208.507 | 2208.5077739 | TP1 |
| 0.115878 | 0.115878 | 0.115878 | 0.115878 | 0.115878 | 0.1158789551 | DTH1 |
| −0.00000 | −0.00000 | −0.00000 | −0.00000 | −0.00000 | −0.000000001 | FN1 |
| 289.4622 | 289.4621 | 289.4621 | 289.4621 | 289.4621 | 289.46214858 | TD2 |
| 2208.507 | 2208.507 | 2208.507 | 2208.507 | 2208.507 | 2208.5077726 | TP2 |
| 0.115878 | 0.115878 | 0.115878 | 0.115878 | 0.115878 | 0.1158789568 | DTH2 |
| 0.000000 | 0.000000 | 0.000000 | 0.000000 | 2.0E-10 | 1.95822E-10 | FN2 |
| 289.4621 | 289.4621 | 289.4621 | 289.4621 | 289.4621 | 289.4621462 | TD3 |
| 2208.507 | 2208.507 | 2208.507 | 2208.507 | 2208.507 | 2208.5077733 | TP3 |
| 0.115878 | 0.115878 | 0.115878 | 0.115878 | 0.115878 | 0.1158789559 | DTH3 |
| 0.000000 | 0.000000 | −0.00000 | 2.0E-10 | −0.00000 | −0.000000000 | FN3 |
| 65.55620 | 65.55620 | 65.55620 | 65.55620 | 65.55620 | 65.55620744 8 | NEW N1 |
| 65.55620 | 65.55620 | 65.55620 | 65.55620 | 65.55620 | 65.556207597 | NEW N2 |
|  |  |  |  | 370.7111 | 370.71110078 | TF3 |

regarding whether or not the product of FN3 and FN1 is negative or positive, *i.e.* whether FN3 is the same sign as FN1 or FN2. Since FN1 and FN3 are of opposite sign, then clearly we must set N2 equal to the value of N3 and leave N1 at its original value. These two new values of N1 and N2 now become the "old" values as far as column 2 is concerned. The process then iterates until the required convergence occurs. Clearly, after about 18 iterations, $N1 = N2 = N3 = 65.556$, whereas after 28 iterations these are seen to be accurate to six decimal places.

The formula for providing the values of A1, A2 and A3 in column 1 of Table 2 is, of course, eqn. (4) with the appropriate value for N1, N2 and N3 from the cells containing "OLD N1", "OLD N2" and "OLD N3". The values for C1, C2 and C3 are given by

$$C = (U * A)/(2.0 * XK)$$

Previous analysis of mild oxidational wear [1] assumed that the plateaux of contact on the disc surface were not oxidized sufficiently to affect the proportion of frictional heat which passes into the pin of a typical pin-on-disc wear machine. The current analysis takes this into account. Thus, if C1, C2 and C3 are greater than 0.1, then the "fictitious" temperatures TD1, TD2 and TD3 of the disc assuming all the heat HT goes into the disc, are given by

$$TD = (-0.1021 * C + 0.8605) * (K1 + K2) \tag{6}$$

where

$$K1 = HT/(PI * A * N * KSD) \tag{7}$$

and

$$K2 = (HT * THD)/(PI * A * A * KOD * N) \tag{8}$$

where HT (the total heat evolved at the interface), KSD and KOD (the thermal conductivities of the steel of the disc and the oxide on the disc) and THD are given in cells at the top of the table. If C1, C2 and C3 are equal to or less than 0.1, then the relevant equation is similar to that for the pin, since this would be the condition for very slow sliding speed. The formula for the "fictitious" temperatures TP1, TP2 and TP3 of the pin are given by

$$TP = HT/(PI * A * KSP * N) + (HT * THP)/(PI * A * A * KOP * N) \tag{9}$$

To alter eqn. (9) to suit TD for $C < 0.1$, one merely replaces KSP by KSD, THP by THD and KOP by KOD.

DTH1, DTH2 and DTH3, the theoretical division of heat into the pin for the three "old" values of N and the differences FN1, FN2 and FN3 between these DTH and DE are readily given by the following equations:

$$DTH = TD/(TD + TP) \tag{10}$$

and

$$FN = DTH - DE \tag{11}$$

The equations relating to the experimental division of heat in terms of the relevant operational and material characteristics of the tribosystem have been published [6]. There is no need for these equations to be reproduced here. Essentially, certain assumptions have been made regarding the heat transfer coefficient that enables an analytical solution to be found for H1, the heat flow rate from the interface into the pin. Clearly, DE is given by

$$DE = H1/HT = H1/(FF*U) \tag{12}$$

Having obtained the values of N3 equal to 65.556 20 which gives DTH and DE equal to 0.115 778 for the measured thicknesses THP3 and THD3 of the oxide plateaux on the pin and the disc, it is then possible to deduce the contact temperature TF3 that is also consistent with these values of N, THP and THD. This is shown at the bottom of the penultimate column (column 28) of Table 2, namely 370.7111 °C. The relevant equation is

$$TF = (DTH*TP) + TPS \tag{13}$$

The general surface temperature TPS of the pin is also given by equations to be found in the literature [6].

### 3.2. The application of spreadsheets to oxidational wear

Table 3 gives a summary of the results of the application of the computer spreadsheet method to the 28 experiments as enumerated in Fig. 1, the graph of "wear rate vs, load". The first 30 or so cells of each column in Table 3 contain the values of the quantities extracted from the appropriate spreadsheet. For instance, the numbers given in the column 3 have been taken from column 29 of Table 2 (which related to experiment 3 only).

The 12 or so cells that appear at the bottom of Table 3 relate to the application of the simple mild oxidational wear model to the analysis of selected pairs of experiments based on the numbers given in the columns appropriate to that pair. For instance, the numbers at the foot of column 1 relate to experiments 1 and 3, the numbers at the foot of column 2 relate to experiments 2 and 4, and so on. The first three numbers in the lower part of column 1 are the result of inserting the appropriate values of TF, WRC, THP, THD and U into the equations for G, S and V. The cell entitled TYPE OF WEAR/ACTIVATION ENERGY either gives the result of putting these values into the equation

$$QPM = G*[LN(S/V)] \tag{14}$$

where QPM is the activation energy for mild oxidational wear or tells us that we have severe oxidational wear occurring if the load W is greater than WT, the transition load. The next cell uses the same calculation to deduce QPS (the activation energy for severe oxidational wear) or it tells us that we have mild oxidational wear if the load is less than the transition load.

The final four cells of Table 3 give the APM and APS (the Arrhenius constants for mild oxidational wear and severe oxidational wear). If both experiments of the pair are in the mild oxidational wear regime (i.e. W < WT), then the table gives the values of APM1 and APM2 in the first two cells and tells us it is mild wear in the last two cells. The calculations are based on the following equation:

$$APM = M/Q \tag{15}$$

where

$$M = WRC*U*P*THP*THP*FO*FO*RH*RH \tag{16}$$

and

$$Q = 2*A*EXP\{-QPM/[R*(TF + 273)]\} \tag{17}$$

190

TABLE 3(a)

List of variables relevant to the oxidational wear of high-chromium ferritic steel: Experiment No. 1

| VARIABLES | EXPT. No. 1 |
| --- | --- |
| SPEED (U) = | 2 |
| LOAD (W) = | 12.5 |
| FRICTION FORCE (FF) = | 5.12 |
| TOTAL HEAT (HT) = | 10.24 |
| TEMP OF PIN SURFACE (TPS) = | 56.25054319 |
| TEMP OF DISC SURFACE (TDS) = | 40 |
| WEAR COEFFICIENT (WRC) = | 1.10000E-14 |
| HEAT FLOW ALONG PIN (H1) = | 0.9849033677 |
| OXIDE THICKNESS, PIN (THP) = | 0.00000325 |
| OXIDE THICKNESS, DISC (THD) = | 0.0000035 |
| PIN HARDNESS (PP) = | 3500000000 |
| THERM COND. OF PIN OXIDE (KOP) = | 6.2070688986 |
| WEAR RATE TRANSITION (WT) = | 65 |
| DISC HARDNESS (PD) = | 3916000000 |
| THERM COND. OF DISC OXIDE (KOD) = | 6.31481 |
| PIN HARDNESS (PP) = | 3500000000 |
| VIRTUAL PIN TEMP (TP) = | 2071.0638048 |
| VIRTUAL DISC TEMP (TD) = | 220.39723636 |
| DIV OF HEAT (THEORY), (DTH) = | 0.0961819697 |
| CONTACT TEMPERATURE (TF) = | 255.44953925 |
| RADIUS OF CONTACT (A) = | 0.0000067813 |
| NUMBER OF CONTACTS (N) = | 24.720747586 |
| REYNOLDS NUMBER (RE) = | 778.09623981 |
| NUSSELDT'S NUMBER (RN) = | 13.680332130 |
| HEAT TRANSFER COEFF (H) = | 58.538006549 |
| EXPTL DIV OF HEAT (DE) = | 0.0961819695 |
| DISC HARDNESS (PD) = | 3916000000 |
| PIN HARDNESS (PP) = | 3500000000 |
| G = (TF1 * TF2 * R)/(TF1–TF2) = | 6006.7151403 |
| S = WRC1 * A2 * U1 * THP1 * THP1 = | 3.19018E-30 |
| V = WRC2 * A1 * U2 * THP2 * THP2 = | 3.52629E-31 |
| TYPE OF WEAR/ACTIVN ENERGY = | 13229.285953 |
| TYPE OF WEAR/ACTIVN ENERGY = | MILD WEAR |
| DENSITY OF OXIDES (RH) = | 5220 |
| FRACTION OXYGEN IN OXIDES = | 0.2945 |
| UNIVERSAL GAS CONSTANT = | 8.314 |
| ARRHENIUS CONSTANT (APM1) = | 0.0028781998 |
| ARRHENIUS CONSTANT (APM2) = | 0.0004915968 |
| ARRHENIUS CONSTANT (APS1) = | MILD WEAR |
| ARRHENIUS CONSTANT (APS2) = | MILD WEAR EXPT 1&2 |

TABLE 3(b)

Summary of results for experiments 2–6

| EXPT. No. 2 | 3 | 4 | 5 | 6 |
|---|---|---|---|---|
| 1 | 2 | 1 | 2 | 1 |
| 12.5 | 31.25 | 25 | 37.5 | 37.5 |
| 6.75 | 13.12 | 11.25 | 15.38 | 18 |
| 7.75 | 26.24 | 11.25 | 30.76 | 18 |
| 49.611492741 | 114.79152586 | 71.517135004 | 97.885648589 | 80.52510588 |
| 25 | 39 | 30 | 32 | 30 |
| 1.30000E-14 | 1.10000E-14 | 1.30000E-14 | 1.10000E-14 | 1.30000E-14 |
| 0.6878627838 | 3.0406638212 | 1.5142771382 | 2.3078118916 | 1.3375479211 |
| 0.000002 | 0.00000325 | 0.000002 | 0.00000325 | 0.000002 |
| 0.000002 | 0.0000035 | 0.000002 | 0.0000035 | 0.000002 |
| 3500000000 | 3500000000 | 3500000000 | 3500000000 | 3500000000 |
| 6.2510858031 | 5.8189421835 | 6.1058513949 | 5.9310281499 | 6.046128548 |
| 60 | 65 | 60 | 65 | 60 |
| 3947500000 | 3918100000 | 3937000000 | 3932800000 | 3937000000 |
| 6.41426 | 6.32144 | 6.38111 | 6.36785 | 6.38111 |
| 3500000000 | 3500000000 | 3500000000 | 3500000000 | 3500000000 |
| 1365.096905 | 2208.5077733 | 1281.7661259 | 2310.4170966 | 1429.1454776 |
| 154.8957597 | 289.4621462 | 199.36362075 | 187.4023892 | 114.72204309 |
| 0.1019055968 | 0.1158789559 | 0.1346024014 | 0.0750263941 | 0.0743082172 |
| 188.7225076 | 370.71110078 | 244.04593364 | 271.22791227 | 186.72235848 |
| 0.0000137286 | 0.0000065843 | 0.0000130319 | 0.0000068821 | 0.0000139331 |
| 6.031695744 | 65.556207448 | 13.387709345 | 72.005781438 | 17.567828719 |
| 389.04811991 | 778.09623981 | 389.04811991 | 778.09623981 | 389.04811991 |
| 9.9041375514 | 13.680332130 | 9.9041375514 | 13.680332130 | 9.9041375514 |
| 42.379707109 | 58.538006549 | 42.379707109 | 58.538006549 | 42.379707109 |
| 0.1019055976 | 0.1158789566 | 0.1346024123 | 0.0750263944 | 0.0743082178 |
| 3947500000 | 3918100000 | 3937000000 | 3932800000 | 3937000000 |
| 3500000000 | 3500000000 | 3500000000 | 3500000000 | 3500000000 |
| 6921.4363165 | 5938.2706318 | 6609.1354336 | 4982.5936858 | 13041.536369 |
| 6.77659E-31 | 3.02829E-30 | 7.24521E-31 | 3.23770E-30 | 7.15365E-31 |
| 7.13887E-31 | 3.42383E-31 | 6.77659E-31 | 3.57871E-31 | 7.24521E-31 |
| 360.47429825 | 12944.375145 | 441.92931002 | 10973.899892 | 165.85798809 |
| MILD WEAR | MILD WEAR | MILD WEAR | MILD WEAR | MILD WEAR |
| 5220 | 5220 | 5220 | 5220 | 5220 |
| 0.2945 | 0.2945 | 0.2945 | 0.2945 | 0.2945 |
| 8.314 | 8.314 | 8.314 | 8.314 | 8.314 |
| 0.0000172071 | 0.0016392806 | 0.0000182891 | 0.0015787809 | 0.0000161195 |
| 0.0000179458 | 0.0003351967 | 0.0000173269 | 0.0002725389 | 0.000016289 |
| MILD WEAR | MILD WEAR | MILD WEAR | MILD WEAR | MILD WEAR |
| MILD WEAR | MILD WEAR | MILD WEAR | MILD WEAR | MILD WEAR |
| EXPT 2&4 | EXPT 3&4 | EXPT 4&6 | EXPT 5&6 | EXPT 6&8 |

TABLE 3(c)

Summary of results for experiments 7–11

| EXPT. No. 7 | 8 | 9 | 10 | 11 |
|---|---|---|---|---|
| 2 | 1 | 2 | 1 | 2 |
| 50 | 50 | 75 | 62 | 81.25 |
| 22 | 22.5 | 28.12 | 26.87 | 30.87 |
| 44 | 22.5 | 56.24 | 26.87 | 61.74 |
| 145.30554737 | 97.886772278 | 246.31904052 | 116.36105529 | 262.47680129 |
| 47 | 35 | 67 | 39 | 98 |
| 1.10000E-14 | 1.30000E-14 | 2.80000E-14 | 1.70000E-14 | 2.80000E-14 |
| 3.6057744377 | 2.2009301402 | 7.7234045954 | 2.5795131324 | 7.9277894712 |
| 0.00000325 | 0.000002 | 0.000002 | 0.0000015 | 0.000002 |
| 0.0000035 | 0.000002 | 0.000004 | 0.000003 | 0.000004 |
| 3500000000 | 3500000000 | 3500000000 | 3500000000 | 3500000000 |
| 5.6166342209 | 5.9310206998 | 4.9469147613 | 5.8085362034 | 4.8397888075 |
| 65 | 60 | 65 | 60 | 65 |
| 3901300000 | 3926500000 | 3859300000 | 3918100000 | 3794200000 |
| 6.2684 | 6.34796 | 6.1358 | 6.32144 | 5.93027 |
| 3500000000 | 3500000000 | 3500000000 | 3500000000 | 3500000000 |
| 2400.4249062 | 1166.0859074 | 1464.4869017 | 1014.5737011 | 1598.2539355 |
| 214.27297232 | 126.43306386 | 233.13311214 | 107.74202269 | 351.2571186 |
| 0.0819494191 | 0.0978191165 | 0.1373293848 | 0.0959997445 | 0.1801770335 |
| 342.01897407 | 211.95226553 | 447.43612579 | 213.75987135 | 550.44545424 |
| 0.0000068491 | 0.000013757 | 0.0000052449 | 0.0000140117 | 0.000006405 |
| 96.934712864 | 24.027205072 | 247.9525622 | 28.720425991 | 180.12372833 |
| 778.09623981 | 389.04811991 | 778.09623981 | 389.04811991 | 778.09623981 |
| 13.680332130 | 9.9041375514 | 13.680332130 | 9.9041375514 | 13.680332130 |
| 58.538006549 | 42.379707109 | 58.538006549 | 42.379707109 | 58.538006549 |
| 0.081949419 | 0.0978191173 | 0.1373293847 | 0.0959997444 | 0.1801770334 |
| 3901300000 | 3926500000 | 3859300000 | 3918100000 | 3794200000 |
| 3500000000 | 3500000000 | 3500000000 | 3500000000 | 3500000000 |
| 4633.7450276 | 208386.95693 | 3402.9272355 | 7034.3524367 | 2056.2156867 |
| 3.19679E-30 | 7.28609E-31 | 3.13863E-30 | 5.35500E-31 | 3.13600E-30 |
| 3.56156E-31 | 5.26206E-31 | 2.00617E-31 | 5.35948E-31 | 2.44990E-31 |
| 10168.911961 | NO SOLN | SEVERE | SEVERE | SEVERE |
| MILD WEAR | NO SOLN | 9358.5265192 | 5.8862540193 | 5242.2914519 |
| 5220 | 5220 | 5220 | 5220 | 5220 |
| 0.2945 | 0.2945 | 0.2945 | 0.2945 | 0.2945 |
| 8.314 | 8.314 | 8.314 | 8.314 | 8.314 |
| 0.0010251736 | 0.0000156325 | SEVERE | SEVERE | SEVERE |
| 0.0001947021 | SEVERE | SEVERE | SEVERE | SEVERE |
| MILD WEAR | MILD WEAR | 0.0001766283 | 0.0000112899 | 0.0001446373 |
| MILD WEAR | 0.0000112899 | 0.0000112899 | 0.0000112993 | 0.0000112993 |
| EXPT 7&8 | EXPT 8&10 | EXPT 9&10 | EXPT 10&12 | EXPT 11&12 |

TABLE 3(d)

Summary of results for experiments 12–16

| EXPT. No. 12 | 13 | 14 | 15 | 16 |
|---|---|---|---|---|
| 1 | 2 | 1 | 3.3 | 3.3 |
| 68.75 | 87.5 | 75 | 7 | 25 |
| 29.56 | 32.81 | 31.5 | 2.24 | 8.25 |
| 29.56 | 65.62 | 31.5 | 7.392 | 27.225 |
| 116.44515008 | TOO HIGH | 156.6268501 | 40.35030443 | 97.003096531 |
| 56 | 98 | 56 | 35 | 25 |
| 1.70000E-14 | 2.80000E-14 | 1.70000E-14 | 8.00000E-15 | 8.00000E-15 |
| 2.3267356716 | TOO HIGH | 3.1590206618 | 0.6173235697 | 2.4352813032 |
| 0.0000015 | 0.000002 | 0.0000015 | 0.0000035 | 0.0000035 |
| 0.000003 | 0.000004 | 0.000003 | 0.0000035 | 0.0000035 |
| 3500000000 | ? | 3500000000 | 3500000000 | 3500000000 |
| 5.8079786549 | ? | 5.5415739838 | 6.3124874816 | 5.93687947 |
| 60 | 65 | 60 | 60 | 60 |
| 3882400000 | ? | 3882400000 | 3926500000 | 3947500000 |
| 6.20873 | ? | 6.20873 | 6.34796 | 6.41426 |
| 3500000000 | ? | 3500000000 | 3500000000 | 3500000000 |
| 1024.986 | 1875.4939534 | 999.1588997 | 2495.5122886 | 2700.8954956 |
| 57.22785 | 167.41522038 | 111.37101422 | 227.39662473 | 265.32936493 |
| 0.05288 | 0.0819494193 | 0.1002863703 | 0.0835123877 | 0.0894501858 |
| 170.6467 | NO SOLN | 256.82886955 | 248.75649409 | 338.59870046 |
| 0.000014 | 0.0000010335 | 0.0000139569 | 0.0000041199 | 0.0000040634 |
| 30.03311 | 4257.1002439 | 35.016050939 | 37.507272273 | 137.70152366 |
| 389.04811991 | 778.09623981 | 389.04811991 | 1283.8587957 | 1283.8587957 |
| 9.9041375514 | 13.680332130 | 9.9041375514 | 17.276038344 | 17.276038344 |
| 42.379707109 | 58.538006549 | 42.379707109 | 73.923998051 | 73.923998051 |
| 0.0528803562 | ? | 0.1002863702 | 0.0835123877 | 0.0894501856 |
| 3882400000 | ? | 3882400000 | 3926500000 | 3947500000 |
| 3500000000 | ? | 3500000000 | 3500000000 | 3500000000 |
| 4227.9937025 | | 8841.9091375 | 7794.5190988 | 20595.6969 |
| 5.33850E-31 | | 1.55426E-31 | 1.31411E-30 | 1.36457E-30 |
| 5.35500E-31 | NO | 4.51365E-30 | 1.33236E-30 | 1.31411E-30 |
| SEVERE | SOLN | NO SOLN | 107.51741503 | 776.04103768 |
| 13.044788927 | | NO SOLN | MILD WEAR | MILD WEAR |
| 5220 | | 5220 | 5220 | 5220 |
| 0.2945 | | 0.2945 | 0.2945 | 0.2945 |
| 8.314 | | 8.314 | 8.314 | 8.314 |
| SEVERE | | SEVERE | 0.000332791 | 0.0003834242 |
| SEVERE | | 0.0003291531 | 0.0003361871 | 0.0003732868 |
| 0.0000112993 | | 0.0000113343 | MILD WEAR | MILD WEAR |
| 0.0000113343 | | MILD WEAR | MILD WEAR | MILD WEAR |
| EXPT 12&14 | EXPT 13&14 | EXPT 14&16 | EXPT 15&16 | EXPT 16&18 |

TABLE 3(e)

Summary of results for experiments 17–21

| EXPT. No. 17 | 18 | 19 | 20 | 21 |
|---|---|---|---|---|
| 3.3 | 3.3 | 3.3 | 3.3 | 3.3 |
| 31.25 | 37.5 | 43.75 | 56.25 | 62.5 |
| 10.62 | 14.62 | 16.84 | 21.94 | 18.44 |
| 35.046 | 48.246 | 55.572 | 72.402 | 60.852 |
| 106.94991103 | 133.47747024 | 160.08819968 | 185.51017139 | 198.45461676 |
| 46 | 39 | 63 | 56 | 70 |
| 8.00000E-15 | 8.00000E-15 | 8.00000E-15 | 8.00000E-15 | 1.10000E-14 |
| 2.528982005 | 3.8748009167 | 4.5242900663 | 5.2843480122 | 5.5198265017 |
| 0.0000035 | 0.0000035 | 0.0000035 | 0.0000035 | 0.0000035 |
| 0.0000035 | 0.0000035 | 0.0000035 | 0.0000035 | 0.0000035 |
| 3500000000 | 3500000000 | 3500000000 | 3500000000 | 3500000000 |
| 5.8709320898 | 5.6950543723 | 5.5186252361 | 5.3500775637 | 5.2642558909 |
| 60 | 60 | 60 | 60 | 60 |
| 3903400000 | 3918100000 | 3867700000 | 3882400000 | 3853000000 |
| 6.27503 | 6.32144 | 6.16232 | 6.20873 | 6.11591 |
| 3500000000 | 3500000000 | 3500000000 | 3500000000 | 3500000000 |
| 2784.2144349 | 2784.2144349 | 3357.4906465 | 3492.7987993 | 2666.9362822 |
| 111.60428854 | 208.60845839 | 297.56989197 | 274.99717152 | 266.04820655 |
| 0.0385398049 | 0.0590490845 | 0.0814131227 | 0.0729862163 | 0.0907090397 |
| 214.25299207 | 297.88278361 | 433.43199753 | 440.43633988 | 440.36984597 |
| 0.0000038616 | 0.0000042194 | 0.0000041287 | 0.0000041329 | 0.0000040182 |
| 190.5841852 | 191.55865364 | 233.41501821 | 299.50222224 | 352.04810686 |
| 1283.8587957 | 1283.8587957 | 1283.8587957 | 1283.8587957 | 1283.8587957 |
| 17.276038344 | 17.276038344 | 17.276038344 | 17.276038344 | 17.276038344 |
| 73.923998051 | 73.923998051 | 73.923998051 | 73.923998051 | 73.923998051 |
| 0.038539805 | 0.0590490844 | 0.0814131229 | 0.072986216 | 0.09070904 |
| 3903400000 | 3918100000 | 3867700000 | 3882400000 | 3853000000 |
| 3500000000 | 3500000000 | 3500000000 | 3500000000 | 3500000000 |
| 6344.8492081 | 7651.7454245 | 226593.14635 | 40273.786963 | 40207.014797 |
| 1.36457E-30 | 1.33657E-30 | 1.33657E-30 | 1.31457E-30 | 1.80754E-30 |
| 1.24886E-30 | 1.36457E-30 | 1.33523E-30 | 1.83779E-30 | 1.78679E-30 |
| 562.22192233 | 158.63094445 | 227.80021573 | NO SOLN | SEVERE |
| MILD WEAR | MILD WEAR | MILD WEAR | NO SOLN | 464.28298065 |
| 5220 | 5220 | 5220 | 5220 | 5220 |
| 0.2945 | 0.2945 | 0.2945 | 0.2945 | 0.2945 |
| 8.314 | 8.314 | 8.314 | 8.314 | 8.314 |
| 0.0003979154 | 0.0003277546 | 0.0003367584 | 0.0003236215 | SEVERE |
| 0.0003568436 | 0.0003323931 | 0.000336292 | SEVERE | SEVERE |
| MILD WEAR | MILD WEAR | MILD WEAR | MILD WEAR | 0.0004576804 |
| MILD WEAR | MILD WEAR | MILD WEAR | 0.0004524258 | 0.0004524258 |
| EXPT 17&18 | EXPT 18&20 | EXPT 19&20 | EXPT 20&22 | EXPT 21&22 |

TABLE 3(f)

Table of results for experiments 22–26

| EXPT. No. 22 | 23 | 24 | 25 | 26 |
|---|---|---|---|---|
| 3.3 | 0.23 | 0.23 | 0.23 | 0.23 |
| 69.75 | 12.5 | 18.75 | 25 | 37.5 |
| 24.06 | 8.5 | 13.88 | 14.5 | 22.94 |
| 79.398 | 1.955 | 3.1924 | 3.335 | 5.2762 |
| 229.78541961 | 35.442601809 | 39.757655459 | 46.757907745 | 46.587318921 |
| 81 | 25 | 25 | 30 | 35 |
| 1.10000E-14 | 4.40000E-14 | 4.40000E-14 | 4.40000E-14 | 4.40000E-14 |
| 6.2564418068 | 0.2735525427 | 0.4165216608 | 0.6131999107 | 0.7278644695 |
| 0.0000035 | 0.0000015 | 0.0000015 | 0.0000015 | 0.0000015 |
| 0.0000035 | 0.0000015 | 0.0000015 | 0.0000015 | 0.0000015 |
| 3500000000 | 3500000000 | 3500000000 | 3500000000 | 3500000000 |
| 5.056532668 | 6.34502555 | 6.3164167443 | 6.2700050717 | 6.2711360756 |
| 60 | 0 | 0 | 0 | 0 |
| 3829900000 | 3947500000 | 3947500000 | 3937000000 | 3926500000 |
| 6.04298 | 6.41426 | 6.41426 | 6.38111 | 6.34796 |
| 3500000000 | 3500000000 | 3500000000 | 3500000000 | 350000000 |
| 3232.3164378 | 1074.952479 | 1178.5531467 | 887.39848969 | 969.68478668 |
| 276.48849923 | 174.88264786 | 176.84237563 | 199.92382071 | 155.17744896 |
| 0.078798481 | 0.1399245741 | 0.1304728935 | 0.1838680388 | 0.1379524035 |
| 484.48704508 | 185.85486964 | 193.52689465 | 209.92212764 | 180.35766583 |
| 0.0000040649 | 0.0000589416 | 0.0000593821 | 0.0000566911 | 0.0000590301 |
| 383.91611248 | 0.3272264156 | 0.4835849572 | 0.7074445643 | 0.9787373777 |
| 1283.8587957 | 89.481067578 | 89.481067578 | 89.481067578 | 89.481067578 |
| 17.276038344 | 4.9932330325 | 4.9932330325 | 4.9932330325 | 4.9932330325 |
| 73.923998051 | 21.365995004 | 21.365995004 | 21.365995004 | 21.365995004 |
| 0.0787984812 | 0.1399245743 | 0.1304728921 | 0.1838680392 | 0.1379524031 |
| 3829900000 | 3947500000 | 3947500000 | 3937000000 | 3926500000 |
| 3500000000 | 3500000000 | 3500000000 | 3500000000 | 3500000000 |
| | 38977.616913 | 22035.637051 | 10647.137635 | 3505.941272 |
| | 1.35213E-30 | 1.34412E-30 | 1.34412E-30 | 1.39226E-30 |
| | 1.34210E-30 | 1.35213E-30 | 1.29086E-30 | 1.34412E-30 |
| | SEVERE | SEVERE | SEVERE | SEVERE |
| | 290.19673076 | 130.9925851 | 430.4692537 | 123.37882337 |
| | 5220 | 5220 | 5220 | 5220 |
| | 0.2945 | 0.2945 | 0.2945 | 0.2945 |
| | 8.314 | 8.314 | 8.314 | 8.314 |
| | SEVERE | SEVERE | SEVERE | SEVERE |
| | SEVERE | SEVERE | SEVERE | SEVERE |
| | 0.0000015977 | 0.0000015858 | 0.0000016611 | 0.0000015953 |
| | 0.0000015858 | 0.0000015953 | 0.0000015953 | 0.0000015401 |
| EXPT 22&24 | EXPT 23&24 | EXPT 24&26 | EXPT 25&26 | EXPT 26&28 |

TABLE 3(g)

Summary of results for experiments 27 and 28

| EXPT. No. 27 | 28 | VARIABLES |
|---|---|---|
| 0.23 | 0.23 | SPEED (U) |
| 43.75 | 50 | LOAD (W) |
| 25.38 | 26.5 | FRICTION FORCE (FF) |
| 5.8374 | 6.095 | TOTAL HEAT (HT) |
| 52.089571578 | 46.985792533 | TEMP OF PIN SURFACE (TPS) |
| 40 | 43 | TEMP OF DISC SURFACE (TDS) |
| 4.40000E-14 | 4.40000E-14 | WEAR COEFFICIENT (WRC) |
| 0.7876337435 | 0.5580245037 | HEAT FLOW ALONG PIN (H1) |
| 0.0000015 | 0.0000015 | OXIDE THICKNESS, PIN (THP) |
| 0.0000015 | 0.0000015 | OXIDE THICKNESS, DISC (THD) |
| 3500000000 | 3500000000 | PIN HARDNESS (PP) |
| 6.2346561404 | 6.2684941955 | THERM COND. OF PIN OXIDE (KOP) |
| 0 | 0 | WEAR RATE TRANSITION (WT) |
| 3916000000 | 3909700000 | DISC HARDNESS (PD) |
| 6.31481 | 6.29492 | TH. COND. OF DISC OXIDE (KOD) |
| 3500000000 | 3500000000 | PIN HARDNESS (PP) |
| 922.19096162 | 866.60506976 | VIRTUAL PIN TEMP (TP) |
| 143.83808795 | 87.337728419 | VIRTUAL DISC TEMP (TD) |
| 0.1349288633 | 0.0915544712 | DIV OF HEAT (THEORY), (DTH) |
| 176.51974982 | 126.32736141 | CONTACT TEMPERATURE (TF) |
| 0.0000591743 | 0.0000611444 | RADIUS OF CONTACT (A) |
| 1.1363023687 | 1.216292667 | NUMBER OF CONTACTS (N) |
| 89.481067578 | 89.481067578 | REYNOLDS NUMBER (RE) |
| 4.9932330325 | 4.9932330325 | NUSSELDT'S NUMBER (RN) |
| 21.365995004 | 21.365995004 | HEAT TRANSFER COEFF (H) |
| 0.1349288628 | 0.0915544715 | EXPTL DIV OF HEAT (DE) |
| 3916000000 | 3909700000 | DISC HARDNESS (PD) |
| 3500000000 | 3500000000 | PIN HARDNESS (PP) |
| 3693.7107768 | | |
| 1.39226E-30 | | |
| 1.34740E-30 | | |
| SEVERE | | |
| 120.97533024 | | |
| 5220 | | |
| 0.2945 | | |
| 8.314 | | |
| SEVERE | | |
| SEVERE | | |
| 0.0000015914 | | |
| 0.0000015401 | | |
| EXPT 27&28 | | |

If both experiments are in the severe oxidational wear regime, *i.e.* if W > WT then the table tells us that we have that type of wear in the first two cells and then gives the values of APS1 and APS2 in the final two cells. Let us now discuss the results summarized in Table 3.

## 4. Discussion

We shall first discuss the variations in TPS, TF and N with load and speed. The estimates of the likely values for QPM, APM, QPS and APS are also discussed.

The variation in TPS the general surface temperature, with load is generally quite linear, as shown in Figs. 2(a), 3(a), 4(a) and 5(a). This is what was expected and merely serves to confirm the consistency of the calculations. The following equations approximately fit the points on these figures:

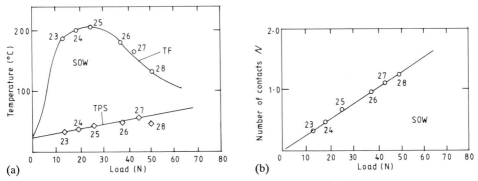

Fig. 2. (a) TF and TPS and (b) number N of contacts as functions of load W at U = 0.23 m s$^{-1}$: MOW, mild oxidational wear; SOW, severe oxidational wear.

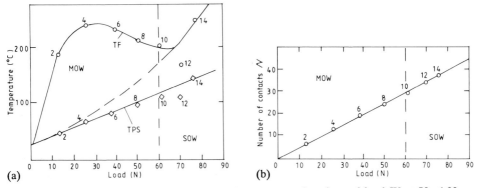

Fig. 3. (a) TF and TPS and (b) number N of contacts as functions of load W at U = 1.00 m s$^{-1}$: MOW, mild oxidational wear; SOW, severe oxidational wear.

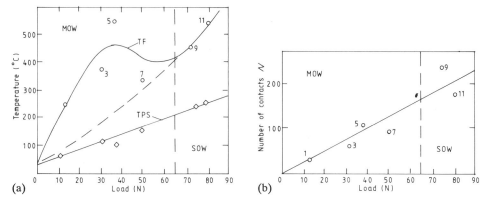

Fig. 4. (a) TF and TPS and (b) number N of contacts as functions of load W at U = 2.00 m s$^{-1}$: MOW, mild oxidational wear; SOW, severe oxidational wear.

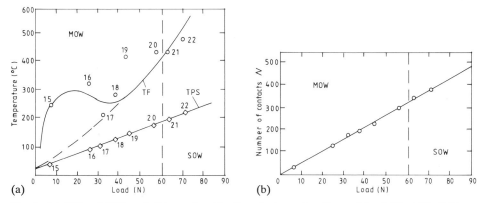

Fig. 5. (a) TF and TPS and (b) number N of contacts as functions of load W at U = 3.30 m s$^{-1}$: MOW, mild oxidational wear; SOW, severe oxidational wear.

$$\text{TPS} = \begin{cases} (0.69W + 25) \ ^{\circ}\text{C} \\ (1.62W + 25) \ ^{\circ}\text{C} \\ (2.60W + 25) \ ^{\circ}\text{C} \\ (2.78W + 25) \ ^{\circ}\text{C} \end{cases} \quad \text{for} \quad \begin{cases} \text{U} = 0.23 \ \text{m s}^{-1} & (18) \\ \text{U} = 1.0 \ \text{m s}^{-1} & (19) \\ \text{U} = 2.0 \ \text{m s}^{-1} & (20) \\ \text{U} = 3.3 \ \text{m s}^{-1} & (22) \end{cases}$$

Apart from the 0.23 m s$^{-1}$ experiments, the contact temperature TF shows a rising trend with increasing load, but with a maximum at about 25 N and a minimum at about 30 N. The experiments carried out at 0.23 m s$^{-1}$ show only the maximum at about 25 N. The values of the contact temperatures TF are consistent with the types of oxide found to be present in the wear debris.

The number N of contacts are all linearly dependent upon the load W, as shown in Figs. 2(b), 3(b), 4(b) and 5(b). The trend can be described by the approximate equation

$$N = k * W \tag{23}$$

where $k = 0.0244$ N$^{-1}$ for the 0.23 m s$^{-1}$ experiments, $k = 0.467$ N$^{-1}$ for the 1.0 m s$^{-1}$ experiments, $k = 2.50$ N$^{-1}$ for the 2.0 m s$^{-1}$ experiments and $k = 2.78$ N$^{-1}$ for the 3.3 m s$^{-1}$ experiments. Note that N is very low, *i.e.* all around $N = 1$, for the 0.23 m s$^{-1}$ experiments, indicating perhaps that very few of the contacts are contributing to the severe oxidational wear which is clearly going on at these low speeds. There seems to be an upward trend in the range of N values as one increases the speed, once again showing how important speed is in the simple oxidational wear model.

In order to discuss the computer analysis for these steels, it is necessary to consider the pairs of experiments chosen for the bottom cells of Table 3 in terms of two categories. The first category is category A, which relates to experimental pairs carried out at similar loads, but different speeds and different wear rate coefficients. The second is category B, which relates to experiments carried out at the same speed and same wear rate coefficient but under different loads.

Let us first consider category A experimental pairs, namely pairs 1 and 2, 3 and 4, 5 and 6, and 7 and 8 for mild oxidational wear and pairs 9 and 10 and 11 and 12 for severe oxidational wear. From the appropriate cells in Table 3, we deduce the following values for QPM, APM, QPS and APS:

QPM $= 11.8$ kJ mol$^{-1}$ (to an accuracy of 10%)

QPS $= 7.3$ kJ mol$^{-1}$ (to an accuracy of 28%)

APM $= 9.0 \times 10^{-4}$ (to an accuracy of 66%)

APS $= 9.0 \times 10^{-5}$ (to an accuracy of 87%)

These values for QPM were obtained from experiments in which the contact temperatures TF were all between the extreme values of 255 and 370 °C. At these temperatures, for the static oxidation of pure iron, it has been shown [7] that QP is 208 kJ mol$^{-1}$ and AP is equal to $1.5 \times 10^6$. Using EN31 steel and assuming that QPM = QP for static oxidation, Quinn [1] obtains APM $= 1.0 \times 10^{16}$ for these temperatures. Clearly, the new values for QPM and APM are considerably less than those obtained with the steels containing virtually no chromium, indicating how important the chromium content is when mild oxidational wear occurs.

If we now consider the category A pairs exhibiting severe oxidational wear, namely 9 and 10, and 11 and 12, we see that the activation energies QPS are about 60% of the QPM values and the Arrhenius constants APS are about an order of magnitude less then the APM values. These results are consistent with the idea that severe oxidational wear is a mixture of severe metallic wear and mild oxidational wear.

The analysis of the pairs in category B that exhibit mild oxidation wear reveals that pairs 2 and 4, 4 and 6, and 6 and 8 (at $U = 1$ m s$^{-1}$), all give very low values for QPM and APM, namely

QPM $= 0.32$ kJ mol$^{-1}$ (to an accuracy of 31%)

APM $= 0.173 \times 10^{-4}$ (to an accuracy of 4%)

Pairs 15 and 16, 16 and 18, 17 and 18, 18 and 20, and 19 and 20 (at 3.3 m s$^{-1}$) all give

QPM $= 0.37$ kJ mol$^{-1}$ (to an accuracy of 66%)

APM $= 3.51 \times 10^{-4}$ units (to an accuracy of 6%)

Low values of QPS and APS are also obtained from the computations for the category B pairs exhibiting severe oxidational wear at 0.23, 1.0 and 3.3 m s$^{-1}$, the most remarkable

200

being QPS = 0.009 kJ mol$^{-1}$ for the pair 10 and 12 (at 1.0 m s$^{-1}$). Such a low tribological oxidation activation energy implies that the contribution of mild oxidational wear towards the total wear is very insignificant in this particular case.

Although the category A values for QPM and QPS are more in line with expected values, the APM and APS values are not. The category B values for QPM and QPS seem much too low, although the APM and APS values are similar to those in category A. Clearly, more research must be carried out with the objective of finding a satisfactory model which gives consistent values of APM, APS, QPM and QPS which the designer can use when faced with allowing for wear and the effects of both surface and contact temperatures in his calculations. This paper has indeed shown that one can use computer techniques that are user friendly to back up one's model. The next step must be to model the effect of "out-of-contact" oxidation on the mild oxidational wear of metal tribo-elements to see whether it can provide oxidational wear constants that are generally applicable. We should also rethink some of the assumptions made in this paper about severe oxidational wear being described by Arrhenius-type equations. For instance, we should be trying to include some of the fatigue-type analyses which possibly are relevant to how long a plateau can stand the repeated stress concentrations before it becomes detached from the metal substrate. The simple oxidational wear theory assumes that, as soon as the critical oxide thickness is reached, the plateau becomes unstable. Possibly 1/K passes are needed for the plateau to build up to a thickness which becomes unstable because of (a) its geometry and (b) its susceptibility to contact fatigue!

### Acknowledgments

The author wishes to acknowledge the support of the National Science Council of the Republic of China and cooperation afforded by the Department of Mechanical Engineering of the National Taiwan University, Taipei, during the summer of 1991, when he was Visiting Research Professor in that department.

### References

1 T. F. J. Quinn, *Physical Analysis for Tribology,* Cambridge University Press, Cambridge, 1991.
2 J. F. Archard, The temperature of rubbing surfaces, *Wear, 2* (1959) 438.
3 C. B. Allen, T. F. J. Quinn and J. L. Sullivan, The oxidational wear of high-chromium ferritic steel on austenitic stainless steel, *J. Tribol., 107* (1986) 172.
4 S. C. Lim and M. F. Ashby, Wear mechanism maps, *Acta Metall., 35* (1987) 1.
5 N. C. Welsh, The dry wear of steels, Philos. *Trans. R. Soc. London, Ser. A, 257* (1965) 31.
6 T. F. J. Quinn, The division of heat and sliding temperatures at sliding steel interfaces and their relation to oxidational wear, *ASLE Trans., 21* (1978) 78.
7 D. Caplan and M. Cohen, The effect of cold work on the oxidation of iron from 100 deg C to 650 deg C, *Corros. Sci., 6* (1966) 321.

*Wear, 153* (1992) 201–227

# The formation of aluminium hydroxide in the sliding wear of alumina

M. G. Gee

*National Physical Laboratory, Teddington, Middlesex TW11 0LW (UK)*

(Received July 28th, 1991)

## Abstract

The wear of ceramics is often affected by tribochemical reactions with the surrounding environment. This paper examines the development of aluminium hydroxide interfacial layers in the wear of alumina at intermediate wear rates and the effect of these layers on wear and friction. Since the humidity of the surrounding atmosphere promotes the formation of these layers, a dramatic effect of humidity on the wear rate is brought about by the changes in layer formation. In supporting experiments, it was found that alpha-alumina reacts directly to form boehmite (Al(OH)) under moderate pressures and high temperatures.

## 1. Introduction

There is increasing interest in the use of ceramics in wear-resistant applications. However, to enable engineers and designers to make the best use of ceramics, it is important that the mechanisms of wear that can occur are understood, and that robust procedures are developed that enable reliable data to be produced which can be used to predict the tribological behaviour of ceramics.

High wear rates in ceramics are often brought about by mechanisms that lead to loss of surface integrity of ceramics. These often involve fracture processes such as direct fracture under the high stresses generated at the contact of asperities between surfaces and fatigue caused by the alternating stresses generated as one specimen moves repeatedly over the other and delamination.

Tribochemical reactions also often occur in the wear of ceramics. In these processes, chemical reactions that might never normally occur, or only occur at very low rates, are enhanced by the high pressure, high temperature conditions that exist at the interface between the surfaces. Thus, alumina can react with moisture in the atmosphere to form aluminium hydroxide [1], and silicon nitride can oxidize to form silica or can react with moisture to form ammonia [2]. Tribochemical reactions can have a beneficial effect if the resultant reaction product is stable, forming a protective layer that separates the two wear surfaces reducing friction and wear. Tribochemical reactions can also be deleterious, if the reaction rate is high and the reaction product is not coherent. In this case the reaction product breaks up and is easily removed from the wear system, giving a high wear rate, and because of the rough surfaces that result, a high level of friction.

This paper discusses the tribochemical reactions to form aluminium hydroxide that occur in the wear of alumina ceramics. This has now been observed in unlubricated

Elsevier Sequoia

sliding wear tests [1, 3], by Gates *et al.* [4, 5] in sliding wear tests carried out in water, and by Hines *et al.* [6] and Czernuska and Page [7] in abrasive wear. Tribochemical reaction with water has also been suggested as the reason for the changes in the wear rate of an alumina ceramic with the percentage of water dissolved in diester by Lancaster *et al.* [8, 9], and also for the change in wear rate with humidity reported for unlubricated sliding tests by Sasaki [10, 11]. Tribochemical reaction may also be the underlying cause of the increase in wear observed by Wallbridge *et al.* for alumina lubricated by water as compared with dry tests [12].

The starting point of the paper is the effect of changes in relative humidity on wear. This is followed by a discussion about the nature of the interfacial films that are formed, and concludes with a description of the processes that are involved in the formation of hydroxide films.

## 2. Effect of humidity

### 2.1. Wear and friction results

At intermediate wear rates where delamination is the major mechanism of loss of material, it was found that there was a considerable effect of the humidity of the air surrounding the test system on the wear of a 95% alumina ceramic (Fig. 1) [1]. In these tests spherically ended pins (5 mm radius) were pressed with an applied load of 40 N against the rotating disc. The relative speed was 0.1 m s$^{-1}$. As the humidity was reduced from 50% RH to 10% RH there was an order of magnitude increase in the wear rate calculated from the final scar diameter; with a further drop in humidity to 4% RH there was a further order of magnitude increase in the wear rate. There was little effect on friction, although in an experiment where the humidity

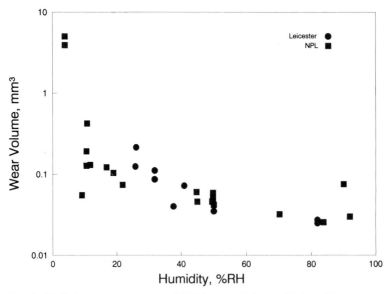

Fig. 1. Variation in wear rate and friction coefficient with humidity at an applied load of 40 N and relative speed of 0.1 m s$^{-1}$ (note that results were confirmed by Dr. John Beynon, University of Leicester).

was inadvertently altered it was found that there was a small increase in the friction coefficient from 0.65 to 0.75 as the humidity decreased from 23% RH to 47% RH.

Further experiments were performed using the same 95% alumina ceramic used in the earlier experiments to get a clearer idea of the effect of humidity. The first of these was to perform several step changes in humidity from near zero humidity to 50% RH (and *vice versa*) and monitor the corresponding changes in wear rate and friction coefficient. After allowing the test to proceed for a sufficient time to allow transient effects to occur and a good measurement of the steady-state wear rate, the test was interrupted without removing the specimens from the wear testing system. The wear scar on the pin was photographed with a 35 mm camera and associated macro lens (this incorporated a 90° bend to ease access in the confined space), and the depth of wear on the disc was measured using a profilometer. The test was then restarted and, after a small period under the old humidity conditions, the humidity was altered to the new value. Because the specimens were not removed from the testing system, misalignment of the specimens, and consequential changes in wear and friction, was minimized. The total system wear (movement of pin towards disc) was measured by a LVDT, and frictional loads by a load cell throughout the test.

The test conditions and main results from this experiment are shown in Table 1. Initially, the humidity was kept at 50% RH while the initial "run-in" wear took place. This resulted in a system displacement of 70 $\mu$m during the first 210 s of the test, but no further wear occurred during this period.

It is evident from the results of Table 1 that little or no measurable wear took place when the humidity was at 50% RH, while a high wear rate was observed when the humidity was 0% RH. The increase in wear rate was also accompanied by a small increase in the friction coefficient, although there was a variation in friction coefficient from one period to the next. The transition in wear and friction did not occur immediately when the humidity was altered, with a delay of 100–200 s before the wear and friction settled to the new levels when the humidity was raised from 0% to 50% RH, and a delay of about 50 s when the humidity was lowered (Figs. 2 and 3). There was nearly always a temporary increase in friction coefficient for both types of transition, with a particularly large peak lasting about 180 s where the friction coefficient rose to over one. This was accompanied by a short-lived increase in the wear rate before wear ceased at 50% RH. Another interesting observation was the presence of short-lived (20–30 s) peaks in the displacement trace (Fig. 4). These indicated that the separation between the surfaces had momentarily decreased

TABLE 1

Results of interrupted test carried out with humidity changes from 0 to 50% RH and vice versa

| Period | Duration at 0% RH | Friction coefficient at 0% RH | Wear rate at 0% RH ($\mu$m$^3$ N$^{-1}$ m$^{-1}$) | Duration at 50% RH | Friction coefficient at 50% RH | Wear rate at 50% RH ($\mu$m$^3$ N$^{-1}$ m$^{-1}$) |
|---|---|---|---|---|---|---|
| Run-in | – | – | – | 27.5[a] | 0.68 | 0 |
| 1 | 31 | 0.8 | 24543 | 5.5 | 0.7 | 0 |
| 2 | 8 | 0.8 | 58489 | 88 | 0.7 | 0 |
| 3 | 31 | 0.83 | 34059 | 4 | 0.7 | 0 |
| 4 | 14 | 0.73 | 82526 | 30 | 0.6 | 0 |

[a]Wear rate after initial "run-in" wear has finished.

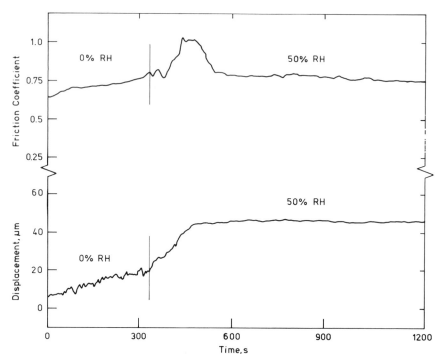

Fig. 2. Effect of transition from 0% RH to 50% RH on wear displacement and friction coefficient in interrupted humidity change experiment.

and then returned very close to the original value before the transient event had occurred.

The second additional experiment was to carry out a series of measurements of wear rate and friction coefficient on a single set of specimens by running the test at several different humidity levels. The test was interrupted when a good measure of friction and wear rate had been obtained. Wear to the pin and disc were measured by photography and profilometry, and the test was then restarted without removing the specimens from the test system. Wear rates and friction coefficients were measured for a complete cycle of humidity conditions from 50% RH up to 90% RH (the maximum that could be achieved in this experiment), down to near zero and then back to 50% RH.

The test conditions and main results from this experiment are shown in Table 2. The major result was that once initial "run-in" had occurred little or no wear occurred until the humidity had been reduced to very close to zero humidity where very significant wear then occurred (Fig. 5). (Note that the error in profilometry measurements, and hence track wear measurements, was quite large after the test, as the wear track was by then somewhat uneven.) In volume terms, the pin wear at 0% RH was 100 times larger than the corresponding wear for the disc. The friction coefficient remained at 0.75 as the humidity was increased to 95% and then down to 4% RH, but then increased to 0.8 at 0% RH. There was a further increase in friction coefficient as the humidity was then increased again, but although there was then a slow decline the friction coefficient was still above 0.8 when the humidity was returned to 50% RH. In this test, in the stage when the humidity was zero the wear rate was

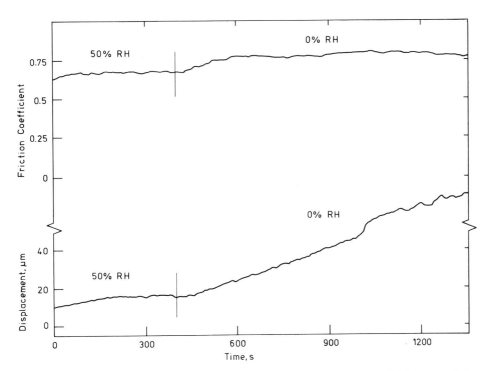

Fig. 3. Effect of transition from 50% RH to 0% RH on wear displacement and friction coefficient in interrupted humidity change experiment.

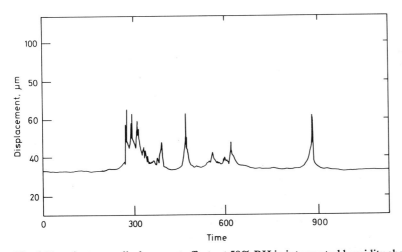

Fig. 4. Transient wear displacement effects at 50% RH in interrupted humidity change experiment.

initially zero with the increase in wear rate occurring over a prolonged period of about 3000 s before a steady high wear rate was observed. In the next stage of the test, when the humidity was 3.6% RH, there was again a period of high wear before the wear rate decreased to near zero, but here the transition only took about 600 s (Fig.

TABLE 2

Results of interrupted test carried out at different fixed humidity levels

| Period | Humidity (% RH) | Duration (min) | Scar diameter (mm) | Track area ($\mu m^2$) | Displacement ($\mu m$) | Friction coefficient |
|---|---|---|---|---|---|---|
| Run-in | 50 | 40 | – | – | 95 | 0.84 |
| 1 | 51 | 35 | 1.65 | – | 112 | 0.73 |
| 2 | 65 | 15 | 1.64 | – | 112 | 0.7 |
| 3 | 83 | 17 | 1.6 | – | 112 | 0.75 |
| 4 | 94 | 28 | 1.68 | 270 | 112 | 0.75 |
| 5 | 75 | 16 | 1.67 | 504 | 112 | 0.7 |
| 6 | 54 | 14 | 1.46 | 350 | 112 | 0.7 |
| 7 | 44 | 17 | 1.58 | 530.5 | 112 | 0.7 |
| 8 | 31 | 21 | 1.72 | 501 | 112 | 0.73 |
| 9 | 25.5 | 23 | 1.75 | 494 | 112 | 0.75 |
| 10 | 17.8 | 30 | 1.76 | 388.5 | 112 | 0.75 |
| 11 | 10 | 24 | 1.75 | 449 | 112 | 0.75 |
| 12 | 6.2 | 39 | 1.72 | 784 | 112 | 0.75 |
| 13 | 3.6 | 13 | 1.81 | 765.5 | 112 | 0.75 |
| 14 | 0 | 97 | 3.26 | 81712.5 | 328 | 0.8 |
| 15 | 4.9 | 40 | 3.47 | 94993 | 359 | 0.83 |
| 16 | 7.6 | 33 | 3.44 | 86384 | 359 | 0.85 |
| 17 | 15.3 | 14 | 15.3 | 82944 | 359 | 0.85 |
| 18 | 51 | 15 | 51 | 87598 | 359 | 0.8 |

6). It is interesting that this transition in wear rate was accompanied by a temporary peak in the friction coefficient to about 0.9.

## 2.2. Microstructural observations

The surfaces of the specimens from the uninterrupted tests [1] were bright and polished in appearance. However, when examined in more detail it was clear that material had broken away from quite much of the surface (this increased with wear rate). Material had broken away in small areas about 20 $\mu m$ across which often joined to form large areas of damage that continued in the direction of relative motion for some distance (Fig. 7).

The worn surfaces of the specimens tested at humidities higher than 10% RH were partially covered with a film of material that gave dark contrast in back scattered imaging in the scanning electron microscope (Fig. 8). The percentage of the dark contrasting layer increased as the humidity increased. Most of the wear surfaces were also covered by a network of cracks that were often at or near the boundary of the dark contrasting layer. Indeed, some small areas of the dark contrasting layer were nearly detached from the surface. The lighter contrasting phase in the back-scattered images resembled the alumina grains in the original microstructure of the material, particularly in specimens tested at high humidity levels. This was not as clear in the specimens tested at lower humidity levels where much more disruption to the surface layers of the material was evident [1].

Examination of worn surfaces at high magnification in the field emission scanning electron microscopy (SEM) showed that some of the light contrasting areas were mottled in appearance, with surface-breaking light contrasting features that continued under the dark contrasting film (Fig. 9). This type of complex image suggests that the light contrasting areas were at one stage somewhat rough, and the dark contrasting layer filled in the depressions in the surface. The light contrasting areas also showed some grooving, suggestive of abrasive action. The dark contrasting layers also show many very small cracks perpendicular to the direction of relative motion, which are related to the network of major cracks traversing the specimen.

In complete contrast to the surfaces worn at higher humidity levels, the surface of the specimen tested at a humidity of 4% RH was dull and rough. When examined

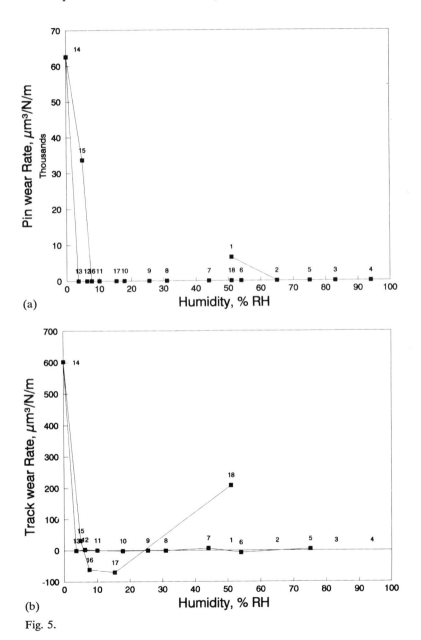

(a)

(b)

Fig. 5.

(*continued*)

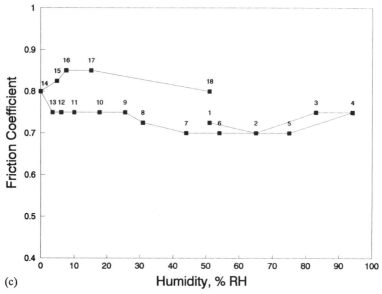

(c)

Humidity, % RH

Fig. 5. Wear rates and friction coefficient for interrupted constant humidity test (Table 2): (a) wear rate calculated from pin scar, (b) wear rate calculated from profilometry measurements of disc wear track area. Numbers by traces give the period in the test at a given humidity, (c) friction coefficient.

in more detail, although there were some small flat areas, most of the worn surface showed evidence of inter-granular fracture, and there was no sign of the dark contrasting film (Fig. 10).

Additional information was obtained from the photographs of the wear scars on pins from the humidity change experiments. The wear surface was smooth and reflective after testing at high humidities (Fig. 11(a)). A feature that was particularly noticeable in the test carried out at different constant humidity levels (Table 2) was the large amount of debris that was attached to the pin (Fig. 11(a)). This was at the leading edge and sides of the scar and extended to some distance behind the scar. When the humidity became very low, damage started to accumulate on the wear scar (evident from the parallel lines of damage across the scar) (Fig. 11(b)). The wear scar of the pin after the period at 0% RH was rough and dull, with a considerable quantity of particulate debris partially covering the scar which had collected on the pin behind the scar (Fig. 11(c)). When the humidity was raised again, the scar again became smooth and polished, but some damage was still visible on the wear surface (Fig. 11(d)).

## 3. Nature of hydroxide film

The dark contrasting film that was formed under humid conditions was studied in several ways to determine its composition and get some feel for its mechanical properties.

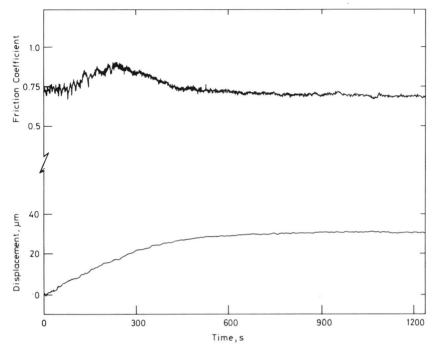

Fig. 6. Variation in wear displacement and friction coefficient at start of period 15 (4.9% RH) in interrupted constant humidity test (Table 2).

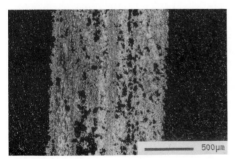

Fig. 7. Optical micrograph of surface of specimen worn at an applied load of 40 N, relative speed of 0.1 m s$^{-1}$ and humidity of 82% RH.

### 3.1. Microanalysis

Analysis of the worn specimen surfaces by X-ray energy dispersive spectrometry in the scanning electron microscope showed that the dark contrasting film was deficient in aluminium compared with the light contrasting areas (Fig. 12). The distribution of the dark and light contrasting areas bore no relationship to the distribution of the components in the second phase in the alumina (calcium, magnesium and chromium). In fact, the distribution of the second phase components is very similar to their distribution in a polished sample of the alumina.

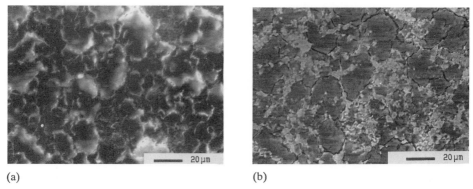

(a)                                                    (b)

Fig. 8. Back-scattered electron micrograph of surface of specimen tested at an applied load of 10 N and a relative speed of 0.3 m s$^{-1}$ (humidity was not controlled in this test) showing high percentage of dark contrasting layer and network of cracks: (a) secondary image, (b) back-scattered image.

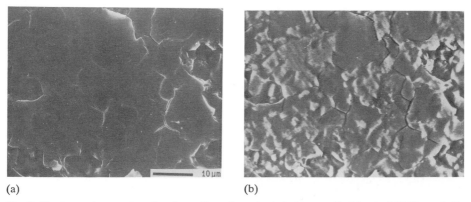

(a)                                                    (b)

Fig. 9. Electron micrographs of surface of specimen tested at an applied load of 10 N, a relative speed of 0.1 m s$^{-1}$ and a humidity of 50% RH: (a) secondary image, (b) back-scattered image.

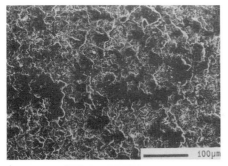

Fig. 10. Secondary electron micrograph of specimen tested at applied load of 40 N, relative speed of 0.1 m s$^{-1}$ and humidity of 4% RH.

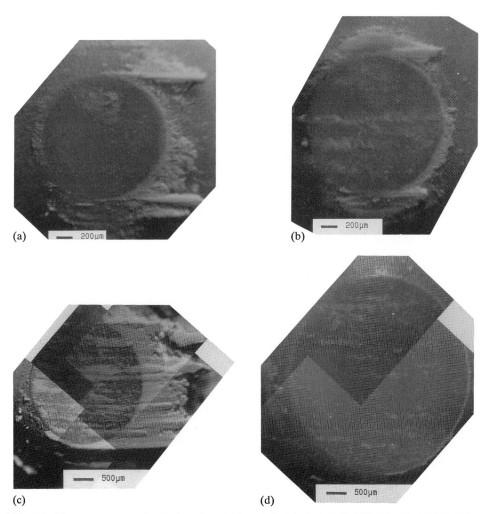

Fig. 11. Wear scars on ends of pins at end of period: (a) 6 at 44% RH, (b) 13 at 3.6% RH, (c) 14 at 0% RH and (d) 15 at 4.9% RH (Table 2) in interrupted constant humidity test.

The worn surface of a specimen tested at a humidity of 50% RH was examined by dynamic secondary ion mass spectrometry (SIMS) [13]. This showed that there was an increase in the hydroxide (OH) signal for the dark contrasting areas. The strength of this hydroxide signal was reduced by the need to flood the surface of the specimen with electrons to eliminate charging. In concurrent SEM experiments, this was found to cause the disappearance of the dark contrasting region, presumably because of the heating brought about by the electron beam.

The worn surface of a specimen tested at a humidity of 50% RH was also examined by Fourier transform infrared spectroscopy (FTIR). The spectra that are shown in Fig. 13 were recorded from an area in the centre of the wear track, and well away from it. There is a clear peak in both spectra at 840 cm$^{-1}$ (11.9 $\mu$m) that is about 60% higher in the spectra from the wear track. However, this peak cannot be positively

212

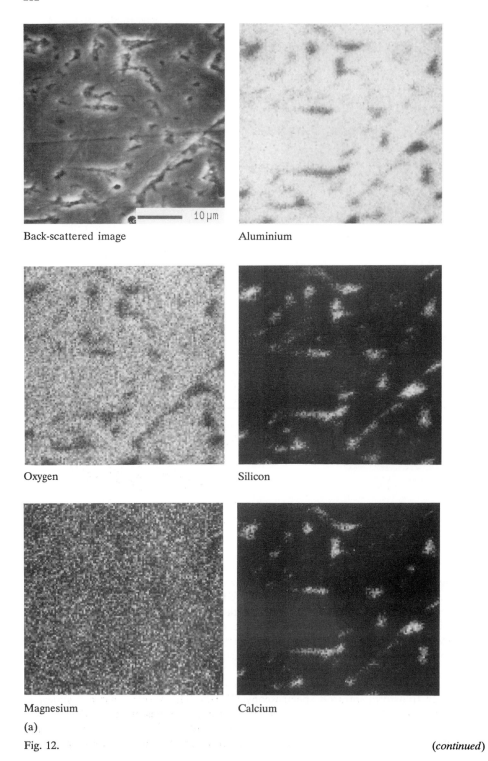

Back-scattered image

Aluminium

Oxygen

Silicon

Magnesium

Calcium

(a)

Fig. 12.

*(continued)*

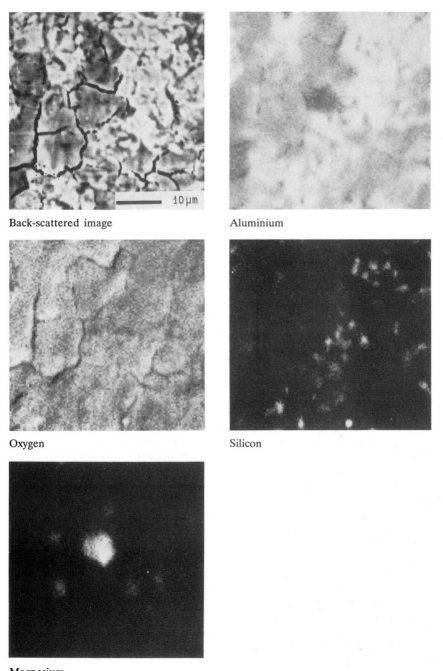

Back-scattered image   Aluminium

Oxygen   Silicon

Magnesium

(b)

Fig. 12. Results of energy dispersive X-ray analysis of surfaces: (a) Polished section of disc material, (b) specimen tested at applied load of 40 N, relative speed of 0.1 m s$^{-1}$ and humidity of 50% RH.

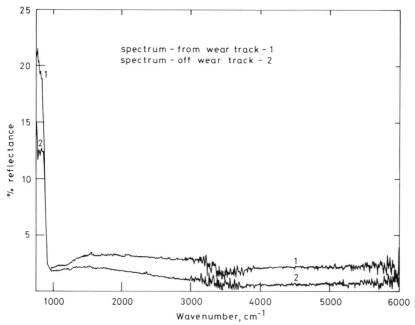

Fig. 13. FTIR spectra from specimen tested at an applied load of 10 N, a relative speed of 0.1 m s$^{-1}$, and a humidity of 50% RH.

identified with either alumina or aluminium hydroxide [14]. There is also a difference in the general level of the two spectra, and a dip in the spectra from the wear track at about 3500 cm$^{-1}$, which could be due to the presence of aluminium hydroxide. However, the ratio of the spectra in Fig. 13 and the spectra from a mirror standard was calculated to get the true materials response, and the minimum at 3500 cm$^{-1}$ is at the same position as a minimum in the mirror spectra, so the features in this region may be due to artefacts.

A diamond stylus was scratched over the surface of a specimen tested at a humidity of 50% RH, and the fragments of material removed from the surface were collected on a carbon film and examined in a transmission electron microscope (Fig. 14). There were some quite large crystalline fragments in the material, but there was also a large percentage of small agglomerated material that gave diffraction rings characteristic of a very small crystallite size material (Fig. 14(b)). A dark-field image of the same area selected some of the small crystallites of size about 20 nm (Fig. 14(c)).

Replicas were made with acetate film of the surface of a 99.997% alumina ring specimen tested under an applied pressure of 0.075 N mm$^{-2}$ [15], and at a humidity of 50%. This test was performed at the lowest temperature in a series of ring-on-ring elevated temperature experiments, and the wear surface showed a similar dark contrasting film to that seen in the pin-on disc tests on 95% alumina ceramic.

When the replicas were examined, some fragments of material from the wear surface were embedded in the surface, presumably those fragments of materials that had been only loosely adherent to the surface of the specimen (Fig. 15). Some areas of the larger fragments were darker and mottled in appearance by comparison with other areas, but the difference was not as large as that for the back-scattered images of the wear surfaces, possibly because of the neighbourhood of the plastic film that

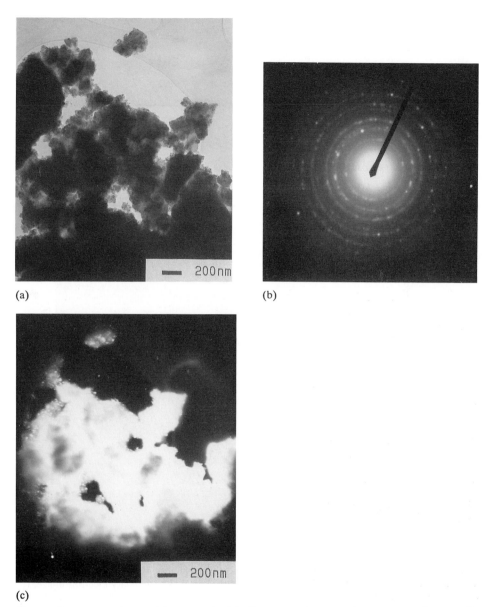

(a)

(b)

(c)

Fig. 14. Fragments of material scratched with diamond stylus away from wear surface on disc of specimen tested at an applied load of 40 N, relative speed of 0.1 m s$^{-1}$ and humidity of 50% RH: (a) bright-field image, (b) diffraction pattern, (c) dark-field image of same area as in (a).

reduced the expansion in contrast that was possible. The areas that had a light even contrast often seemed to have originated from a single particle that had then been subject to considerable cracking. There was also particulate material on the surface of the specimen that had apparently been compressed into the fragment.

216

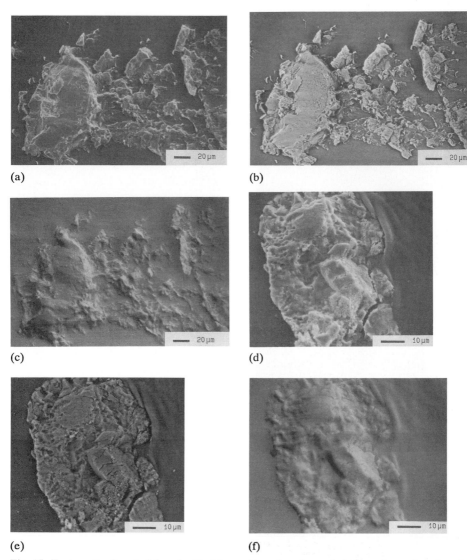

Fig. 15. Fragments of material embedded in replica of surface of ring specimen tested under applied pressure of 0.075 N mm$^{-2}$ and humidity of 50% RH: (a) secondary electron image, (b) compositional back-scattered image of (a), (c) topographic back-scattered image of (a), (d) secondary electron image, (e) compositional back-scattered image of (d), (f) topographic back-scattered image of (d).

## 3.2. Mechanical characteristics

In an attempt to get a feel for the mechanical properties of the dark contrasting film, scratches were made across the worn surface of a specimen tested at a humidity level of 50% RH. These were made at applied loads from 0.098 N to 0.49 N with a 0.2 mm tip radius Rockwell indentor and a Vickers indentor. At low loads, little further damage was observed to the wear surface, indicating that the dark contrasting film had some mechanical strength. As the applied load was increased more damage was caused to the surface, with plates of material that were often the dark contrasting layer pushed out from the path of the indentor (Fig. 16). There was more damage to the wear surface with the scratches produced by the sharper Vickers indentor than with the Rockwell indentor, but insufficient tests were done to get any quantitative measure of the load below which no damage occurred.

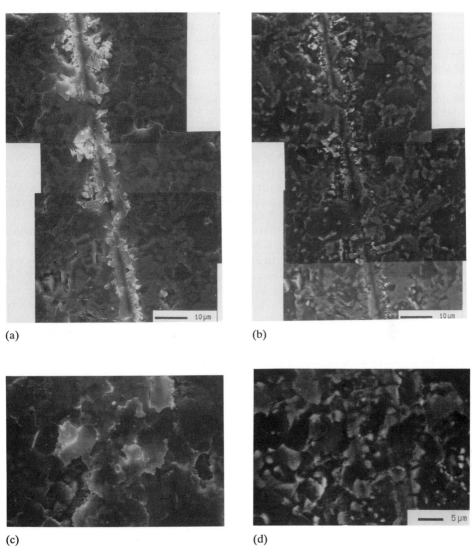

(a)

(b)

(c)

(d)

Fig. 16. Scratches produced on a specimen tested at an applied load of 10 N, a relative speed of 0.1 m s$^{-1}$, and a humidity of 50% RH: (a) secondary image of scratch made by a Vickers indentor loaded at 10 g, (b) back-scattered image of (a), (c) secondary image of scratch produced by Rockwell indentor loaded at 50 g, (d) back-scattered image of (c).

## 4. Formation of hydroxide layers

### 4.1. Reaction of alumina with water

From the evidence reported above, it is quite likely that the dark contrasting film is aluminium hydroxide formed by reaction with moisture in the air surrounding the specimens. Although the formation mechanism is not completely clear, it is suggested that it is more likely that the hydroxide is formed indirectly by reaction of wear debris with moisture than the direct reaction of the surface of the alumina itself. This is because it is known that very fine particulate alumina debris is generated in the wear of alumina, with particle sizes as low as 20 nm observed in X-ray diffraction (XRD) experiments [16] and transmission electron microscopy (TEM) observations [17].

Experiments were carried out to confirm this point by heating different alumina samples with water in a closed container (bomb) at 200 °C for 48 h. Equal weights of water and the sample were placed in the bomb, with the sample in a holder that was designed to keep the alumina out of any liquid water that was present. Several samples of alumina debris, stock alumina powder of various sizes, and a piece of single crystal alumina were tested as listed in Table 3. XRD and thermogravimetric analysis (TGA) was used to examine the resultant powders. It was found that a significant amount of aluminium mono-hydroxide (boehmite) was formed in all the experiments except the sapphire (Fig. 17). All of the powder debris samples showed a high percentage conversion to boehmite (Al(OH)) [14], but with the stock alumina powders, there was an increase in the percentage of hydroxide formed with decreasing nominal powder size (note the hydroxide peak at a two-theta of 28°), with a barely detectable (by XRD) amount of hydroxide formed for the 3 $\mu$m size powder.

TGA of the powders shows that the powders gave a total mass loss of about 1.5% for the untreated specimens, with the major loss in mass occurring below 200 °C (Fig. 18). By contrast, in the treated samples where aluminium hydroxide was formed in significant quantities, most of the mass was lost at 420–450 °C, with a small fraction of the mass loss occurring below 200 °C. In the debris samples there was also a smaller mass loss at 650 °C. Although the mass loss at 200 °C is likely to be due to the removal of adsorbed water, the mass loss at 420–450 °C is further evidence for the formation of boehmite which dehydrates at this temperature [14]. The mass loss at 620 °C could not be explained.

The powders were examined before and after treatment in the scanning electron microscope (Fig. 19) Little gross change was observed to the stock alumina powders

TABLE 3

Bomb experiments

| Powder | Load in wear test (N) | Speed in wear test (m s$^{-1}$) | Hydroxide formed (detected by XRD) | TGA mass loss (%) |
|---|---|---|---|---|
| Debris A | 150 | 0.37 | Yes, large amount of boehmite | 7.81 |
| Debris B | 50 | 0.37 | Yes, large amount of boehmite | 7.11 |
| Debris C | 50 | 0.1 | Yes, large amount of boehmite | 7.8 |
| 0.05 $\mu$m $\alpha$-alumina | – | – | Yes, large amount of boehmite | 11.84 |
| 0.3 $\mu$m $\alpha$-alumina | – | – | Yes, small amount of boehmite | 2.56 |
| 50 $\mu$m $\alpha$-alumina | – | – | No | 0.24 |
| Sapphire | – | – | No | – |

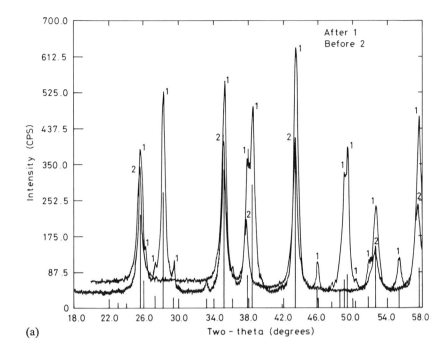

(a)

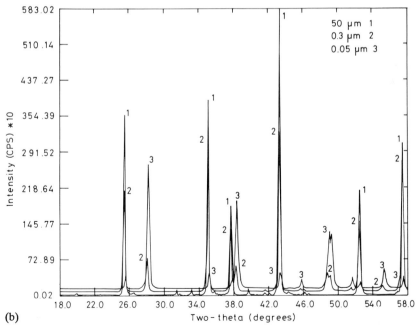

(b)

Fig. 17. XRD traces for samples before and after heat treating in bomb with water: (a) wear debris C, (b) alumina powders after treatment.

220

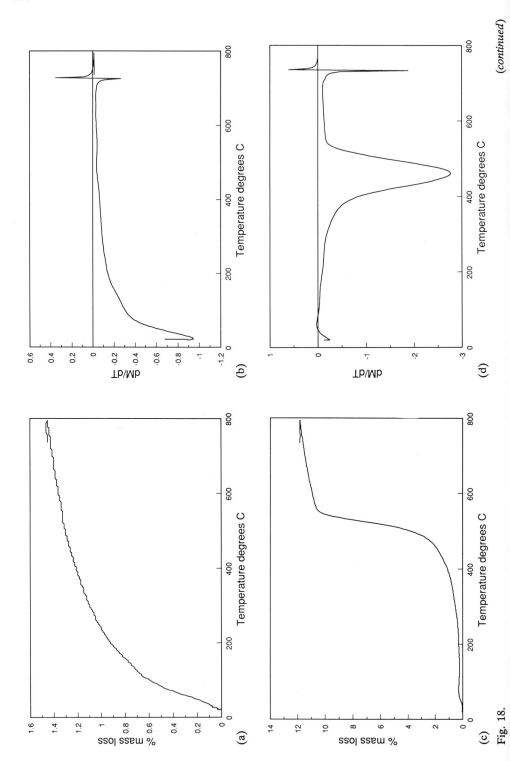

Fig. 18. *(continued)*

221

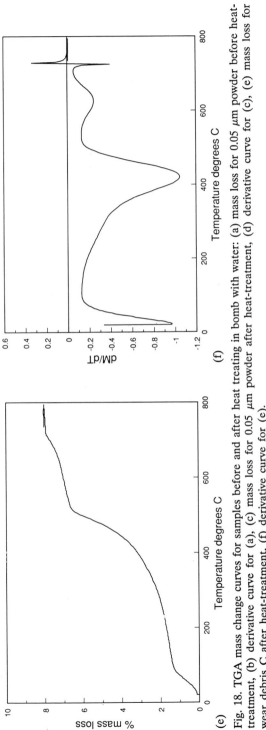

Fig. 18. TGA mass change curves for samples before and after heat treating in bomb with water: (a) mass loss for 0.05 μm powder before heat-treatment, (b) derivative curve for (a), (c) mass loss for 0.05 μm powder after heat-treatment, (d) derivative curve for (c), (e) mass loss for wear debris C after heat-treatment, (f) derivative curve for (e).

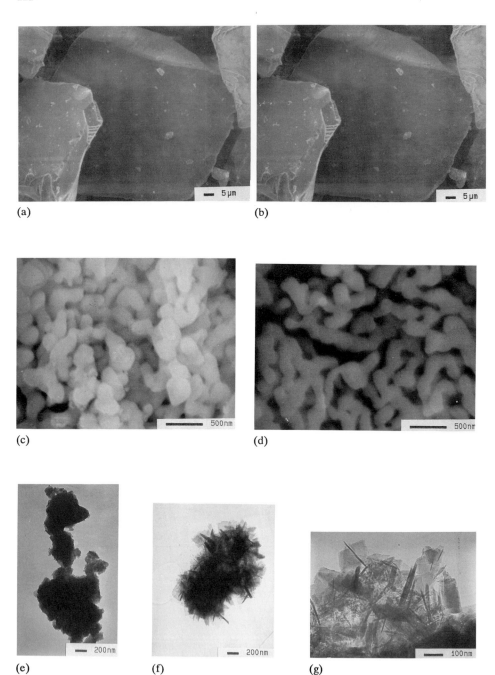

Fig. 19. Micrographs of powders heat-treated with water in bomb: (a) 50 $\mu$m alumina powder before heat-treatment, (b) 50 $\mu$m alumina powder after heat-treatment, (c) 0.3 $\mu$m alumina powder before heat-treatment, (d) 0.3 $\mu$m alumina powder after heat-treatment, (e) wear debris C before heat-treatment, (f) wear debris C after heat-treatment, (g) wear debris C after heat-treatment.

and to the sapphire, although there were small crystals on the surface of the 50 $\mu$m grit and the sapphire. However, these may have been artefacts caused by the crystallization of impurities in the water. SEM and TEM examination of one debris sample before and after treatment showed that the original powder consisted of some large crystalline fragments agglomerated with many smaller crystallites. The treatment had formed fibrous particles on the surface of these agglomerates (Fig. 19(f)), which were very similar to the morphology recorded for boehmite [18].

### 4.2. Aluminium hydroxides

Before the formation route for the hydroxide is discussed, it is useful to describe some information about the chemistry of aluminium hydroxides.

A useful starting point is Fig. 20, which describes the routes for thermal *dehydration* of alumina [14, 18]. This diagram shows the complexities of the chemistry of aluminium hydroxides, and may offer some clues regarding the likely products of hydration reactions if it is assumed that some of these reactions are reversible. Alpha-alumina, or corundum, is the stable unhydrated alumina that is the eventual product of the dehydration reactions. The various forms with other Greek names are transition aluminas that contain some hydroxyl radicals but which are intermediate in the transformation from the hydroxides to alpha-alumina. Transition path a is favoured for moist air, large particle sizes and a fast reaction, whereas path b is favoured for small particles, slow reaction rates and dry air. Gibbsite and bayerite are forms of aluminium tri-hydroxide Al(OH)$_3$. There is also another crystallographic form of the tri-hydroxide which is norstrandite. Boehmite and diaspore are aluminium mono-hydroxides, Al(OH).

It is also useful to consider the Al$_2$O$_3$–H$_2$O phase diagram (Fig. 21). This shows that at elevated pressures and temperatures, the hydroxides are stable with the formation of bayerite favoured at low temperatures, and boehmite at higher temperature. In fact if the conditions for the bomb experiments are considered (the H$_2$O liquid/vapour boundary is shown) giving a pressure of 23 bar at a temperature of 200 °C, then the formation of boehmite in these experiments is not surprising.

### 4.3. Formation route

The formation of hydroxide films is suggested to occur as follows. The most important prerequisite for the formation of the hydroxide film is the presence of finely divided alumina wear debris (Fig. 22). This mass of debris is forced under the very high pressure of local contacts between the surfaces into any depressions in the surface and, under the action of the elevated temperatures and pressures at the wear interface,

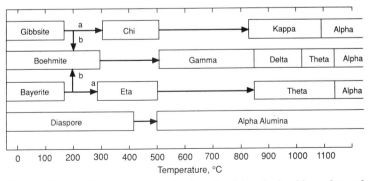

Fig. 20. Dehydration reaction routes for aluminium hydroxides, after ref. 14.

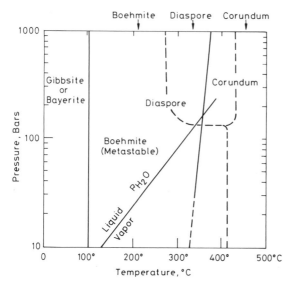

Fig. 21. $Al_2O_3$–$H_2O$ phase diagram, after ref. 18.

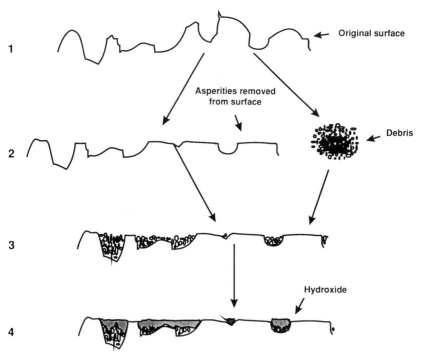

Fig. 22. Schematic diagram indicating formation route of hydroxide layers.

reaction of the alumina wear debris to form hydroxide takes place. (It should be noted that the flash temperatures at the interface are likely to be much higher [19], and the pressures lower than those encountered in the bomb experiments.) This process continues until hydroxide film fills the depressions in the original surface. With the flattening of asperities on the original surface, this results in the very flat surfaces that have been observed.

The hydroxide film is obviously beneficial as the wear of the alumina decreases in the uninterrupted tests as the percentage of the surface that is covered by the film is increased, with a particularly marked decrease in wear rate from 4% RH (where no hydroxide was formed) to 10% RH, where hydroxide was first observed. There was also increasingly less disruption to the microstructure of the surface layers of the material as the formation of hydroxide increased. In the interrupted tests where the humidity was changed there was no observable wear at any significant humidity level, presumably because of the formation of hydroxide.

One reason for the protection afforded by the hydroxides may be because they have layered crystallographic structures [14, 18], which might offer similar lubrication properties to those of graphite which also has a layered structure. However, this conclusion is not supported by the small reduction in friction coefficient that is observed when the hydroxide is formed.

The suggested route for the formation of the hydroxide films leaves the question of the formation of the original finely divided wear debris unanswered. Although some of the fine debris may be produced directly by polishing or micro-abrasion of the surface, it is much more likely that the fine debris is produced by comminution of larger particles that are formed by fracture processes such as indentation fracture or fatigue cracking. In this regard, it is interesting that high wear rates always occurred in the initial few minutes of tests where the formation of hydroxide films was found. If the test was interrupted in this early high wear period, no sign of the hydroxide films was found [1], suggesting that the reduction in wear rate after the first few minutes is due to the onset of hydroxide formation, giving protection to the underlying alumina wear surface.

The effect of humidity on the time needed to create a significant amount of hydroxide film may explain the discrepancy in the results for the variation in wear rate with humidity for the two types of test. In the uninterrupted tests, there was a slow drop in apparent wear rate with humidity after the initial sharp drop. By contrast, in the uninterrupted tests the wear was not measurable except at very low humidity levels. This may be because in the uninterrupted tests the wear rate was calculated from the total volume lost, including the initial period of high wear during the test. Thus if, as is likely, it takes longer to create a hydroxide film that is useful in protecting the underlying alumina at lower humidity levels, then higher wear can occur in this initial period giving the observed apparent dependency. This explanation has implications for testing, since it is obviously not sufficient to record only the total volume of wear, but it is necessary to develop ways of monitoring wear, and indeed wear rate, continuously through the test.

This conclusion is supported to some extent by the observation of incubation times before the wear rate decreased with an increase in the humidity. This is interpreted as the time need to create a sufficiently large and stable hydroxide film under the continuing wear conditions. Additional experiments need to be performed with increases in the humidity to different levels so that the change in incubation time with humidity level can be characterized. Further experiments are also needed to characterize the kinetics of the hydration reactions more closely so that a full model of the hydroxide film formation can be made.

Incubation times were also observed before the wear rate started to increase after a reduction in humidity, presumably due to the length of time needed to remove this film at the lower humidity level. Again, additional experiments would show if this incubation time varied with the humidity level.

The bomb experiments on alumina powders show that a direct reaction to form aluminium hydroxide from alpha-alumina can occur. This result is in contrast to the conclusions of Gates *et al.* [4] who stated that the direct reaction was not possible, and the formation of hydroxide occurred indirectly through the formation of the transition δ-alumina. The key point seems to be the size of the debris; if this is small enough then the direct reaction will proceed at a high enough rate to give significant formation of aluminium hydroxide.

One surprising feature that was observed in the tests was that although there was a large variation in wear rate with humidity there was only a small effect on the friction coefficient. The work done by moving the two surfaces against the frictional forces generated at the interface is the source of the energy that causes damage to the surfaces and ultimately to wear. Thus there is normally an expectation that as the wear rate is reduced the frictional forces should also be lowered, which was not observed in these experiments. The reasons for this discrepancy are not completely understood, but part of the explanation may be due to the decrease in roughness of the wear surface when hydroxide films are formed, since it is known that a large contribution to friction can often arise from the interlocking of rough surfaces.

## 5. Conclusions

(1) In uninterrupted pin-on-disc wear tests a strong effect of humidity has been found on the wear rate of alumina. However, very little effect was found of humidity on the friction coefficient.

(2) In contrast with the results of the uninterrupted tests, when humidity change experiments were performed, no measureable wear was observed except in dry conditions.

(3) The effect of humidity was due to the formation of thin protective layers of aluminium hydroxide at the wear interface.

(4) The discrepancy between the two sets of results was thought to be due to the effect of humidity on the rate of formation of aluminium hydroxide.

(5) Al(OH) (boehmite) was found to form directly from alpha alumina in hydrothermal experiments.

## References

1 A. J. Perez-Unzueta, J. H. Beynon and M. G. Gee, The effect of surrounding atmosphere on the sliding wear of alumina, *Wear, 146* (1991) 179.
2 T. E. Fischer and H. Tomizawa, *Wear, 105* (1985) 29–45.
3 G. Kapelski, F. Platon and P. Boch, Wear and friction properties of some engineering ceramics, *Science of Ceramics, Vol. 14*, Institute of Ceramics, 1987, pp. 781–786.
4 R. S. Gates, S. M. Hsu and E. E. Klaus, *Tribol. Trans., 32* (1989) 357–363.
5 R. S. Gates, S. M. Hsu and E. E. Klaus, Ceramic tribology: methodology and mechanisms of wear of alumina, NIST Special Publication 758, US Department of Commerce, 1988.
6 J. E. Hines, R. C. Bradt and J. V. Biggers, Delta alumina formation during the abrasive wear of a polycrystalline alumina, *Proc. Int. Conf. on the Wear of Materials,* ASME, 1979, pp. 540–549.
7 J. T. Czernuska and T. F. Page, Characterising the surface contact behaviour of ceramics, *J. Mater. Sci., 22* (1987) 3917–3923.

8   J. K. Lancaster, Y. Mashal and A. G. Atkins, The role of water in the wear of ceramics, to be published.

9   J. K. Lancaster, A review of the influence of environmental humidity and water on friction, lubrication and wear, *Tribol. Int., 23* (1990) 371–389.

10  S. Sasaki, The effects of surrounding atmosphere on the friction and wear of alumina, zirconia, silicon carbide and silicon nitride, *Proc. Int. Conf. on the Wear of Materials,* ASME, 1989, pp. 409–417.

11  S. Sasaki, The effects of water on friction and wear of ceramics, *J. JSLE, 33* (1988) 620–628.

12  N. Wallbridge, D. Dowson and E. W. Roberts, *Proc. Int. Conf. on the Wear of Materials,* ASME, 1983, pp. 202–211.

13  H. E. Bishop, private communication, 1990.

14  K. Wefers and G. M. Bell, Oxides and hydroxides of aluminium, Technical paper 19, Alcoa Research Laboratories, 1972.

15  M. G. Gee, C. S. Matharu, E. A. Almond and T. S. Eyre, The measurement of sliding friction and wear of ceramics at high temperature, *Wear, 138* (1990) 169–187.

16  M. G. Gee and E. A. Almond, The effect of surface finish on the wear of alumina, *J. Mater. Sci., 25* (1990) 296–310.

17  M. G. Gee, to be published.

18  C. Misra, *Industrial Alumina Chemicals,* Americal Chemical Society, 1986, p. 17.

19  M. F. Ashby, private communication, 1989.

*Wear, 153* (1992) 229–243

# Sliding wear mechanism of polytetrafluoroethylene (PTFE) and PTFE composites

T. A. Blanchet and F. E. Kennedy

*Thayer School of Engineering, Dartmouth College, Hanover, NH 03755 (USA)*

(Received June 12, 1991)

## Abstract

The previous literature regarding the wear of polytetrafluoroethylene (PTFE) is discussed, as are the mechanistic theories proposed to date for wear reduction via fillers. The mild–severe transition for unfilled PTFE is investigated as a function of sliding speed and temperature, and guidelines for maintenance of mild wear are developed. A fracture-based model describes the onset of severe wear and attendant changes in debris morphology. The wear-reducing effectiveness of three fillers is investigated as a function of speed. Under severe sliding conditions (when fillers are most effective) it is proposed that fillers reduce wear by interrupting subsurface deformation and crack propagation which would otherwise lead to large wear sheets.

## 1. Introduction

The high melting point of polytetrafluoroethylene (PTFE) of about 327 °C and its low coefficient of friction make this polymer useful as a solid lubricant in a variety of dry sliding tribosystems. The desirable frictional characteristics of PTFE result from the low shear strength surface films which it generates while sliding against smooth counterfaces [1, 2]. However, the transfer films which form atop such counterfaces are easily removed as sliding continues. The repetitive, cyclic process of film formation and removal results in unacceptably high rates of PTFE transfer wear [3]. These rates can be decreased by over three orders of magnitude through incorporation of any of a variety of fillers [4]. (It should be noted that fillers can actually harm the *abrasive* wear resistance of PTFE if sliding against *rougher* surfaces, by reducing its ductility [5, 6].) The mechanism by which fillers impart transfer wear resistance to PTFE in sliding contact with *smooth* counterfaces remains unclear and thus is the focus of this research.

## 2. Background

Lancaster [6] initially proposed that hard inorganic fillers reduce the wear of PTFE by preferentially supporting the applied load. High aspect ratio fillers should therefore provide the best wear resistance [4]. However, particulate or lamellar fillers (aspect ratios approximately unity and zero respectively) have also been shown to provide reasonable performance [7]. Even other soft polymers have been incorporated as fillers to reduce wear [8], but they do not impart any additional hardness to PTFE [9].

Briscoe *et al.* [10], on the other hand, demonstrated that a lead oxide–copper oxide filler reduced the wear of high density polyethylene (HDPE) (another linear, low friction polymer which suffers similar wear) by increasing the adhesion of its transfer films to the counterface, halting the repetitive transfer wear process. Briscoe *et al.* [11] invoked the same argument to describe the wear-reducing effect of carbon fillers on PTFE, though the adhesion mechanism was unclear. Brainard and Buckley [12] observed that PTFE fragments remained adherent to a tungsten field ion microscope (FIM) tip following static contact and concluded that the strength of this adhesion was likely due to chemical bonding directly between carbon atoms on the polymer backbone and the metal tip. Subsequent spectroscopic studies of chemical interactions between PTFE and various filler and counterface materials revealed the generation of various metal fluorides [13–17]. However, it is not clear that bonds to fluorine, being monovalent, could provide adhesion between the counterface and the rest of the PTFE molecule [18]. Additionally, the effect of the excitation radiation upon PTFE in these spectroscopic studies has not been fully considered [19].

Briscoe *et al.* [10] based their theory of reduced wear via transfer film adhesion on the observation that the wear rate of HDPE could be reduced by 75% if sliding took place atop a predeposited filled transfer film. For PTFE, however, Bahadur and Tabor [20] and Gong *et al.* [21] have shown that this theory does not hold. The insensitivity of the wear process of PTFE to predeposited films [20, 21] or the chemical composition of the counterface is due to the layering of transfer films. The locus of failure during transfer film removal is not at the interface between the counterface and the first layer of PTFE transfer; therefore the adhesion at this interface is not rate determining [21, 22].

Tanaka [23] proposed a theory which focuses on PTFE's banded structure. Makinson and Tabor [24] found that the 20 nm thickness of transfer films formed by PTFE corresponded to the thickness of crystalline slices which comprise this banded structure and inferred that film formation occurred via slip between these slices. Tanaka *et al.* [3] thought this to be the cause of PTFE's unusually high rate of transfer wear and proposed that the filler's wear-reducing role was the prevention of large-scale destruction of this special structure [23]. The banded structure has, however, been called into question [2], as has its relevance to the transfer process, after observation of films with dimensions considerably smaller than the proposed slice thickness [2, 18, 25, 26]. PTFE instead forms its low shear strength surface films via orientation of individual molecules [1, 2]. Although fillers accumulate at the PTFE wear surface [7, 27, 28], film formation still occurs atop these fillers and across the counterface, providing low friction similar to that of the unfilled polymer [4, 21]. Although fillers do not completely prevent surface film formation, their effect on the initial removal of PTFE from the surface warrants further study.

## 3. Experimental details

Sliding tests were performed in air on a pre-existing oscillatory pin-on-disk rig, previously described in detail [29, 30]. The PTFE composite pins were placed in a stationary specimen holder, which was dead-weight loaded against a metallic flat specimen held in place against an oscillating disk. Thermoelectric modules placed beneath the metallic flat and against the pin holder control the bulk temperatures of those components. The disk was driven at a preset amplitude and frequency by an accurately controlled d.c. motor through a crank–rocker linkage. Friction force was measured continuously by a piezoelectric transducer and linear wear by a linear variable differential transformer (LVDT) which monitored changes in height of the wearing polymer pin.

The four commercially produced pin materials tested were (1) unfilled PTFE, (2) 15% graphite-filled PTFE, (3) 25% glass-filled PTFE and (4) 40% bronze-filled PTFE. These were the same compositions used earlier by Tanaka [4]. The graphite flakes, bronze particles and discontinuous glass fibers each had diameters of several tens of micrometers, with the glass fiber length ranging between 50 and 100 $\mu$m. The pins had a 2 mm $\times$ 4 mm cross-section, with the 4 mm dimension oriented along the sliding direction. The contacting end of the pin was final machined flat while in the pin holder using a clean end mill. A 2.5 mm length of the pin was left extending from the holder.

Flat counterface specimens were 316 stainless steel, an alloy containing nickel, an element often supposed to take part in tribochemical reactions with PTFE [15, 17]. The samples, 12.5 mm $\times$ 25 mm $\times$ 6 mm thick, were ground flat and polished using 0.3 $\mu$m alumina particles in water. Polishing was quickly followed by cleansing, water rinsing, air-blown drying and ultrasonic bathing in methanol. The resulting roughness of $R_a = 0.02$ $\mu$m allowed adhesive mechanisms to predominate over any abrasion by the counterface.

Each test used new or resurfaced pin and flat specimens. A 52.4 N load was placed atop the pin holder to cause an average contact pressure of 6.55 MPa. The pins were allowed to creep in place for at least 36 h, while thermal equilibrium was allowed to develop at the desired test temperature, until the initially high creep rate diminished to a low steady state value (on the order of 0.001 mm h$^{-1}$ for the 2.5 mm length of pin extending from the pin holder). The drive motor was then turned on to a preset speed, yielding a desired oscillation frequency of the flat at an amplitude of 4 mm. This amplitude produced a wear track 12 mm long, large enough relative to the 4 mm length of the pin in the sliding direction that no region on the steel counterface was constantly overlapped by the pin (no mutual overlap). At such an amplitude the tribological behavior of unfilled PTFE was similar to that seen in unidirectional contacts and was not overwhelmed by oscillatory kinematical effects [31]. Average oscillatory sliding speeds ranged up to 0.2 m s$^{-1}$.

Instantaneous friction force was displayed on a storage oscilloscope, while its filtered magnitude was recorded along with wear measurements from the LVDT. Test durations were at least long enough for a steady state, linear wear rate to be easily recognizable, as determined by the correlation coefficient of the wear volume *vs.* sliding distance data. Average friction coefficients were also determined for this steady state region, with 95% confidence intervals determined for both wear rate and friction coefficient.

## 4. Results

Steady state wear rates (volume per unit sliding distance per unit normal load) and kinetic friction coefficients measured as a function of speed at 23 °C are displayed in Figs. 1(a) and 1(b) respectively. For unfilled PTFE, friction steadily increases with increasing speed while wear remains relatively mild, generally at a rate of about $10^{-5}$ mm$^3$ N$^{-1}$ m$^{-1}$ for speeds up to $8 \times 10^{-3}$ m s$^{-1}$. At this point wear goes through a mild–severe transition, with higher speeds (and correspondingly higher kinetic friction)

232

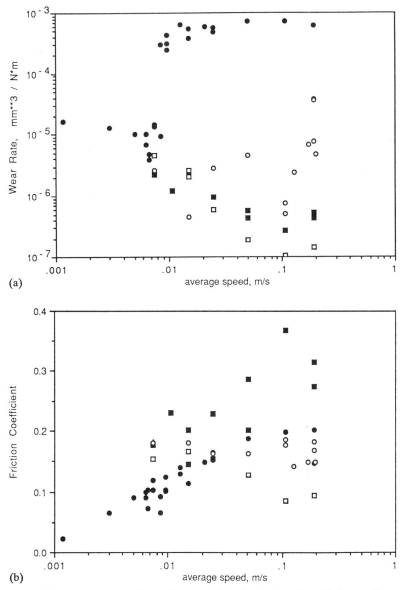

(a)

(b)

Fig. 1. (a) Wear rate and (b) coefficient of kinetic friction of unfilled as well as graphite-, glass-fiber- and bronze-filled PTFE as a function of average oscillatory sliding speed at 23 °C. ●, unfilled PTFE; ○, 15% graphite; ■, 25% glass; □, 40% bronze.

yielding severe wear with rates approaching $10^{-3}$ mm$^3$ N$^{-1}$ m$^{-1}$. A similar monotonic increase in friction and transition to higher wear, brought on by increasing speed, has been demonstrated for unfilled PTFE in unidirectional contacts [3]. The frictional behavior is thought to be a reflection of the viscous nature of the film-drawing process, since sliding speed is closely related to strain rate within these surface films and the kinetic friction $\mu_k$ is proportional to $V^n$. At a critical velocity the shear stresses associated with the film-drawing process at the sliding surface become great enough to cause failure in the PTFE subsurface, leading to the more severe wear process [3].

The frictional behavior of the filled PTFEs is less systematic (Fig. 1(b)). All three composites have friction coefficients near 0.2 at a sliding speed of 0.01 m s$^{-1}$, in the vicinity of the wear transition speed for the unfilled polymer. As speed is increased from that value, friction tends to increase for the glass-filled, decrease for the bronze-filled and remain fairly constant for the graphite-filled PTFE.

At speeds just below the transition the mild wear rate of the unfilled polymer is not too much greater than that observed for the filled materials (Fig. 1(a)). Wear reduction by fillers is most evident above unfilled PTFE's transition speed, since the wear rates of the filled PTFEs generally remain below $10^{-5}$ mm$^3$ N$^{-1}$ m$^{-1}$. (Wear rates of the glass- and bronze-filled polymers actually tend to decrease with increasing speed within this range.) The role of fillers must therefore be related to the obstruction of processes which cause the transition to severe wear in the unfilled PTFE.

Figure 2(a) shows the wear *vs.* speed behavior of unfilled PTFE at temperatures ranging up to 66 °C. At each temperature a similar mild–severe wear transition is observed, with mild rates of about $10^{-5}$ mm$^3$ N$^{-1}$ m$^{-1}$ below the transition speed and nearly $10^{-3}$ mm$^3$ N$^{-1}$ m$^{-1}$ above the transition speed. Lines have been included to highlight these transitions. As the temperature increases, a higher speed is needed to induce the transition to severe wear. Increases in temperature reduce the viscosity associated with the surface-film-drawing process (reflected in the coefficient of proportionality relating $\mu_k$ to $V^n$); thus a higher speed is needed to attain the high wear condition of failure within the subsurface. (Frictional heating affects the transition speeds very little compared to bulk temperature, since analytical and thin film thermocouple measurements show that the dissipation contribution to the average contact temperature at the transition speed will be less than 2–3 °C even at about 0.1 m s$^{-1}$ [31].)

The tribological behavior of PTFE is closely related to its viscoelastic properties (and therefore rate- and temperature-dependent properties). For a semicrystalline polymer below its glass transition temperature the tribological behavior (as a function of speed or shear rate) for many temperatures can be represented by a single master curve by use of a shift factor ($a(T)$) with an Arrhenius temperature dependence [32]

$$a(T) = \exp\left[\frac{\Delta H}{R}\left(\frac{1}{T} - \frac{1}{T_0}\right)\right] \tag{1}$$

where $T$ is the absolute temperature, $T_0$ is a reference temperature (the temperature at which the shift factor is unity and no shift occurs, 296 °C in this case), $R$ is the universal gas constant and $\Delta H$ is the activation energy. The master curve for wear rate *vs.* shifted speed (Fig. 2(b)) was constructed using an activation energy calculated to be approximately 9.2 kcal mol$^{-1}$ [31]. Tanaka *et al.* [3] constructed a very similar curve, having determined a slightly lower activation energy of 7 kcal mol$^{-1}$. Both values are within the 7–10 kcal mole$^{-1}$ range proposed for tribological process in which only van der Waals bonds are broken [33].

In a unidirectional contact the sliding speed exponent $n$ describing kinetic friction was found to be 0.26 for unfilled PTFE for test temperatures ranging from 23 to 100 °C [3]. For the oscillatory results presented here that exponent is closer to $n = 0.4$. Since the friction data for several temperatures could also be represented on a master curve (Fig. 2(c)) using the same shift factor as employed for the wear data, kinetic friction can be generally described over the range of tests speeds as

234

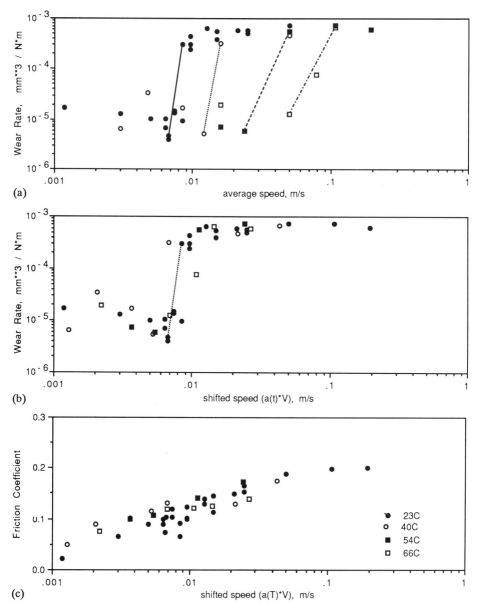

Fig. 2. (a) Wear rate of unfilled PTFE as a function of speed at temperatures of 23, 40, 54 and 66 °C. At each temperature a line has been included to denote transition to severe wear. (b), (c) Master curves of wear rate and friction coefficient superimposed as a function of shifted speed, using an Arrhenius factor with $\Delta H = 9.2$ kcal mol$^{-1}$.

$$\mu_k(V,T) = c[a(T)V]^n \tag{2}$$

where $c$ has a value of approximately 0.7 when describing speed with units of meters per second.

## 5. Discussion

Figure 3 illustrates the drawing of strips of oriented low shear strength film across the surface of an unfilled PTFE pin after a short sliding duration at low speed. With increased sliding distance a surface film fully develops atop the bulk PTFE, with a corresponding transfer film upon the counterface. Under these mild wear conditions the cyclic process of formation of strips of transfer film, followed by the eventual detachment, discards these strips as debris primarily at the ends of the wear track (Fig. 4(a)). The strips of debris still show surface striations running along their length, having previously been in sliding contact with the pin.

The filled PTFEs tested here share this mild wear process, with similar strip debris discarded at wear track ends (Figs. 4(b)–4(d)). Strips of transfer are not produced as generously by the filled PTFE as they are by the unfilled polymer. The fillers, which accumulate at the sliding surface of the pin as the wear process continues [4, 28, 34], slow the transport of the neat matrix polymer to the sliding interface and thus cause wear to take place at a slightly lower rate. However, as previously mentioned, the resulting differences in wear between the filled and unfilled PTFEs are less than dramatic in this mild regime (Fig. 1(a), $V < 8$ mm s$^{-1}$).

Since increasingly higher speeds induce severe wear of unfilled PTFE, a simultaneous change in the morphology of the transferred material is observed. This change is a result of the shear strain rates associated with surface film formation becoming large relative to the reciprocal of the relaxation time of the polymer, which has a temperature dependence of the form $t_r \propto \exp(\Delta H/RT)$. The constant $\delta$ which relates shear strain rate to speed ($d\gamma/dt \propto V/\delta$), under the assumption of occasional instants of stick at the sliding interface, would approximately be equal to the thickness over which relative sliding displacement is being accommodated (likely the sum thickness of the transfer film on the counterface and the running film on the PTFE pin surface). The drawing of surface films in the mild regime is overwhelmed in the severe regime by subsurface deformation and fracture processes which result in more massive transfer [35, 24, 18, 3, 31, 34]. The fragmented sheets of transfer (Fig. 5(a)) are quickly removed from the contact and deposited about the periphery of the wear track as flakes of debris

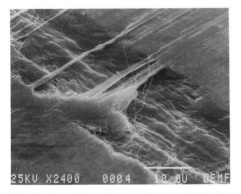

Fig. 3. Secondary electron image of thin film of PTFE drawn over sliding surface of unfilled pin following a very short sliding duration. (Machine grooves from the milling operation, running from upper left to lower right, are not yet worn away, helping to illustrate the drawing process as the film spans these grooves.)

Fig. 4. Secondary electron images of (a) strips of PTFE transfer and debris upon the counterface following mild wear of unfilled PTFE; also wear tracks from (b) graphite-, (c) glass-fiber- and (d) bronze-filled PTFE.

(Fig. 5(b)). Such sheets can be several hundred micrometers in diameter, easily visible with the naked eye.

Profilometric traces across the wear track showed these transferred wear sheets to range in thickness from a few micrometers to 20 $\mu$m, raising the lightly loaded profilometer stylus by such a dimension above the rest of the wear track (Fig. 6). This sheet thickness, which is about the same as that found by Bahadur and Tabor [20], should correspond to a depth at which subsurface processes responsible for the

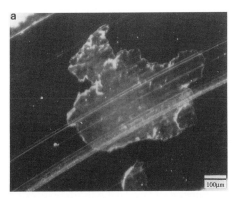

Fig. 5. (a) Optical image of transferred sheet of unfilled PTFE upon counterface. (b) Secondary electron image of transferred sheets as well as wear sheet debris existing about the periphery of a severe wear track.

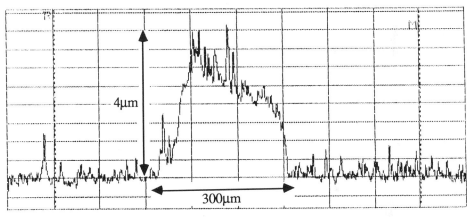

Fig. 6. Stylus profilometry trace along counterface following severe wear, as stylus climbs over transferred sheet several micrometers in thickness.

severe wear of the unfilled polymer are activated. Sections of the unfilled pins (about 20 $\mu$m in thickness) were microtomed at room temperature normal to the sliding surface following severe wear. These sections revealed the existence of a worked layer, which in some locations was separated from the bulk PTFE by cracks running parallel to the sliding surface (Fig. 7). The thickness of the transferred sheets is indeed similar to the thickness of this worked layer and may result from the propagation of these subsurface cracks. (Worked layers were not observed in thin sections of unfilled PTFE after mild wear tests.) These observations suggest severe wear is a consequence of delamination, a process discussed with increasing frequency relative to polymer wear [36–41].

Figure 8 is a crude representation of a subsurface crack parallel to a sliding surface subject to kinetic friction, with a friction coefficient (0.1) similar to that found for unfilled PTFE. For such a situation the uniform resultant loads imposed at the sliding surface deviate from being normal to that surface by only a small angle $\alpha$ (note that $\mu_k = \tan \alpha$). If these uniform resultant loads are considered to be applied over a relatively wide contact length, the smaller crack will therefore be considered

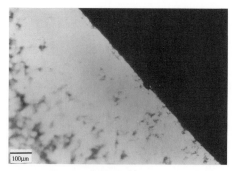

Fig. 7. Cross-polarized optical thin section of unfilled PTFE pin following severe wear: section taken normal to sliding surface, displaying formation of deformed layer and subsurface cracking.

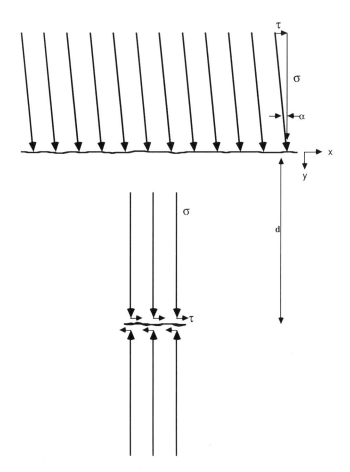

Fig. 8. Schematic drawing of crack at a depth $d$ below a sliding surface subject to a widely distributed load and having a coefficient of kinetic friction of about 0.10.

in a state of compression–shear, yielding a mode II problem studied in detail by Rosenfield [42–45]. (Note that with a friction coefficient of 0.1 any tensile region existing behind the load will be very shallow and will increase in depth only slightly with increasing distance behind that load. The load would have to move considerably beyond the crack before that crack passed from the compressive to the tensile zone. Since the stress associated with tensile crack opening decreases with increasing distance from the load, it is anticipated that mode I contributions will be overshadowed by mode II contributions.) Shieh [46] experimentally demonstrated that cracks can propagate under such combinations of compression and shear. This mode of propagation with a trajectory that is parallel to the sliding surface is greatly favored by the anisotropy of the near-surface region [42], resulting from the molecular orientation process.

Crack-sliding displacement is resisted by static friction between the opposing crack faces, described by the coefficient $\mu_{cf}$. Under conditions of low kinetic friction the shear stress existing between the crack faces will equal that found at the sliding surface $y=0$ under the wide uniform load ($\tau_d=\tau_0$). The normal stresses are approximately equal under all conditions for the stated geometry, $\sigma_d=\sigma_0=\sigma$. This situation will persist as long as $\mu_k<\mu_{cf}$ (such that $\tau_d<\mu_{cf}\sigma$ under the stated assumptions). Therefore all shear stress on the crack faces in compressive contact is equilibrated by static friction and thus the effective shear stress causing stress intensification at the tips is zero. However, since $\tau_d$ on the crack faces cannot exceed $\mu_{cf}\sigma$, sliding conditions where $\mu_k>\mu_{cf}$ result in $\tau_0>\tau_d$. (Several crack lengths away, the far-field shear stress on the plane $y=d$, $\tau_{d,ff}$, is still equal to that imposed at the sliding surface, $\tau_0$.) The effective shear stress contribution between the crack faces which cannot be supported by static friction,

$$\tau_{eff}=\tau_0-\mu_{cf}\sigma \tag{3}$$

must instead be supported by stress intensifications at the crack tips (note the convention that compressive $\sigma$ is positive):

$$K_{II}=\tau_{eff}(\pi a)^{1/2} \tag{4}$$

where $a$ is the crack half-length. $\Delta K_{II}$, which is twice this value for oscillatory motion, may lead to propagation of such a shear crack parallel to the sliding surface. This trajectory would be favored by the texture of the near-surface material which can develop by the molecular orientation processes, and delamination of wear sheets results.

The friction existing between the crack faces should be similar to that measured in static contacts between PTFE and itself. Makinson and Tabor [24] measured such friction to have a coefficient between 0.10 and 0.16, within the range of kinetic values measured (0.03–0.35). More precise measurements indicative of $\mu_{cf}$ are difficult owing to the effects of an unknown environment existing within the subsurface crack [47] and the degree of roughness and molecular orientation generated on its faces. $\mu_{cf}$ may also have a temperature dependence [2], though it is likely to be slight relative to the dependence of the kinetic friction. In the severe wear criterion $\mu_k(V,T)=\mu_{cf}$, any slight temperature dependence of $\mu_{cf}$ could likely be lumped with that of the kinetic term when determining an empirical value for crack face friction. Such a value can be estimated from Fig. 9, since at all test temperatures the mild–severe wear transition occurs approximately at a value of kinetic friction of $\mu_k=0.105\pm0.015$. Using this value as $\mu_{cf}$ and eqns. (1) and (2), design guidelines of maximum speed or minimum temperature to maintain mild wear of unfilled PTFE can be developed (since increases in speed or decreases in temperature can bring about severe wear by causing the kinetic friction to rise above the threshold level):

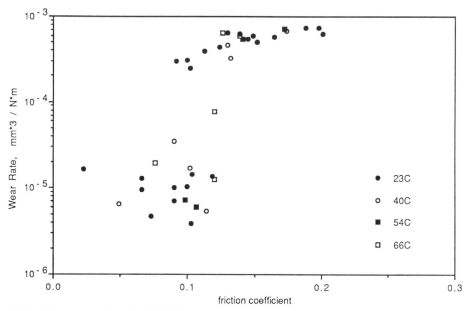

Fig. 9. Wear rate of unfilled PTFE at several temperatures as a function of kinetic friction.

$$V_{\max} = [a(T)]^{-1}\left(\frac{\mu_{cf}}{c}\right)^{1/n} \tag{5}$$

$$T_{\min} = \left[T_0^{-1} + \frac{R}{n\Delta H}\ln\left(\frac{\mu_{cf}}{cV^n}\right)\right]^{-1} \tag{6}$$

The values of $\Delta H$, $\mu_{cf}$, $n$ and $c$ (9.2 kcal mol$^{-1}$, 0.105, 0.4 and 0.7 respectively) quoted here apply strictly to this specific tribosystem. For example, in the unidirectional contact of Tanaka et al. [3] where $\Delta H = 7$ kcal mol$^{-1}$ and $n = 0.26$, the values for $\mu_{cf}$ and $c$ estimated from the published figures are instead approximately 0.2 and 0.45 (when speed is expressed as meters per second and the reference temperature $T_0 = 296$ °C).

Analysis using deformation properties quoted from Bilik [48] reveals that the real area of contact for these test conditions will be a fraction of the apparent area. As a result, the actual stress at the sliding surface will be somewhat higher than the apparent stress and will be distributed over finite contact lengths, yielding stress distributions $\tau(x,y)$ and $\sigma(x,y)$. Contact length effects have been coupled with crack face friction analysis on such mode II wear problems by Hills and Ashelby [47, 49]. Finite contact lengths imply that free surface outside of the contact should be accounted for, though ignorance of this matter yields errors which are small [45] relative to other problems inherent in trying to apply fracture mechanics to cracks with sizes on the order of the microstructure in a plastically strained material [42]. The simplified model for the onset of wear of unfilled PTFE presented here should, however, remain self-consistent, since the constants for the model ought to be determined empirically using data obtained directly from the tribosystem of interest.

As presented in Fig. 1(a), the wear-reducing role of the filler must be a preventive one in light of the severe wear that is induced without the filler. In spite of other previously published theories, Ricklin [50] suggested that the wear-reducing role of fillers within PTFE was merely to prevent the production of larger wear particles. Bahadur and Tabor [20] similarly stated that the reduced wear rate of filled PTFE was attributable to the filler's ability to govern the size and shape of the wear fragments. These viewpoints are backed further by the differential scanning calorimetry (DSC) analysis of the molecular weights of PTFE debris by Arkles and Schireson [35]. Under mild sliding the characterization of unfilled PTFE debris was similar to that found upon its sliding surface, while the characterization of debris under severe sliding was more similar to the bulk PTFE, since deeper subsurface failure was activated. Under severe conditions, however, the debris formed by glass-filled PTFE retained mild wear characteristics, since failure at greater depths within the surface was prevented.

In light of the model proposed here to describe the onset of severe wear of unfilled PTFE, it is suggested that the role of the filler is to prevent this onset by retarding subsurface crack propagation which would otherwise lead to the larger wear sheets as previously described (Figs. 5(a) and 5(b)). This process is observed upon the sliding surface of glass-fiber- and bronze-filled pins shown in Figs. 10(a) and 10(b). As a subsurface crack encounters a large filler particle, the trajectory turns to the sliding surface. This in turn leads to the finer debris observed in Figs. 4(c) and 4(d), considerably smaller than the several hundred micrometer scale of wear sheets of unfilled PTFE. The accumulation of fillers at the composite's sliding surface during the initial stages of sliding likely accentuates the role of these fillers. Additionally, the presence of these fillers at the sliding surface may also limit the contact area

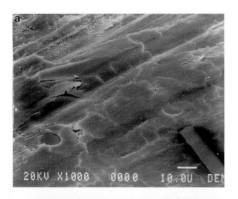

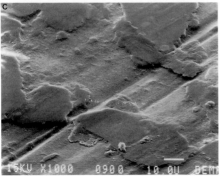

Fig. 10. Secondary electron images of (a) glass-fiber-, (b) bronze- and (c) graphite-filled pin surfaces.

within which frictional tractions are applied directly to the PTFE matrix. As a result of these smaller traction areas, the worked surface layer will not be as deep [51] and the wear debris will in turn be thinner than that generated by unfilled PTFE.

Tanaka [23] claimed that lamellar fillers were not as effective at reducing wear because they do not remain embedded deeply within the sliding surface. The explanation of less effective wear reduction, as evidenced in Fig. 1(a), is also valid within the context of this model. Flakes of graphite tend to lay atop the plane of the sliding surface (Fig. 10(c)) and will not interfere with subsurface crack propagation as effectively as spherical or fiber fillers. Along these same lines, Sung and Suh [52] found wear of fiber-filled PTFE to be lowest when fibers were primarily oriented normal to the sliding surface, and highest when fibers all lay in planes parallel to the sliding surface. Instead of invoking the load support theory often cited to explain such wear–fiber orientation relationships [6], the authors noted that with the latter geometry cracks can still propagate parallel to the sliding surface under cyclic loading, resulting in large-scale fiber separation and higher rates of wear.

## 6. Conclusions

(1) The mild sliding wear of unfilled PTFE gives way to severe wear upon an increase in sliding speed or a decrease in temperature. This transition is related to kinetic friction reaching a threshold value. The effects of sliding speed and temperature are intermingled through the viscoelastic shear properties of this polymer and can be superimposed using an Arrhenius shift factor.

(2) Severe wear of unfilled PTFE occurs via subsurface cracking, which generates wear sheets several micrometers thick and several hundred micrometers in diameter. A fracture-based model is presented to describe the onset of severe wear, and design limitations of maximum sliding speed and minimum temperature are developed for the maintenance of mild wear of PTFE.

(3) While PTFE wear is greatly reduced by fillers under severe conditions, their effect is not dramatic under mild sliding conditions. It is therefore proposed that the role of the filler must be preventive in nature and is associated with interrupting subsurface deformation and crack propagation that would otherwise produce large wear sheets.

## Acknowledgment

The authors wish to thank the NASA Graduate Student Researchers Program for support funding.

## References

1 R. P. Steijn, *Wear, 12* (1968) 193.
2 C. M. Pooley and D. Tabor, *Proc. R. Soc. Lond. A, 329* (1972) 251.
3 K. Tanaka, Y. Uchiyama and S. Toyooka, *Wear, 23* (1973) 153.
4 K. Tanaka and S. Kawakami, *Wear, 79* (1982) 221.
5 J. Bijwe, C. M. Logani and U. S. Tewari, *Wear, 138* (1990) 77.
6 J. K. Lancaster, *J. Phys. D: Appl. Phys., 1* (1968) 549.
7 K. Tanaka, Y. Uchiyama, S. Euda and T. Shimizu, in T. Sakurai (ed.), *Proc. Joint JSLE–ASLE Int. Lubrication Conf., Tokyo, 1976,* Elsevier, Amsterdam, 1976, p. 110.
8 B. Arkles, J. Theberge and M. Schireson, *Lubr. Eng., 33* (1977) 33.

9 M. Hong and S. Pyun, *Wear, 143* (1991) 87.

10 B. J. Briscoe, A. K. Pogosian and D. Tabor, *Wear, 27* (1974) 19.

11 B. J. Briscoe, M. D. Steward and A. J. Groszek, *Wear, 42* (1976) 99.

12 W. A. Brainard and D. H. Buckley, *Wear, 26* (1973) 75.

13 G. Pocock and P. Cadman, *Wear, 37* (1976) 129.

14 P. Cadman and G. M. Gossedge, *Wear, 51* (1978) 57.

15 P. Cadman and G. M. Gossedge, *Wear, 54* (1979) 211.

16 P. Cadman and G. M. Gossedge, *J. Mater. Sci., 14* (1979) 2672.

17 J. Gao and H. Dang, *J. Appl. Polym. Sci., 36* (1988) 73.

18 D. R. Wheeler, *Wear, 66* (1981) 355.

19 D. R. Wheeler and S. V. Pepper, *J. Vac. Sci. Technol., 20* (1982) 226.

20 S. Bahadur and D. Tabor, *Wear, 98* (1984) 1.

21 D. Gong, B. Zhang, Q. Xue and H. Wang, *Wear, 137* (1990) 25.

22 D. Gong, B. Zhang, Q. Xue and H. Wang, *Wear, 137* (1990) 267.

23 K. Tanaka, in K. Friedrich (ed.), *Friction and Wear of Polymer Composites,* Elsevier, Amsterdam, 1986, p. 137.

24 K. R. Makinson and D. Tabor, *Proc. R. Soc. Lond. A, 281* (1964) 49.

25 J. L. Lauer, B. C. Bunting and W. R. Jones, *Tribol. Trans., 31* (1988) 282.

26 S. V. Pepper, *J. Appl. Phys., 45* (1974) 2947.

27 K. Tanaka, *J. Lubr. Technol., 99* (1977) 408.

28 M. N. Gardos, *Lubr. Eng., 37* (1981) 641.

29 F. E. Kennedy, L. Smidhammar and D. Play, *Eurotrib 85, Proc. 4th Eur. Tribological Conf., Lyon, 1985,* Elsevier, Amsterdam, 1985, p. 5.1.2.

30 V. R. Evans and F. E. Kennedy, *Proc. Int. Conf. Wear of Materials, 1987,* ASME, New York, 1987, p. 427.

31 T. A. Blanchet, F. E. Kennedy and X. Tian, *Proc. Int. Conf. Wear of Materials, 1991,* ASME, New York, 1991, p. 689.

32 K. G. MacLaren and D. Tabor, *Nature, 197* (1963) 856.

33 R. P. Steijn, *ASLE Trans., 11* (1968) 235.

34 T. A. Blanchet and F. E. Kennedy, *Tribol. Trans., 134* (1991) 327.

35 B. C. Arkles and M. J. Schireson, *Wear, 39* (1976) 177.

36 N. P. Suh, in D. A. Rigney (ed.), *Fundamentals of Friction and Wear of Materials,* ASM, Metals Park, OH, 1980, p. 43.

37 M. Clerico, in N. P. Suh and N. Saka (eds.), *Fundamentals of Tribology,* MIT Press, Cambridge, MA, 1978, p. 769.

38 J. R. Youn and N. P. Suh, *Proc. Society of Plastics Engineers, 39th ANTEC, Boston, MA, 1981,* p. 20.

39 P. S. Walker, M. Ben-Dov, M. J. Askew and J. Pugh, *Eng. Med., 10* (1981) 33.

40 M. M. Landy and P. S. Walker, *J. Arthroplasty, Suppl.,* (October 1988) S73.

41 T. C. Ovaert and H. S. Cheng, *J. Tribol., 113* (1991) 150.

42 A. R. Rosenfield, in D. A. Rigney (ed.), *Fundamentals of Friction and Wear of Materials,* ASM, Metals Park, OH, 1980, p. 221.

43 A. R. Rosenfield, *Wear, 61* (1980) 125.

44 A. R. Rosenfield, *Wear, 72* (1981) 97.

45 A. R. Rosenfield, *Wear, 116* (1987) 319.

46 W. T. Shieh, *Eng. Fract. Mech., 9* (1977) 37.

47 D. A. Hills and D. W. Ashelby, *Wear, 54* (1979) 321.

48 G. M. Bartenev and V. V. Lavrentev, *Friction and Wear of Polymers,* Elsevier, Amsterdam, 1981, p. 75.

49 D. A. Hills and D. W. Ashelby, *Eng. Fracture Mech., 13* (1980) 69.

50 S. Ricklin, *Lubr. Eng., 33* (1977) 487.

51 F. E. Kennedy and L. P. Grotelueschen, *J. Appl. Mech., 51* (1984) 687.

52 N. Sung and N. P. Suh, *Wear, 53* (1979) 129.

*Wear, 153* (1992) 245–261

# An investigation of the interaction of model asperities of similar hardness

A. J. Black, E. M. Kopalinsky and P. L. B. Oxley

*School of Mechanical and Manufacturing Engineering, University of New South Wales, PO Box 1, Kensington, NSW 2033 (Australia)*

(Received June 25, 1991)

## Abstract

Experiments are described in which records were obtained of the forces and deformation during the life cycle of the interaction of model wedge-shaped asperities of similar hardness and geometry. The results show that the asperities moved past each other by a combination of plastic deformation of the asperities and sliding at their common interface. It appears that the fracture process which in previous work has been assumed to end the cycle did not occur. Slipline field models are presented to describe the deformation and good agreement is shown between stresses and velocities calculated from the slipline fields and those measured experimentally.

## 1. Introduction

The plane strain slipline field in Fig. 1 has been successfully applied to the modelling of asperity interactions when a hard surface slides over a relatively soft one. With this model the friction force is taken to be the force needed to push waves of plastically deformed material along the soft surface ahead of asperities on the hard surface. The field is completely defined in terms of $\alpha$, the slope of the hard asperity, and the normalized interfacial film strength $f = \tau/k$ along DE, where $\tau$ is the shear strength of the film and $k$ is the shear flow stress of the deforming material. It can be seen that $\alpha$ and $f$ are in effect surface roughness and lubrication parameters respectively. The resulting theory [1], based on the stress analysis of the slipline field in Fig. 1, predicts in agreement with experience that the coefficient of friction $\mu$ increases with increase in $\alpha$ and $f$. Good quantitative agreement between predicted and experimental values of $\mu$ has been shown for both scaled-up model asperity experiments [2, 3] and for experiments using actual surfaces [4]. The model has also been used to make predictions of wear in terms of $\alpha$, $f$ and the low cycle fatigue properties of the wearing material [5] by considering the strain increment occurring as material flows through the wave, which can be calculated from Fig. 1. Good agreement has been shown with experimental wear results [6].

The model in Fig. 1 represents a relatively simple case in that the hard asperity is assumed to be rigid. Therefore only one surface deforms and the process can be assumed to be steady state. When the interacting asperities are of similar hardness and both deform, the deformation geometry changes with time and the problem is far more complex. This problem is considered in the present paper. It is appropriate to start by reviewing some of the more important previous investigations in this area.

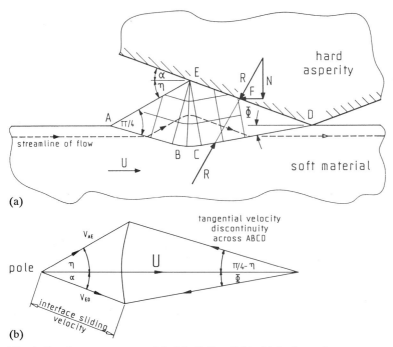

Fig. 1. Steady state wave model: (a) slipline field; (b) hodograph.

Most investigations of the interaction of asperities of equal hardness have been made against a background of the classic Bowden–Tabor adhesion theory of friction [7]. In this the friction force is considered to be the force needed to shear the welded junctions formed by adhesion at the tips of contacting asperities. If account is taken of junction growth under the combined action of the shear and normal stresses acting on the junction during deformation, then, as shown by McFarlane and Tabor [8], the resulting theory gives values of $\mu$ which obey the basic laws of friction and are in good quantitative agreement with experimental results. The theory cannot account for the influence of surface roughness unless a separate ploughing term is introduced and it is usual to assume that this will be very small compared with the adhesion term.

In his detailed analysis of the Bowden–Tabor junction model Green [9, 10] applied plasticity theory to estimate the forces involved in asperity deformation. Both plane strain and plane stress conditions were considered. He pointed out that, while during the initial junction growth period the two surfaces moved closer together, they must under steady sliding conditions move parallel to each other. He then showed that the necessary imposition of this condition on each individual junction determined both its manner of deformation and the forces exerted through it. To investigate the influence of the strength of adhesion, etc. on the value of the coefficient of friction, Green argued that if there are many junctions on the contacting surfaces at different stages of development, then the coefficient of friction can be estimated by taking the ratio of the average values of the forces acting tangentially and normally to the surfaces over the life cycle of a typical junction. He assumed the life cycle to consist of formation, deformation and fracture. Lacking a method for predicting the change in shape of an asperity and the corresponding forces during a life cycle, Green carried out experiments using scaled-up model asperities made of plasticine to give some indication of the type of deformation that might be expected. Green's results in Fig. 2 show that for wedge-shaped asperities the change in shape can be roughly characterized by an increase in the angle $\eta$ and a decrease in the angle $\alpha$. For the part of the life cycle in which $\eta$ is in the range $0-\frac{1}{4}\pi$ Green used plane strain slipline field solutions which he had derived for wedge-shaped asperities to estimate tangential and normal forces. For $\eta$ values in the range $\frac{1}{4}\pi-\frac{1}{2}\pi$, where no such solutions existed, he deduced the probable way in which these forces might be expected to vary by considering some solutions he had obtained for plane-sided symmetrical junctions. In this way he showed how the direct stress normal to the sliding direction could become tensile towards the end of the life cycle and hence cause fracture of the junction. Green could not make accurate quantitative estimates of the coefficient of friction because neither the forces over the life cycle nor the point of fracture were known with sufficient accuracy. However, he was able to show in a general way how the coefficient of friction might be expected to vary with such factors as the strength of adhesion and the ductility and hardness of the contacting materials and the resulting trends were in good agreement with experiment. Green mainly concentrated on what he termed strong junctions in which the adhesion at the interface between the contacting asperities was sufficiently large to prevent interface sliding. However, he also gave some consideration to weak junctions in which sliding did occur at the interface in the same way as for the field in Fig. 1. Even in this case he considered the life cycle of the asperity interaction to be ended by fracture. In support of this he showed from the appropriate slipline field solution that the normal stress at the end of the cycle, although smaller in magnitude than for strong junctions, was nevertheless still tensile.

Greenwood and Tabor [11] made a comprehensive experimental study of Green's asperity deformation models. It should be noted, however, that their experimental conditions were in most cases nearer to plane stress than plane strain. In their experiments they measured the tangential and normal forces acting on model asperities during the deformation cycle. The specimen materials used were plasticine, lead, indium and aluminium. Various interface conditions were considered ranging from strong to negligible adhesion. Strong adhesion was achieved by making the model asperities from a single piece of material, which completely eliminated the possibility of interface sliding. Weak and negligible adhesion was achieved by using two-piece model asperities under both dry and lubricated conditions. The measured forces were found to be in reasonable quantitative agreement with Green's theoretical forces. However, only in the case of the strong adhesion experiments was the normal force observed to go negative, thus indicating a tensile normal stress at the end of the cycle. Although for the weak and negligible adhesion experiments one might have expected

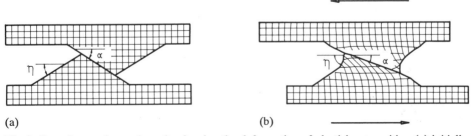

(a)                  (b)

Fig. 2. Green's experimental results showing the deformation of plasticine asperities: (a) initially; (b) during deformation.

some interface sliding, it is not possible to determine from Greenwood and Tabor's results whether or not this was the case.

Edwards and Halling [12] conducted experiments under approximately plane strain conditions on wedge-shaped model asperities which were manufactured from rolled lead sheet. Like Greenwood and Tabor, they achieved strong adhesion conditions by using one-piece specimens and weaker adhesion conditions by using two-piece specimens with and without lubrication. The force results obtained by Edwards and Halling are similar to those of Greenwood and Tabor. A most useful feature of the Edwards and Halling paper are photographs taken of the sides of the specimens (view as in Fig. 2) at various stages of the deformation. For lubricated conditions these appear to indicate that sliding was taking place at the interface and that the model asperities were moving past each other without any obvious indications of fracture. In analysing asperity deformation, Edwards and Halling [13] did in fact at first include interface sliding and proposed a Green-type slipline field of the form shown in Fig. 3. Because the field in Fig. 3 was not valid over the complete cycle of asperity deformation, Edwards and Halling used an equivalent pattern of velocity discontinuities to approximate the slipline field. This pattern of velocity discontinuities was applicable for all stages of the deformation and could be used with the upper bound method to estimate forces for the complete cycle. The best upper bound is assumed to be that which minimizes the rate of energy dissipation and, somewhat unfortunately, this was found to coincide with the condition of zero sliding at the interface. Recognizing that in some cases sliding must occur, Edwards and Halling obtained an approximate solution

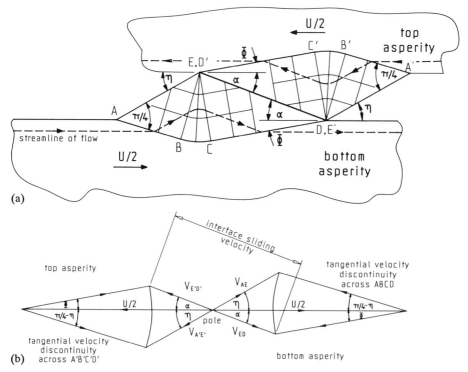

Fig. 3. Green-type slipline field for the deformation of asperities of similar hardness: (a) slipline field; (b) hodograph.

for such cases which in essence combined the upper bound and slipline field solutions. In considering Edwards and Halling's analysis, it should be noted that the upper bound method is not strictly applicable to the problem of asperity deformation because of its undefined free-surface boundary.

It can be seen from the above review of previous work that investigations of asperity interactions, both experimental and theoretical, have been greatly influenced by the Bowden–Tabor adhesion model [7]. Challen and Oxley [1] have reasoned that at least for the case of a hard surface sliding over a relatively soft one the adhesion model is far too severe, especially for smooth, well-lubricated surfaces. This is because the fracture process involved implies far greater wear than observed in practice. It was for this reason that Challen and Oxley introduced the slipline field model given in Fig. 1, since with this model a friction force could be accounted for without fracture being involved. The same reasoning might also be expected to apply in many cases for surfaces of similar hardness in sliding contact. The present paper describes an investigation of the interaction of model asperities of approximately the same hardness under well-lubricated conditions. The motivation behind this work was to see if such asperities could interact and move past each other without the occurrence of fracture, as is indeed suggested by some of the results of Edwards and Halling [12]. If this was the case, then by analysing the deformation taking place it was hoped to provide an asperity interaction model which would serve as a basis for future work on the sliding contact of surfaces of similar hardness.

## 2. Experiment and experimental results

The aim of the experiments was to obtain a record of the plastic deformation and associated forces during the interaction of model wedge-shaped asperities of as near as possible the same geometry and hardness. The plastic deformation in the tests had to approximate closely to plane strain conditions.

The test rig used to achieve these objectives is shown schematically in Fig. 4. A milling machine was employed as the basic drive unit in the rig. The top specimen was located in a holder which was clamped to a rigid structure attached to the milling machine head. The bottom specimen was held between two hardened steel guide

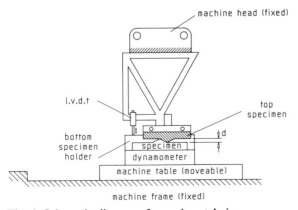

Fig. 4. Schematic diagram of experimental rig.

250

plates which located the specimen on the specimen stage. The stage was bolted to the milling machine table, which could be traversed automatically in the horizontal direction during a test. The guide plates were used to prevent lateral flow of material and thus to maintain conditions as close to plane strain as possible. They also provided the sides of a bath for tests in which liquid lubricants were used. The front guide (not shown in Fig. 4) had a slot cut in it and a 126 mm × 16 mm × 16 mm piece of Perspex was fitted in this slot flush with the inner face of the guide. This provided a window with a viewing area of 120 mm × 10 mm through which the deformation could be observed and photographs taken during a test. A piezoelectric three-component dynamometer formed an integral part of the specimen stage and was aligned so as to measure the horizontal and vertical forces ($F$ and $N$ in Fig. 1). These were referred to as the tangential and normal forces in the earlier papers reviewed in Section 1. The third component which was measured was perpendicular to these two directions. For the plane strain test conditions used, this component was found to be close to zero. The experimental rig provided extremely rigid support. Nevertheless, it was desirable to measure any changes in the vertical distance between the top and bottom specimens (dimension $d$ in Fig. 4) which occurred as a result of the forces acting during a test. This was achieved using a linear variable displacement transducer (LVDT) located as shown in Fig. 4. The measuring systems were calibrated before each test and the errors in the measured forces and distances were negligible when compared with the magnitudes of the measured values in the tests. A 35 mm SLR time lapse camera was used to take photographs at various stages of the deformation. A timing circuit was developed to drive the camera to take photographs at a time lapse of between 2 and 3 s. A square wave was produced by the timing circuit and sent to an IBM XT personal computer. This signal together with the signals from the dynamometer and the displacement transducer, which were also sent to the computer, enabled each photograph to be associated with the corresponding forces and displacements. A fibre optic dual light source was used for taking photographs. This enabled the light intensity to be sufficiently high to give well-defined photographs of the area of interest.

The specimens used in the present investigation were made from Wood's metal. This metal was chosen since it was a soft material with high ductility and enabled specimens to be cast in a mould to near final shape. Because of its softness, relatively large model asperities could be used without exceeding the force capability of the dynamometer. The specimens had a nominal size of 150 mm × 25 mm × 12 mm with a wedge-shaped asperity of approximately 16 mm base length and 4 mm height positioned near the centre of one of the 150 mm × 12 mm faces. This face will be referred to as the test surface. The specimens were machined on the side faces so that each pair of specimens had the same width for locating between the guide plates. The face opposite the test surface was also machined so that it was square to the side faces and parallel to the test surface. Also, two holes 6 mm in diameter were drilled in each specimen for location purposes. The test surface and the asperity were left in the as-cast condition, with the surface finish closely resembling the good finish on the mould. The side surface to be viewed in a test was polished on 1200-grade wet-and-dry paper to remove machining marks. A square grid having 0.5 mm sides was then scribed on this surface on an NC machining centre. The scribing directions were such that the grid sides were parallel and normal to the specimen test surface. The grid covered an area of approximately 40 mm × 20 mm which included the asperity. Once scribed, the specimens were cleaned using an ultrasonic cleaner to remove debris. The grid area was painted and the paint was left raised above the specimen surface.

The surface was then polished to remove the upper layer of paint until the metal surface was exposed and a clear grid could be seen.

In preparation for a test the top and bottom specimens were located in their respective holders. Care was taken to ensure that they were properly seated so that the horizontal grid lines were parallel to the milling machine table and hence to the direction of motion. After the specimens were carefully aligned, the table was raised to give the required interference and then moved horizontally to bring the asperities into close proximity. The specimens were then securely clamped between the guides. The camera and light source were put in position. To make a test, the camera circuit and dynamometer were activated and the milling machine table traverse engaged. The test was ended once the asperities were no longer in contact as indicated by the vertical force falling to zero.

Tests have been made for various wedge angles and lubrication conditions and for pure aluminium specimens as well as for Wood's metal specimens. In this paper attention is limited to the results for a pair of Wood's metal specimens having a wedge angle ($\alpha$ in Fig. 2(a)) of 25° with Shell Vitrea 100 used as the lubricant. A milling machine table speed of 0.31 mm s$^{-1}$ was used in the test. The time lapse between photographs was 2.6 s. Results for the force and vertical displacement are given in Figs. 5 and 6 and examples of the photographs are given in Fig. 7. This set of results was chosen for analysis because the model asperities deformed more or less equally. This was not always the case with the Wood's metal specimens since it was not easy to ensure similar hardness for the two specimens used in a test.

## 3. Analysis and discussion of results

The force results obtained (Fig. 5) are similar in shape to those of Greenwood and Tabor [11] and Edwards and Halling [12]. However, unlike with some of these earlier results, the vertical force remained positive throughout the deformation cycle. The photographs (Fig. 7) show similar deformation patterns to those obtained by Edwards and Halling for lubricated conditions.

It appears from the force results (Fig. 5) that initial asperity contact in the experiment took place at a time $t \approx 5$ s. This is confirmed by the results in Fig. 6

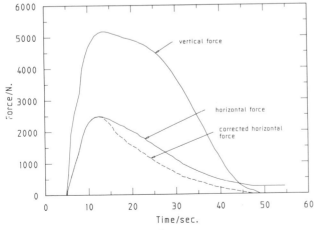

Fig. 5. Experimental force results.

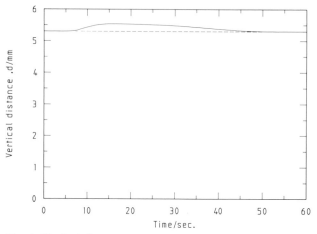

Fig. 6. Vertical displacement results.

which show that the vertical distance $d$ (Fig. 4) started to change at about the same time. During the test $d$ has changed very much in line with the observed changes in the vertical force (Fig. 5) and has returned to its initial value once this force fell to zero. This indicates that change in $d$ resulted mainly from the elasticity of the machine–specimen system. The results show that the maximum change in $d$ was small compared with the interference between the asperities. The forces acting in the first stages of asperity contact appear to indicate a bedding-in period. During this period there was no bulk plastic deformation within the asperities as can be seen from the results for $\alpha$ and $\eta$ (Fig. 2) measured from the photographs and given in Fig. 8. These angles could be measured with good accuracy since the interface and free surfaces in each photograph were well defined and remained approximately straight. The results show that $\alpha$ and $\eta$ remained constant at a value of approximately 25° up to $t \approx 14$ s, at which point $\alpha$ started to decrease and $\eta$ to increase, thus indicating the start of plastic deformation within the asperities. This point also almost coincided with the occurrence of the maximum vertical and horizontal forces in the test. The angle $\alpha$ can be seen to have decreased to 0° at $t \approx 40$ s while $\eta$ for the bottom asperity increased to 90° at $t \approx 37$ s. The top asperity kept deforming plastically until $t \approx 42$ s and in this case $\eta$ attained a value of 120°.

It can be seen from Fig. 5 that while the vertical force reduced to zero at the end of asperity contact a residual horizontal force remained. This must have resulted from the top specimen, which was in sliding contact with the guide plates, rubbing on these plates. Since no such force existed at the start of a test, it must have been caused by material which had plastically deformed sideways during the test. The measured horizontal force was corrected to allow for this in the following way. The back guide plate was removed and a test made under similar conditions to those described above. This allowed the normal force (side force) acting on the front guide plate, as well as the horizontal force, to be measured during the test. The side force on the guide plate was observed to first occur at a point corresponding to the maximum vertical and horizontal forces in the test, *i.e.* at the point where the asperity started to deform plastically. The coefficient of friction between the specimen and guide was calculated from the values of the side force on the guide plate at the end of the test and the residual horizontal force. It was then assumed that the friction coefficient

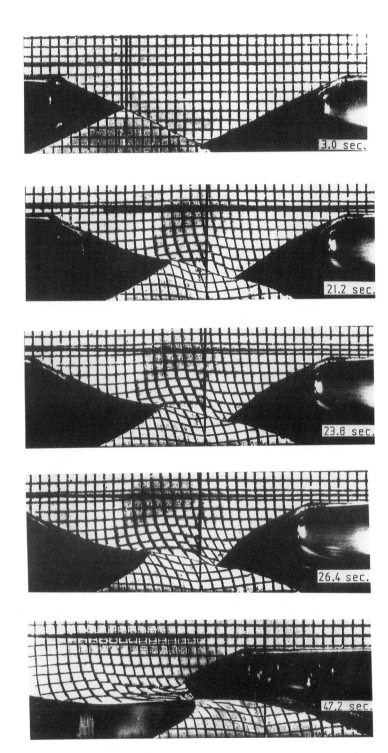

Fig. 7. Examples of photographs taken in test (grid 0.5 mm sides).

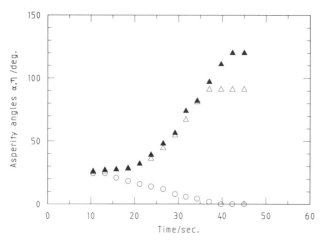

Fig. 8. Angles measured from photographs: ▲, $\eta$ top asperity; △, $\eta$ bottom asperity; ○, $\alpha$.

would have been constant throughout the test and that the horizontal force on the guide at each stage of the test could be found from the product of the coefficient of friction and the corresponding side force. This could then be subtracted from the measured horizontal force to give the true horizontal force acting at the asperity interface. In applying these results to the results from the present test, in which there were two guide plates, it was assumed that the distribution of side force on each plate would have the same form as in the single-guide test and that the coefficient of friction would be the same as in the single-guide test. The unknown magnitude of the side force at the end of the test was determined by equating twice its product with the coefficient of friction to the measured residual horizontal force. Once this side force had been estimated, the side force distribution for the single-guide test was scaled accordingly and the horizontal force was then corrected in the way described above. The results obtained are indicated by the broken line in Fig. 5. The value of the coefficient of friction between the specimens and side plates was calculated to be 0.18. For true plane strain this should have been zero and in future work it will be necessary to try and lubricate the guide–specimen interface more effectively.

Values of the coefficient of friction $\mu$ calculated as the ratio of the corrected horizontal force to the vertical force (Fig. 5) are shown plotted against the experimental values of $\alpha$ (Fig. 8) in Fig. 9. Also given in Fig. 9 are the theoretical values of $\mu$ calculated from the slipline field in Fig. 1. In order to compare the experimental and theoretical values of $\mu$, it is necessary to know what the value of $f$ was in the test. The normal stress $n$ and the shear stress $\tau$ acting at the interface during the test are given in Fig. 10. These were calculated by resolving the measured forces, corrected as above, normally and tangentially to the interface and dividing the resolved forces by the interface area. The interface area was determined as the product of the specimen width and the length of the interface measured from the photographs. This procedure assumed, on the basis of the experimental observations, that the interface length was constant across the specimen width. Once $\tau$ was known, then $f = \tau/k$ could be determined as long as $k$ was also known. Compression tests made on the Wood's metal used in the asperity tests showed that its flow stress was highly strain rate sensitive and that it had an approximately constant value over a range of strain values for a given strain rate. For a strain rate similar to that in the asperity tests it was found that

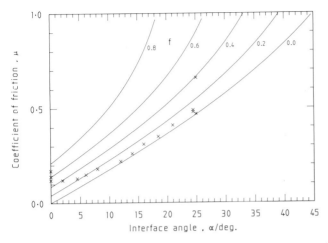

Fig. 9. Experimental and theoretical values of the coefficient of friction.

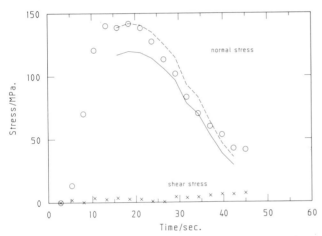

Fig. 10. Interface stresses. Lines represent values of normal stress calculated from slipline fields: —, taking $k=35$ MPa; – – –, taking $k=41$ MPa.

$k \approx 35$ MPa and this value was used in the initial calculations. From the results in Fig. 10 $\tau$ was assumed to have an average value of 3.2 MPa. Therefore the average value of $f$ in the tests was about 0.09. The experimental results in Fig. 9 mainly fall in the theoretical range defined by $f=0$ and 0.2, thus indicating good agreement between the theoretical and experimental results. It is tempting on this basis to assume that the deformation in the present tests can be represented as shown in Fig. 1 or more appropriately by the model in Fig. 3 where both asperities are deforming. However, the dangers in doing this can be seen from the following argument. If $\tau=0$, then the resultant force must act normally to the interface irrespective of the asperity deformation model assumed. For $\tau=0$, $\mu=\tan \alpha$, which corresponds to the $f=0$ line in Fig. 9. The good agreement between theoretical and experimental values of $\mu$ might therefore indicate nothing more than $\tau \rightarrow 0$ in the test. If, however, it can be shown that the magnitude of the normal stress at the interface calculated from the slipline field in Fig. 3 is in good agreement with the experimental values, then this would give strong support to the use of a model of this type. This is now considered.

For those conditions in the test where the asperities were deforming plastically the normal stress at the interface can be calculated from the slipline field in Fig. 3. This is done by starting at the free surface AE and working along sliplines such as ABCD. At the free surface the hydrostatic stress $p_f=k$ and applying the appropriate Hencky equation along ABCD gives the value of the hydrostatic stress adjacent to the interface, $p_i$, as

$$p_i=k[1+2(\tfrac{1}{4}\pi+\Phi-\eta)] \tag{1}$$

where $\tfrac{1}{4}\pi+\Phi-\eta$ is the fan angle, with all angles as given in Fig. 3. The stress normal to the interface, $n$, can now be expressed in terms of $p_i$ as

$$n=p_i+k\sin 2(\Phi+\alpha) \tag{2}$$

When $\eta>\tfrac{1}{4}\pi+\Phi$, the field in Fig. 3 and eqn. (1) are no longer applicable. For such cases a possible solution is given by the field in Fig. 11. In this the fan is replaced by a stress discontinuity EC which must bisect the angle $\pi-\beta$, where $\beta$ is as shown in Fig. 11. For this field the hydrostatic stress adjacent to the interface is given by

$$p_i=k(1-2\sin\beta) \tag{3}$$

where $\beta$ can be determined from the geometric relation

$$\beta=\eta-\tfrac{1}{4}\pi-\Phi \tag{4}$$

Once $p_i$ is known from eqn. (3), $n$ is determined from eqn. (2) as before. The field in Fig. 11 is similar to the one used by Challen and Oxley [1] as their wear model. The full line given in Fig. 10 represents the values of $n$ calculated from eqns. (1)–(4) using experimental values of $\alpha$ and $\eta$ (Fig. 8). The values of $\Phi$ used in the calculations were found from the interface relation

$$\alpha+\Phi=\tfrac{1}{2}\cos^{-1}f \tag{5}$$

with $f$ values corresponding to the experimental values of $\tau$ given in Fig. 10; $k$ was taken as 35 MPa as before. For most stages of the test the values of $\eta$ for the top and bottom asperities (Fig. 8) were nearly equal and an average value was used in the calculations. However, towards the end of the test only the top asperity continued to deform plastically and therefore in calculating $n$ it was appropriate to use the values of $\eta$ measured from the top asperity. The experimental values for $n$ and those calculated

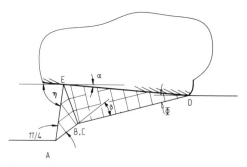

Fig. 11. Slipline field with stress discontinuity replacing fan.

from the above equations can be seen (Fig. 10) to follow the same trend; the calculated values, however, were somewhat less than the experimental values, particularly for higher values of $n$. If $k$ is taken as 41 MPa, then the agreement is improved in this range as can be seen from the broken line in Fig. 10. This good agreement between experimental values of $n$ and those calculated from the fields in Figs. 3 and 11 gives strong support to the use of these fields in modelling the observed asperity deformation. It now remains to be seen how closely these fields model the velocities associated with the deformation.

To measure velocities, tracings were made from the photographs of the asperity outlines and of the grids. Also included on the tracings were the vertical and horizontal lines shown on each photograph. These were lines scribed on the Perspex viewing window to serve as a datum. To facilitate the velocity measurements, the tracings were digitized and reconstructed by representing the grid sides by straight lines. Reconstructed tracings for photographs taken at known time intervals were then overlaid as shown in Fig. 12. In this case the tracings were for the photographs taken at $t = 21.2$ and 26.4 s, both of which are given in Fig. 7. The tracings were located so that the midpoints on the interfaces and the horizontal grid lines in the undeformed region of the top specimen coincided. In this way the deformation was represented as in the hodograph in Fig. 3 with the midpoint of the interface assumed stationary and with material flowing into and out of the top and bottom asperities as indicated. The distances moved by individual nodal points of the grid in a given time interval were represented by straight lines and arrows as shown in Fig. 12. Because the scale of the tracings was known from the grid size, the real distance could be found and with the known time interval the velocity magnitude calculated. In measuring velocities, one source of error could have resulted from the elastic deflections occurring during a test. It can be seen in Fig. 12 that the originally horizontal grid line nearest the horizontal datum line is not parallel to this datum. Calculations showed that the elastic deflections measured in the test (Fig. 6) could account for this. The errors introduced in this way would be small. Nevertheless, in future work attempts should be made to make the machine–specimen system even more rigid.

Values of the magnitude of the horizontal velocity in the non-deforming regions of the top asperity found in the way described above are given in Fig. 13. Also given are the values of table speed measured during the test from the horizontal movement of the vertical datum line. In this case the tracings were overlaid so that the same section of undeformed grid in the top asperity coincided in each tracing. As already mentioned, the nominal table speed in the test was 0.31 mm s$^{-1}$. The results in Fig.

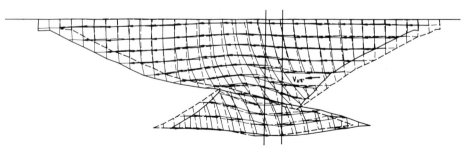

Fig. 12. Overlaid tracings of photographs taken at $t = 21.2$ s (broken lines) and $t = 26.4$ s (full lines). Lines with arrows indicate velocities. Bold line with arrow indicates velocity $V_{A'E'}$ found from hodograph in Fig. 15.

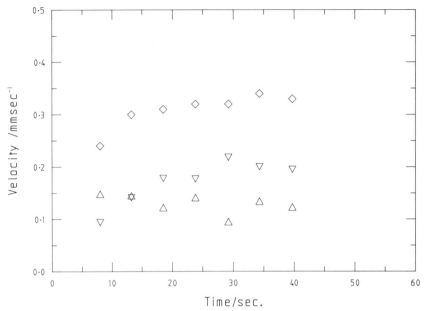

Fig. 13. Velocities measured from tracings of photographs: ◇, table speed in test; ▽, horizontal velocity in non-deforming regions of top asperity, △, horizontal velocity in non-deforming region of bottom asperity.

13 show that at the start of the test the table speed was well below this value, presumably because of the backlash in the machine. For the remainder of the test the speed varied between 0.31 and 0.34 mm s$^{-1}$, with an average value of just over 0.32 mm s$^{-1}$. Had the deformation of the asperities in the test been perfectly symmetrical, then the velocities in their non-deforming regions as defined in Fig. 3 would have been half this value, *i.e.* 0.16 mm s$^{-1}$. The results in Fig. 13 show that for the top asperity this velocity had an average value of about 0.17 mm s$^{-1}$, which means that it was deforming somewhat more easily than the bottom asperity. For the bottom asperity it was not possible to measure this velocity directly because the field of view was limited and an insufficient area of the non-deforming region could be included in the photographs for this asperity. However, it was possible to calculate this velocity from the horizontal movement of the vertical line measured from the tracings overlaid as in Fig. 12. These values are given in Fig. 13, from which the average velocity of the non-deforming region of the bottom asperity was found to be 0.13 mm s$^{-1}$. It can be seen that the sum of the velocities in the non-deforming regions of the two asperities is approximately equal to the table speed as would be expected.

Measurements of the interface sliding velocity were made in the region adjacent to the midpoint of the interface. This was done to avoid the complications which arise away from the midpoint as a result of the rotational velocity of the interface. In this connection the results for $\alpha$ in Fig. 8 show that the angular velocity of the interface about its midpoint was approximately constant over the plastic deformation part of the cycle. Results for the magnitude of the interface sliding velocity for both the top and bottom asperities ($V_{ED}$ and $V_{E'D'}$ in Fig. 3) together with the resultant sliding velocity ($V_{ED} + V_{E'D'}$) are given in Fig. 14. Measurements could not be made near the end of the test because of the lack of grid lines as the interface shortened. It can

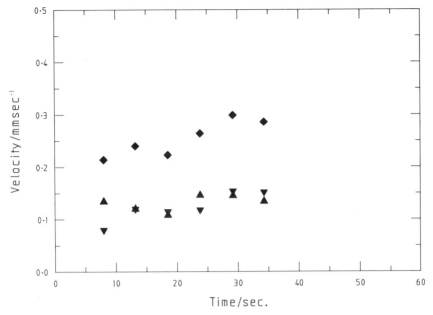

Fig. 14. Interface sliding velocities measured from tracings of photographs: ▼, top asperity; ▲, bottom asperity; ◆, resultant sliding velocity (▼ plus ▲).

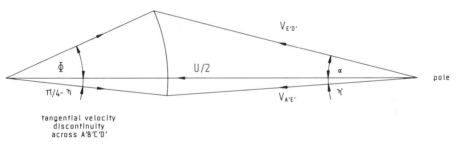

Fig. 15. Hodograph constructed from velocities and angles measured from photographs.

be seen that except at the start of the test, *i.e.* during the bedding-in period, the sliding velocities for each asperity were approximately equal. The results for the resultant sliding velocity show that this velocity increased as the test progressed. These latter results, if extrapolated to $t = 40$ s, which corresponds to $\alpha$ becoming 0° (Fig. 8), indicate an interface sliding velocity approximately equal to the table speed. This is what would be expected once bulk plastic deformation had ended in the asperities and the interface became horizontal.

The final part of the velocity analysis was to see how closely the hodograph given in Fig. 3 would fit the measured velocities. It was realized that in a more complete analysis the hodograph would also have to account for the velocities resulting from a rotating interface. This will be considered in a future paper. The hodograph given in Fig. 15 was constructed for the top asperity using velocities measured from the photographs taken at $t = 21.2$ and 26.4 s and angles measured from the intermediate photograph taken at $t = 23.8$ s. All three photographs are given in Fig. 7. The top asperity was chosen because greater detail of the deformation was available for this asperity. The measured values used were, referring to Fig. 3, $U/2=0.18$ mm s$^{-1}$, $V_{E'D'}=0.12$ mm s$^{-1}$, $\alpha=14°$ and $\eta=39°$. In the construction, lines representing $U/2$ and $V_{E'D'}$ were drawn using a suitable scale from the pole with $V_{E'D'}$ making an angle $\alpha$ with $U/2$. A line was then drawn to join the end points of these two vectors. This line defined the angle $\Phi$ and the magnitude of the velocity discontinuity across the boundary slipline. With the magnitude of the velocity discontinuity and the angle $\eta$ known, the hodograph was completed as shown. The value of $\Phi$ found from the construction is $24°$. This compares reasonably well with the value of $\Phi=30°$ which was calculated from eqn. (5) using the experimental value of $f$, i.e. $f=0.02$. A most significant difference between the hodographs in Figs. 3 and 15 is that in the latter $\eta'$, the angle made by $V_{A'E'}$ with $U$, is no longer equal to the slope of the free surface, $\eta$; the respective values were $\eta'=4°$ and $\eta=39°$. This indicates that in the present case, where both asperities are deforming, the free surface is not a streamline of the flow as it is for the steady state wave model given in Fig. 1. The magnitude of $V_{A'E'}$ measured from Fig. 15 is 0.11 mm s$^{-1}$ and this is shown to scale and acting at an angle $\eta'=4°$ in Fig. 12. It can be seen that $V_{A'E'}$ found from the hodograph is in good agreement with the measured velocities in the region adjacent to the free surface.

## 4. Concluding remarks

It has been shown how asperities of similar hardness can move past each other by a combination of plastic deformation and interfacial sliding with no apparent fracture taking place. Slipline fields have been presented which model the observed deformation well. However, in considering velocities, so far no account has been taken of the velocities normal to the interface resulting from the rotation of the interface during the plastic deformation part of the cycle. Slipline fields which can allow for this are now being sought. Also in future work, experiments will be made on non-symmetric wedge-shaped asperities to check the respective roles of $\alpha$ and $\eta$ (Fig. 2) in determining interface normal stresses and hence coefficients of friction. The stress analysis presented in this paper shows that an increase in $\eta$ for given values of $\alpha$ and $f$ would decrease the normal stress at the interface and hence increase the coefficient of friction and it will be interesting to see if the proposed experiments confirm this. It is also intended to investigate the influence of different specimen materials and lubrication conditions, including dry, on the process.

## Acknowledgment

The authors wish to thank the Australian Research Council for financial support of the project described in this paper.

## References

1  J. M. Challen and P. L. B. Oxley, Wear, 53 (1979) 229–243.
2  J. M. Challen, L. J. McLean and P. L. B. Oxley, Proc. R. Soc. Lond. A, 394 (1984) 161–181.
3  A. J. Black, E. M. Kopalinsky and P. L. B. Oxley, Wear, 123 (1988) 97–114.
4  H. Moalic, J. A. Fitzpatrick and A. A. Torrance, Proc. Inst. Mech. Eng., 201 (1987) 321–329.

5  J. M. Challen, P. L. B. Oxley and B. S. Hockenhull, *Wear, 111* (1986) 275–288.
6  J. M. Challen, E. K. Kopalinsky and P. L. B. Oxley, *Conf. on Tribology, C156/87,* Institute of Mechanical Engineers, London, 1987, pp. 957–964.
7  F. P. Bowden and D. Tabor, *The Friction and Lubrication of Solids,* Oxford University Press: Clarendon, Oxford, 1950.
8  J. S. McFarlane and D. Tabor, *Proc. R. Soc. Lond. A, 202* (1950) 244–253.
9  A. P. Green, *J. Mech. Phys. Solids, 2* (1954) 197–211.
10  A. P. Green, *Proc. R. Soc. Lond. A, 228* (1955) 191–204.
11  J. A. Greenwood and D. Tabor, *Proc. Phys. Soc. B, 68* (1955) 609–619.
12  C. M. Edwards and J. Halling, *J. Mech. Eng. Sci., 10* (1968) 121–132.
13  C. M. Edwards and J. Halling, *J. Mech. Eng. Sci., 10* (1968) 101–110.

*Wear, 153* (1992) 263–275

# Microscopic origins of the interface friction of organic films: the potential of vibrational spectroscopy

B. J. Briscoe, P. S. Thomas and D. R. Williams

*Department of Chemical Engineering and Chemical Technology, Imperial College of Science Technology and Medicine, Prince Consort Road, London SW7 2BY (UK)*

(Received July 30, 1991)

## Abstract

This paper begins by reviewing the history of interface friction of organic films in terms of the measurement and interpretation of these phenomena using microscopic models. The interface friction is considered to arise from the shear or flow of the organic film and the prime characteristic is taken as the interface shear stress, denoted as $\tau$. The influence of contact pressure, temperature and sliding velocity is described in general terms.

The essence of the established models is based upon the belief that microscopic entities, such as side groups or chain segments, are engaged within the shear plane and thereby transfer frictional work into the film which is ultimately dissipated as heat by phonon wave damping. The value and success of these models is assessed.

An alternative approach is suggested which seeks to use vibrational spectroscopy as a means of identifying the characteristics of the microscopic units active in the shear plane. The data are preliminary, but indicate that this method has potential for identifying the species responsible for accommodating the microscopic strain and also for characterizing the environment in which these species flow.

## 1. Introduction

The understanding of the mechanisms of the processes which accommodate plastic flow in a material or at the interface has been the subject of debate for centuries. In this paper we propose to carry the debate one step further by characterizing the processes of flow in terms of molecular entities. This in its own right is not unusual as many authors have previously also attempted to explain flow through molecular deformation [1–3]. However, the examination of the molecular characteristics of the processes of flow remain relatively unexplored via the use of vibrational spectroscopy [4, 5]. Vibrational spectroscopy has the virtues of being both molecularly specific as well as being environmentally sensitive. Therefore, by characterizing the spectrum under thermal or compressive perturbation it may be possible to gain a better understanding of the molecular processes which accommodate plastic flow.

### 1.1. History

The term interfacial rheology is a convenient description of the processes of flow which may be induced, by a variety of means, in the interfacial regions between solid bodies. The subject, in its most general sense, has a long history. The idea of flow at contacting solid asperities is central to the asperity contact models of friction and lubrication. Euler [6, 7], for example, using a triangular asperity model of spheres, introduced $\mu$, the coefficient of friction, differentiated between static and kinetic friction and, using the geometry of triangular asperities, formulated the relationship between $\mu$ and $\alpha$, the inclined angle to the horizontal where $\mu = \tan \alpha$. Coulomb [8] studied the interfacial rheology of pork fat thickened with lime in his studies of the friction of marine slipways. Sir William Hardy with Ida Doubleday [9] investigated the interfacial rheology of certain aliphatic carboxylic acids in model glass contacts over seventy years ago. They introduced the phrase "boundary lubrication" to describe the process of frictional work dissipated in thin organic layers which they presumed to be monomolecular bilayers. More recently lubrication engineers, studying the rheology of thin oil layers under high contact pressures, have noted certain similarities between the rheology of solid organic layers and fluids under high contact stresses [10–12]. Philip Bowden and David Tabor [13] invoked the ideas of interfacial rheology in their development of the adhesion model of friction and its application to boundary lubrication. Similar ideas have been adopted by many other authors to describe the friction of polymers and polymeric coatings between relatively rigid counterfaces [14–17]. Smooth glass substrates have been frequently used for these studies. There are also important, but relatively few, published studies on well defined molecular lubricants in model contacts. Many of these papers have used mica substrates [18–23, 2].

## 1.2. Interface shear yield stress

These studies, a spectrum in their diversity, provide a number of quite general ideas and experimental trends. The first concept is that of the interface shear yield stress; the work required per unit area of contact to maintain motion or the energy per unit area required to initiate this motion. This quantity is given the symbol $\tau$ in this paper. Its physical significance is considered later, but for the moment it will be regarded simply as a characteristic of the interface zone rheology during continuous shear or at the initiation of shear. As such, it reflects the property of a certain type of kinetic friction or static friction respectively. For brevity here, we will not consider the static friction cases.

As a matter of experimental fact, $\tau$ seems to be a function of several important contact mechanical variables. Significantly, $\tau$ has been shown, to a good approximation, to have a linear dependence on the contact (usually the mean value) pressure, $P$:

$$\tau = \tau_0 + \alpha P \tag{1}$$

where $\tau_0$ and $\alpha$ are material constants. The mean contact pressure, $P$, is taken as the ratio of the normal load, $W$, to the real contact area, $A$. This relationship is quite general for solids with only a few exceptions. This expression, or other forms of it, had a rather special significance in the early studies of friction. This point is considered at a later stage. The temperature variation of the quantity $\tau$ has been found to have two empirical forms:

$$\tau = \tau_0' - \beta T \tag{2a}$$

$$\tau = \tau_0'' \exp(\gamma/T) \tag{2b}$$

where $\tau_0'$, $\tau_0''$, $\beta$ and $\gamma$ are material constants. Expression (2b) has been observed to be more common, where $\gamma$ is either zero or has some negative characteristic temperature value. The dependence of $\tau$ on strain rate is more complex and follows, as far as is known, a logarithmic dependence:

$$\tau = \tau_0''' + \theta \ln V \tag{3}$$

where $\tau_0{}'''$ and $\theta$ are constants and $V$ is the relative velocity between substrates in a model contact. The sign of $\theta$ may be either positive or negative. The significances of these empirical relationships have been reviewed by several authors in the context of the approaches adopted to describe bulk shear processes for energy dissipation in organic polymers [24–26].

## 1.3. Interpretation of the empirically observed relationships

### 1.3.1. The continuum approach

For many organic species, where suitable data are available, the comparison between the film response and the bulk response is sufficiently good to indicate that the interfacial shear processes are generally similar in character to those which occur during bulk shear. These comparisons are naturally tentative for reasons described elsewhere [27(a)]. For example, the nominal rates of strain may be *ca.* $10^6$ s$^{-1}$ in films: such rates of deformation cannot be reproduced in bulk shear. However, comparable pressure coefficients, $\alpha$, have been identified. The absolute values of $\tau_0$ are found to be rather different; a factor of ten is typical for the ratio of $\tau_{0(bulk)}/\tau_{0(film)}$. For films, the pressure is taken as the mean contact pressure. It has a significant hydrostatic component. For the bulk data the prevailing hydrostatic pressure is utilized. A popular way of interpreting the bulk yield data has been to adopt a stress-modified chemically activated rate limiting process developed by Eyring [27(b)]. The model has many weaknesses, but has the virtue of accounting well for the trends observed in experimental studies.

If it is assumed that plastic flow in shear is a thermally activated process involving segmental motion over a potential energy barrier (Fig. 1), we may apply an activated rate equation of the form

$$\dot{\epsilon} = A \, \exp - \left(\frac{\Delta E + \Omega P}{kT}\right) \, \sinh\left(\frac{\tau\nu}{kT}\right) \tag{4}$$

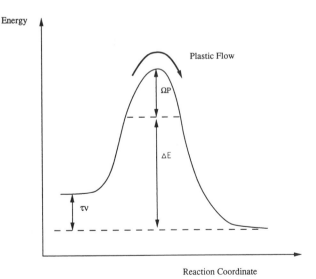

Fig. 1. Potential barrier in Eyring's thermal activation model for plastic flow, modified from a chemically activated rate limiting process by a stress gradient induced by the influence of pressure, $P$, and shear stress, $\tau$.

where $\dot{\epsilon}$ is the strain rate, $A$ is the pre-exponential factor related to the natural frequency of the deformed segment, $\Delta E$ is the activation energy required for a segment to pass over the potential energy barrier, $\Omega$ and $\nu$ are the pressure activation and shear stress activation volumes respectively and $k$ and $T$ are the Boltzmann constant and temperature, respectively. It has been common to interpret the notional values of $\Omega$ and $\nu$ as the sizes of the characteristic local volumetric relaxations ($\Omega$) which occur as a characteristic segmental volume ($\nu$) is displaced in the shear gradient.

As eqn. (4) was originally derived utilizing microscopic stress fields across molecular planes, it has led to attempts to model molecular mechanisms for the processes involved in these deformations. Howard and Thakray [26], for example, attempted to relate the volume of the statistical link of a polymer in solution to the Eyring stress activation volume. The calculated volume was found to be an order of magnitude greater than that of the likely active statistical link. This inconsistency was ascribed to the flow of several links simultaneously. Foot et al. [28] in their studies on poly(ethylene terephthalate) alluded to the deformation behaviour being associated with the segmental motion of the relevant second-order transitional relaxation at the appropriate temperature. Thus, the correlation of prediction with experimental observation adopting the Eyring model has been shown to contain certain weaknesses in the interpretation of bulk deformation. One of the major difficulties in applying the Eyring approach to bulk deformation is the common absence of well defined shear planes.

Other authors have attempted to extend the Eyring activation theory by dividing the polymer states into discrete energy bands. Robertson [29] has described a two-energy-state model which includes the *cis* and *trans* rotation around the carbon–carbon backbone chain, the *cis* orientation being the high-energy state and the *trans* being the low-energy state. This application has met with similar difficulties, although there is some evidence for the relative distribution of the different states under pressure afforded from vibrational studies of polystyrene [30].

### 1.3.2. The Eyring interpretation

Arguably, the Eyring model has been applied more successfully to plastic yield where the shear plane is known. This situation is the case for the interface shear process. The interfacial shear strength, $\tau$, of organic lubricants, sheared between hard substrates in model contacts, is consistent with the high stress limit of eqn. (4). Furthermore, on the application of Eyring theory it is possible to gain an arguably useful understanding of the significance of the parameters appearing in eqns. (1) to (3). In the high stress limit, where $\tau\nu/kT > 1$, the Eyring plasticity equation reduces to

$$V = V_0 \exp - \left( \frac{\Delta E + \Omega P - \tau\nu}{kT} \right) \tag{5}$$

where $V$ is assumed to be the relative velocity of the contact pair, which will be proportional to the strain rate, accommodated by a new pre-exponential factor, $V_0$, which is considered to be a characteristic velocity. Rearranging (5) we have:

$$\tau = \frac{kT}{\nu} \ln\left( \frac{V}{V_0} \right) + \frac{1}{\nu} (\Delta E + \Omega P) \tag{6}$$

which provides the following into relationships between $P$, $V$, $T$ and $\tau$

$$\tau = \tau_0 + \alpha P \qquad \text{const. } T, V$$

where

$$\tau_0 = \frac{kT}{\nu} \ln\left(\frac{V}{V_0}\right) + \frac{\Delta E}{\nu} \qquad \alpha = \frac{\Omega}{\nu} \tag{7}$$

and

$$\tau = \tau_0' - \beta T \qquad \text{const. } P, V$$

where

$$\tau_0' = \frac{1}{\nu}\left(\Delta E + \Omega P\right) \qquad \beta = \frac{k}{\nu} \ln\left(\frac{V}{V_0}\right) \tag{8}$$

and

$$\tau = \tau_0''' + \theta \ln V \qquad \text{const. } T, P$$

where

$$\tau_0''' = \frac{1}{\nu}\left(\Delta E + \Omega P - V_0\right) \qquad \theta = \frac{kT}{\nu} \tag{9}$$

In the high-stress limit the Eyring relationship conforms to the equations derived from observation. It must be emphasized, however, that in the low-stress region, where $\tau\nu/kT < 1$, exponential temperature dependence occurs (eqn. (2b)).

### 1.3.3. Molecular or microscopic models

The important facet of the Eyring model of plasticity is the accommodation of a microscopic mechanism which is potentially capable of accounting for the dissipation of energy in friction. Although it is not intrinsically dissipative in its own right, it is still necessary to invoke a mechanism for the dissipation of the frictional work as heat. Other models have been derived to provide mechanisms of plastic flow; however they also tend not to be dissipative of the frictional energy. Euler [6, 7] proposed a triangular asperity model in which the geometry of spherical entities allowed the calculation of the inclination of the asperity sides and thus the coefficient of friction and the force required to maintain motion of the asperities over one another. A more recent example of this type of model is the molecular deformation of methyl terminal groups in rigid stearic acid boundary lubricant layers devised by Cameron and his co-workers in the 1970s [1, 2]. Tabor [3] has also provided a similar model. These models consist of crystal lattices of Langmuir–Blodgett layers of surfactants which lock together as a Euler type model. When a shear stress is applied the atomic force fields of repulsion between the sterically strained hydrogen atoms force a parting of the surfaces so that the methyl groups may pass over one another, retaining their crystal lattice, to the adjacent potential well. Unfortunately, the energy required to deform the methyl groups will be recovered in the relaxation of these strained bonds. Homola et al. [23] have recently progressed with this model, likening it to the passage of a cart over a cobbled street. But, again, the problem of dissipation of energy in friction has not been addressed.

In some respects the molecular topographical models do resemble the essence of the Eyring argument. The size of a molecular asperity, or Euler asperity, is related to the stress activation volume, $\nu$, in a simple picture. Of course, the asperity dimension may not be the size of the characteristic element, $\nu$, which is moved discretely to accommodate the microscopic strain; a group of asperities, or a dislocation, may be involved. The pressure activation volume similarly may be likened to the relative height of the physical barriers. If a normal pressure is applied the resistance to molecular motion will increase, as overlap between the layers increases. This will have the effect of increasing the size of the physical barrier to motion.

### 1.3.4. Summary

It is true to say that neither the Eyring nor the topographical models inherently provide a clear and unequivocal mechanism for the dissipation of energy in frictional motion. It is most certainly the case that the dissipation of the frictional energy occurs, not at the contact zone, but in isotropic phonon wave damping in the adjacent bodies. The molecular models provide a means of transferring work into the system.

In summary, there appear to be three ways of interpreting interfacial rheological data. The first involves a correlation with conventional bulk flow data. This approach has serious practical limitations and does not, of course, provide a microscopic interpretation. The Eyring model has often been applied to bulk types of rheological processes. Its true value is unclear, although it does provide the basis for the understanding of the mechanisms of plastic flow. The microscopic topological models have been relatively unexplored, but seem an attractive basis for first-order prediction trends in interface friction. Like the Eyring model, they have the means of describing the primary resistance of the shear process within a chosen shear plane. Essentially, all these models simply provide no more than geometric parameters which may be related to the architecture of the shear plane.

The rheological response of a material, at the interface, may be characterized by the measurement of the interfacial shear strength, $\tau$. The variations in $\tau$ may be ascribed to the deformation of molecular entities or segmental flow: however these entities may not be identified via examination of the rheological properties alone. Identification of these entities must be conducted by the specific analysis of the molecular environment. We propose to utilize vibrational spectroscopy. The vibrational modes of a molecule are both chemically and environmentally unique. Thus, by perturbing the environment in which a vibrational mode exists, the characteristics of that mode will vary. Flow, within a shear plane, occurs via activation of segmental motion through the application of a stress gradient. Once plastic flow has been induced frictional energy is dissipated through the dispersion of thermal energy in phonon wave damping. Inherently, vibrational spectroscopy is also dispersive. The activation of vibrational modes occurs through the interaction of light with a dynamic dipole. The energy absorbed must also be dissipated. This occurs through the dispersive remission of the absorbed light and thermal dissipation via phonon wave damping. This approach is consistent with the application of Eyring's stress-modified thermally activated rate process.

### 1.4. The relationship between $\Omega$ and $\nu$ and pressure and temperature coefficients

#### 1.4.1. Pressure coefficient

Classical, the measurement used to characterize the frictional properties of film materials is the friction coefficient, $\mu$. The interrelationship between $\mu$ and $\alpha$ may be shown to be:

$$\mu = \frac{\tau_0}{P} + \alpha \tag{10}$$

Therefore, at high contact pressures $\mu \to \alpha$. On the application of the Eyring model to interfacial shear, it is found that $\alpha$ is a ratio of the pressure activation volume to the shear activation volume (eqn. (7)). If the Eyring model is considered to be a topographical model of segmental molecular motion constrained between two planes, $\alpha$ becomes the ratio of the volumetric space between the planes (equivalent to the height of a molecular asperity) to the volume of the segment in motion (equivalent to the size of a molecular asperity). Thus, $\alpha$ becomes a ratio of lengths which could be likened to Euler's frictional gradient of an asperity. The effect of molecular topography on the shear strength of an organic film has been studied by varying the length of the alkyl chain in poly($n$-alkyl methacrylate) [31]. Increasing the chain length initially produced an increase in the value of $\alpha$ for the homologous series. Once the chain length reduced the glass transition temperature ($T_g$) to below the operating temperature, the value of $\alpha$ reduced to a value below that of the primary member. It was assumed that the molecular topography of the polymer affected the size of the segment in flow. Thus, by studying the variation in the values of $\alpha$ as a function of the "molecular roughness", the significance of $\Omega$ and $\nu$ may be investigated. The evidence in Amuzu's paper does not directly show an existence of rate-limited flow; however, the Eyring interpretation does model the empirical observations closely. Briscoe and Evans [22] found that, for the shear of carboxylic acids, the calculated values of $\nu$ correlated to the size of an ethylene group in the backbone chain. However, other authors [24, 26] have found that for polymer films the volume of $\nu$ calculated was orders of magnitude greater than the volume of a single ethylene segment. This anomaly has been ascribed to the motion of dislocations in the film.

### 1.4.2. Temperature coefficient

The temperature dependence of the shear process is important in two ways. Firstly, frictional energy is dissipated in heat, probably through the hysteresis of phonon wave damping and the emission of electromagnetic radiation in the low-energy region of the spectrum. Lauer et al. [32] sought to identify the modes involved in frictional relaxation of molecular entities by detecting these emissions using emission Fourier transform infrared spectroscopy (FTIR) with fairly little success due to the problem of grey emission and the weak nature of the frictionally excited emissions. Secondly, the parameters involved in the Eyring model are thermally activated. The temperature coefficient, $\beta$, of eqn. (7), from the Eyring interpretation, is proportional only to the stress activation volume, $\nu$. It has been shown experimentally that there are two regimes of behaviour or the temperature dependence of the shear strength; temperature independence and a form of exponential dependence [31, 33]. In the regime of temperature independence eqn. (2) applies. However, if both $\nu$ and $\Omega$ are temperature dependent in the same fashion, then

$$\tau = \frac{\tau_0'}{\nu_0}\left(\Delta E \exp\left(\frac{Q}{kT}\right)\right) - T\frac{k}{\nu_0}\exp\left(\frac{Q}{kT}\right)\ln\left(\frac{V}{V_0}\right) \tag{11}$$

where

$$\nu = \nu_0 \exp\left(\frac{Q}{kT}\right) \qquad \Omega = \Omega_0 \exp\left(\frac{Q}{kT}\right)$$

and $Q$ is an activation parameter. If the value of $Q=0$ then eqn. (11) reduces to eqn. (2). This type of temperature dependence of the activation coefficients does not affect the value of pressure coefficient as this quantity is the ratio of the two volumes; $\Omega/\nu$.

Another possible explanation for the temperature dependence of $\tau$ can be seen as a change in the size of the segment in motion. From the experimental results of

Briscoe and Smith [33] and Amuzu *et al.* [31] it is found that $\tau$ is independent of $T$ up until $T_g$. Below $T_g$ the natural thermal vibrations within the polymer are limited to less than 10 chain atoms whose energy levels will be almost completely occupied, thus allowing little change in the stress activation coefficient over the temperature range to $T_g$. From the onset of $T_g$ the possible thermal vibrations may vary between 10 and 50 chain atoms. Thus, as the temperature is raised more energy levels will progessively become occupied. The segmental size in motion continually increases reducing the value of $\tau$. At higher temperatures, as the vibrational energy levels become increasingly filled, the size of the segment in motion tends to a maximum, variation in size is reduced and $\tau$ once again becomes temperature independent. This behaviour would also apply to the $\beta$ relaxations. However, due to the relative size of the vibrations, maximum occupation of the energy levels may occur over a shorter temperature range and the variation in magnitude is less.

*1.5. Correlation of spectroscopy and the rheological response*

It is natural to turn to other means of prescribing the identity of the species which are in microscopic motion during the accommodation of macroscopic shear. Whilst the previous models are essentially static in character, that is they consider the migration of time-invariant geometric entities, it is possible to include time-dependent effects. For example, the stress activation volume could be ascribed to the time-averaged size of the array of oscillators which would undergo segmental flow. The pressure activation volume could be ascribed to the time-averaged summation over the range of pressures transmitted through molecular contact. The Eyring model does also contain a frequency term (or terms) as a characteristic velocity, $V_0$ (eqn. (5)). For segmental motion to occur, stress, or ultimately thermal, activation is required. Thus segmental flow will be a function of the natural frequency of the segmental entities concerned. Vibrational spectroscopy, in principle, offers a means of identifying these species and also provides a basis for understanding their characteristics. The remainder of this paper considers this approach in the context of the temperature dependence of the interface shear stress.

## 2. Experimental details

Solutions of polystyrene (0.5%), of both the isotactic (iPS) (Polyscience MW $1.7 \times 10^6$) and atactic (aPS) (BDH MW 100 000) polymer, were prepared in nominally "good" and "poor" solvents: chloroform ($CHCl_3$) and carbon tetrachloride ($CCl_4$) respectively. Thin films (200–500 nm) of the polymers were prepared by solvent casting onto potassium bromide (KBr) windows. The samples were then mounted in a converted Linkam microscope temperature stage (THMS600) which was subsequently mounted into a Bomem Michelson Fourier transform IR spectrometer (Ramspec 152), fitted with a liquid nitrogen cooled MCT detector, for the acquisition of spectra in transmission. Spectra were taken at room temperature ($\approx 20$ °C) and at 10 °C intervals up to 210 °C, using a resolution of 4 cm$^{-1}$ averaged over 200 scans. The data, plotted in Figs. 2 and 3, are presented as relative intensity normalized to the largest stable vibrational band in the polystyrene spectra as a function of temperature. The reference band chosen was an out-of-plane bending mode of the benzene ring at 698 cm$^{-1}$. The relative intensities of two vibrational modes are shown: 760 cm$^{-1}$ (Fig. 3), an out-of-plane bending mode of the benzene ring and 2925 cm$^{-1}$ (Fig. 2), an asymmetric C–H stretch of the backbone chain. The data acquired in this study are compared with the rheological data for polystyrene (Fig. 4) published by Briscoe and Smith [33].

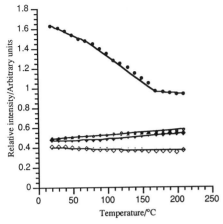

Fig. 2. Relative intensity of the asymmetric C–H stretching mode of the backbone chain at 2925 cm$^{-1}$ to the out-of-plane bending mode of the benzene ring at 698 cm$^{-1}$ for four samples: aPS and iPS samples cast from both HCCl$_3$ and CCl$_4$. ♦, aPS/CHCl$_3$; ◇, aPS/CCl$_4$; ●, iPS/CHCl$_3$; ○, iPS/CCl$_4$.

Fig. 3. Relative intensity of the out-of-plane bending mode of the benzene ring at 760 cm$^{-1}$ to the out-of-plane bending mode of the benzene ring at 698 cm$^{-1}$ for four samples: aPS and iPS samples cast from both CHCl$_3$ and CCl$_4$. ♦, aPS/CHCl$_3$; ◇, aPS/CCl$_4$; ●, iPS/CHCl$_3$; ○, iPS/CCl$_4$.

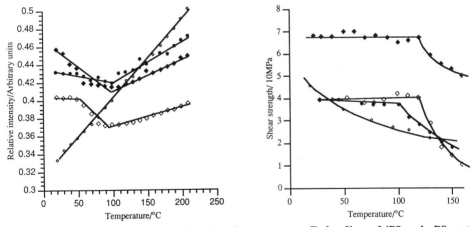

Fig. 4. The shear strength, $\tau$, as a function of temperature, $T$, for films of iPS and aPS cast from "good" and "poor" quality solvents. The films had been sheared while raising and lowering the temperature in the range 20–160 °C until the temperature dependence of the shear strength was reversible. (Data taken from ref. 33.) ♦, aPS/ Propanol; ◇, aPS/CCl$_4$; ●, iPS/Toluene; ○, iPS/CCl$_4$.

## 3. Results

Molecular vibrational modes are sensitive to their molecular environments as their vibrational frequencies are a function of the bond strength. The intensity of a vibrational band is primarily dependent on the average direction and magnitude of the transition moment as well as the concentration of that specific molecular species. Thus, the physical environment of a functional group within a molecule may influence the frequency or the intensity of a vibrational mode. This thesis has been supported by a variety of authors working on the effects of tensile strain [34, 35, 30] and also on the effect of thermal history [36, 4]. Fowkes and Tischler [37] have shown that for acid–base interactions between polymers and solute species, spectral shifts in frequency, of up to 40 cm$^{-1}$, may be observed. In this study, we have chosen to utilize the variation of the intensity of the vibrational modes as an indication of the active segment environment. This may be accomplished since, if a molecule is subjected to steric strain and distortion, it will deform, and thus disrupt the symmetry associated with the functional group. This alters the transition moment and consequently changes the intensity of the adsorbed band.

iPS and aPS films were cast from solvents described as "good" (CHCl$_3$) and "poor" (CCl$_4$). From the good solvent, due to the complete solvation of the individual polymer molecules, polymer–polymer interactions in solution are limited. This structure facilitates elongation and the ordering of the polymer chains during casting. Such cast films would be expected to exhibit a coordinated order, which is open and affine in nature. This process, in principle, would produce the equivalent effect to be found in the slow cooling of a film produced from the melt. The casting of a film from poor solvent mimics thermal quenching and produces a greater interaction between the polymer chains as the solvation is not complete. As a result this process provides a more disordered film which is less affine and more closely packed. In some regions, the iPS polymer chains may also crystallize to form $3_1$ helical lamellae [38, 39]. This structure is the ideal conformation for a tetrahedral coordination of the polymer backbone. This conformation minimizes the structural steric strain from the structure and allows the maximum symmetry for vibrational interaction with the incident light. The formation of a helical structure affects only the intensity of the C–H stretching modes associated with the backbone chain. The stereochemistry of the helix does, however, "split" a number of the out-of-plane bending modes of the benzene ring [36]. Painter and Koenig [36] have also found that the intensities of the C–H stretching modes of the backbone chain increase for samples of iPS which contain crystalline regions. In this study only iPS cast from the good solvent (Fig. 2), due to the nature of the solvent–polymer interactions, showed the increase in the intensity of the backbone C–H stretch. Also, only results for the most prominent C–H stretching mode have been included; the other C–H stretching modes of the backbone chain, however, do behave similarly. In Fig. 2, the relative intensity of the vibrational mode at 2925 cm$^{-1}$ has been plotted as a function of temperature. The results show that, for the sample iPS cast from the good solvent, the increase in intensity of this mode is nearly threefold relative to those for aPS and iPS cast from the poor solvent. These differences are due to the differing types of structural order, previously noted, which are present in the various films. As the temperature of the polymer is raised, the molecular order diminishes until the intensity of the mode tends to that of a disordered structure. It is interesting to point out at this stage that if the iPS film is cast from a saturated solution in CHCl$_3$ ($\approx 2\%$), the effect of the deposition tends towards that of simulated quenching. The ordering is reduced and, as a result, the intensity of the vibrational mode tends to that seen for the sample cast from the poor solvent.

The trend in the temperature-dependent nature of the intensity of the aromatic out-of-plane bending mode at 760 cm$^{-1}$ correlates with the interface shear stress $vs.$ temperature data shown in Fig. 4. Briscoe and Smith [33] characterized two types of temperature-dependent behaviour of the shear strength, $\tau$, from eqn. (2b); Type I (linear behaviour), where the activation energy for plastic flow is zero, and is associated with a mechanism of brittle fracture at the interface, and Type II (exponential behaviour), where the activation energy for plastic flow takes a positive value (calculated at $\simeq 15$ kJ mol$^{-1}$), associated with plastic flow within the film. The data shown in Fig. 4 follow a Type I trend up to the glass transition temperature ($T_g$) at which point occurs the onset of Type II behaviour. The data show one anomaly; for iPS cast from CCl$_4$ there is no region of interfacial brittle fracture. These trends are paralleled in the spectroscopic data. The vibrational modes for all the samples, except for iPS cast from CCl$_4$, reduce in intensity up to $T_g$. At the onset of $T_g$, the gradients change to positive values. For iPS cast from the poor solvent the behaviour is quite different. There are no obvious inflections associated with a change in the internal structure and, as paralleled with the rheological experiments, the gradient is that of the post-$T_g$ behaviour. The relative intensity of the vibrational modes in the spectra of iPS cast from CCl$_4$ system increases by 70% over the temperature range studied (Fig. 3). For the other three systems the relative intensities only vary by a maximum of $\pm 20\%$ with a trend for a decreasing of the intensity up to $T_g$ and an increasing of the intensity post-$T_g$.

## 4. Discussion

Polystyrene does not contain polar functional groups. Hence, the only molecular interactions present are dispersive non-polar van der Waals forces. The formation of a glassy phase is associated with the intramolecular straining of molecular bonds [40, 5]. Due to the structure of polystyrene, rotation around the carbon–carbon backbone is inherently constrained by the size of the benzene ring. Therefore, an activation energy is required to institute flow. This is also true for the long-range molecular vibrations. In a stress gradient, for flow to occur in the material, the activation energies required to attain segmental or molecular motion must be reached. Therefore, the resistance to flow will arise from the continual deformation of the polymer molecules, which on relaxation will convert the stress activation into thermal energy which is subsequently dissipated through phonon wave damping.

Below $T_g$, the relative variations in the bulk volume are small. Thus, with an increase in the thermal energy input into the system the thermal energy must be dissipated by some means other than an increase in macromolecular freedom. The amplitudes of the molecular relaxations and the available short-range multi-atomic vibrations must increase. In consequence, straining of the molecular bonds, through intermolecular interactions, occurs and the intensity of the vibrational mode decreases. Although band broadening and shifts in frequency might be expected to occur, they do not appear to a significant extent in the spectra. We have assigned the intensity variations in the C–H asymmetric stretch to the relative concentration of the helical structure in iPS. This type of structure allows good orientation of the polymer in the cast films and gives a large effective cylindrical volume to the polymer chains. Therefore, for flow to occur a large segmental volume must be displaced. The nature of atacticity also affords a large effective cylindrical volume for the polymer chains. iPS cast from the poor solvent, however, forms a disordered molecular array which is not as rigid as the helical structure. It has a smaller effective cylindrical volume, almost planar, which allows relatively less constraint to flow and, therefore, deforms more easily.

The sub-$T_g$ variations in the spectral intensity follow two types of temperature dependence. The "rigid" structures of aPS and iPS, cast from the good solvent, show a decrease in the intensity of the 760 cm$^{-1}$ mode contrasting with the increase in intensity for iPS cast from the poor solvent. These results parallel well with the rheological data of Fig. 4. Above $T_g$, the active segmental unit is continually altering in size. Structures associated with solvent history are continually relaxing. This is shown by the temperature lag in the decrease in intensity of the C–H asymmetric stretch in Fig. 2 for iPS cast from $CHCl_3$. The polymer arguably retains a degree of sub-$T_g$ structure as the decrease in the intensity continues up to a temperature associated with the liquid–liquid transition $(T_{l-l})$ of the polymer.

The post-$T_g$ dependence of the intensities for the mode at 760 $cm^{-1}$ show a similar behaviour for all samples. The increasing intensities are now associated with the relaxation of the strain initially built up in the accommodation of thermal (strain) energy in the glassy region. This behaviour is also well paralleled in Fig. 4 where the temperature dependence of the shear strength, for all the samples, is exponential. The volume of the segment in motion is now continually increasing allowing less restrained flow.

## 5. Conclusions

The macroscopic strain induced during the friction process in the organic film is accommodated by a multitude of microscopic strain relaxations. Particularly, the idea is of side groups or segments engaging with one another in the shear plane. As the microscopic strain is relaxed, work is done in the film which is ultimately dissipated as heat. As a first stage in the microscopic modelling of the origins of the work done, but not dissipated, it is desirable to identify the microscopic species involved and also the environment in which they flow under shear. This type of data is not readily available from studies of the interfacial rheology as a function of, say, the contact pressure at ambient temperature.

In this paper we have explored the use of vibrational spectroscopy in the infrared region as a means of characterizing the molecular relaxation characteristics of species which may engage within a shear plane. To do this we have examined the spectral characteristics of various polystyrene films cast from a number of solvents as a function of temperature. These data, when compared with the temperature-dependent rheology of similar films, show reasonable trends. We have thus inferred that vibrational spectroscopy provides a means of interpreting the temperature-dependent interfacial rheology of polystyrene films.

## References

1 M. J. Sutcliffe and A. Cameron, *Special Discuss. Faraday Soc., No. 2* (1972) 26.
2 M. J. Sutcliffe, S. R. Taylor and A. Cameron, *Wear, 51* (1978) 181.
3 D. Tabor, in J. M. George (ed.), *Proc. 34th Int. Conf. Societe de Chimie Physique, Microscopic Aspects of Adhesion and Lubrication.*
4 S. N. Magonov, D. Shen and R. Qian, *Makromol. Chim., 190* (1989) 2563.
5 B. Jasse, L. Bokobza, B. Froelich and L. Monnerie, *J. Mol. Struct., 73* (1981) 1.
6 L. Euler, *Mém. Accad. Sci. Berlin, No. 4* (1748) p. 122.
7 L. Euler, *Mém. Accad. Sci. Berlin, No. 4* (1748) p. 133.
8 C. A. Coulomb, *MCT. Math. Phys. (Paris), X* (1785) p. 161.
9 N. B. Hardy and I. Doubleday, *Proc. R. Soc. London A, 104* (1923) 25.
10 K. L. Johnson and A. D. Roberts, *Proc. R. Soc. London A, 337* (1974) 217.
11 W. Hirst and A. J. Moore, *Proc. R. Soc. London A, 337* (1974) 101.

12  K. L. Johnson and J. Tevaarweck, *Proc. R. Soc. London A, 256* (1977) 215.
13  F. P. Bowden and D. Tabor, *The Friction and Lubrication of Solids,* Oxford University Press, Oxford, 1950.
14  J. N. Gregory, *Nature: London, 157* (1946) 443.
15  F. P. Bowden and J. E. Young, *Proc. R. Soc. London A, 208* (1951) 311.
16  L. C. Towle, *J. Appl. Phys., 42* (1971) 2368.
17  R. C. Bowers, *J. Appl. Phys., 42* (1971) 4961.
18  A. I. Bailey and J. S. Courtney-Pratt, *Proc. R. Soc. London A, 227* (1955) 500.
19  D. A. Roberts and D. Tabor, *Special Discuss. Faraday Soc., No. 1* (1970) 243.
20  B. J. Briscoe, B. Scruton and F. R. Willis, *Proc. R. Soc. London A, 333* (1973) 99.
21  J. N. Israelachvili and D. Tabor, *Wear, 24* (1973) 386.
22  B. J. Briscoe and D. C. B. Evans, *Proc. R. Soc. London A, 380* (1982) 389.
23  A. M. Homola, J. N. Israelachvili, P. M. McGuiggan and M. L. Gee, *Wear, 136* (1990) 65.
24  L. A. Davis and C. A. Pampillo, *J. Appl. Phys., 42* (1971) 4659.
25  I. M. Ward, *J. Mater. Sci., 6* (1971) 1397.
26  R. W. Howard and G. Thackray, *Proc. R. Soc. London A, 302* (1968) 453.
27  (a) B. J. Briscoe, in P. Feltham (ed.), *Reviews on the Deformation Behaviour of Materials III (1),* 1980, p. 172.
    (b) H. Eyring, *J. Chem. Phys., 4* (1936) 283.
28  J. S. Foot, R. W. Truss, I. M. Ward and R. A. Duckett, *J. Mater. Sci., 22* (1987) 1437.
29  R. E. Robertson, *J. Chem. Phys., 44* (1966) 3950.
30  M. Theodorou, B. Jasse and L. Monnerie, *J. Poly. Sci.:Poly. Phys. Ed., 23* (1985) 445.
31  J. K. A. Amuzu, B. J. Briscoe and D. Tabor, *ASLE Trans., 20* (1977) 152.
32  J. L. Lauer and M. E. Peterkin, *J. Lubric. Technol., 98* (1976) 230.
33  B. J. Briscoe and A. C. Smith, *J. Macromol. Sci.-Phys., B, 22* (1983) 53.
34  H. Jahankani, C. Vlattas and C. Galiotis, in F. R. Jones (ed.), *Interfacial Phenomena in Composite Materials '89,* Butterworth, London, 1989, p. 125.
35  I. M. Robinson, R. J. Young, C. Galiotis and D. N. Batchelder, in F. L. Matthews, N. C. R. Bushell, J. M. Hodgkinson and J. Morton (eds.), *6th Int. Conf. Composite Materials,* Vol. 1, p. 333.
36  P. C. Painter and J. L. Koenig, *J. Poly. Sci.: Poly. Phys. Ed., 15* (1977) 1885.
37  F. M. Fowkes and D. O. Tischler, *J. Poly. Sci.: Poly. Phys. Ed., 22* (1984) 547.
38  C. Y. Liang and S. Krimm, *J. Poly. Sci., 27* (1958) 241.
39  E. D. T. Atkins, D. H. Isaac and H. H. Keller, *J. Poly. Sci.: Poly. Phys. Ed., 18* (1980) 71.
40  G. E. Roberts and E. F. T. White, in R. N. Haward (ed.), *The Physics of Glassy Polymers,* Ch. 3, pp. 168–171.
    F. P. Bowden and Hughes, *Proc. R. Soc. London A, 160* (1939) 575.
41  J. L. Lauer and A.-J. Ahn, *STLE Trans., 31* (1987) 120.
42  Z. Xu, B. Jasse and L. Monnerie, *J. Poly. Sci.: Poly. Phys. Ed., 27* (1989) 355.

*Wear, 153* (1992) 277–295

# Micro-mechanisms of wear — wear modes

Koji Kato

*School of Mechanical Engineering, Tohoku University, Sendai (Japan)*

(Received July 28, 1991)

## Abstract

Grooves are formed on a wear surface in sliding contact and even when the contacting surfaces are of the same material the wear on the contact interface results in free particles. The abrasive friction and the abrasive wear have been proven to be the representative type of friction and wear in general sliding of surfaces from such observations.

This means that the micro-mechanisms of groove formation and wear particle generation at one abrasive contact point should be analyzed in detail and the macroscopic wear properties should be explained by summarizing the unit phenomena at the macroscopic interface.

The *in-situ* scanning electron microscopy (SEM) wear study is one of the most effective methods for this purpose. It was started in 1974, and some fruitful results have been accumulated in the past sixteen years.

Possible wear modes in abrasive sliding were made clear and effective parameters were introduced to describe the abrasive wear mode diagram for metals. The practical usefulness of the diagram was shown in the estimations of abrasive wear resistance and wear mode transitions in the repeated process of sliding.

Similar results are being obtained for ceramics.

The present understanding on the micro-mechanisms of wear is summarized in this paper by reviewing these results of *in-situ* SEM wear studies.

## 1. Introduction

The volume loss as wear in sliding friction between metals is observed as a result of groove formation on the surface and wear particle generation. Therefore, the micro-mechanism of groove formation and wear particle generation will provide an introduction for the understanding of macroscopic wear properties.

Parallel grooves are formed on a wear surface even in the case of sliding friction between similar metals. This means that hard abrasive asperities are formed on the wear surface because of e.g. such as work hardening, phase transitions and third body formation at the interface [1–4]. This viewpoint tells us that abrasive friction is the most general situation in the wear of metals.

An important point in this case is that abrasive asperities would not always be much stronger than a mating surface. So a question is how the abrasive asperity itself would be worn and how the mating surface would be worn. Depending on the possibility of wear of abrasive asperities, short or large parallel grooves are formed on a mating surface which always tell the direction of sliding. The degree of adhesion at the contact interface would be closely related to the change of wear mode.

The representative abrasive friction between hard grains and a soft surface is not an exceptional case in wear. It should be assumed as an extreme case of general wear in sliding friction. The micro-mechanism of groove formation in abrasive friction should be a key point for the understanding of sliding wear mechanisms of metals in this meaning.

The shape, size, structure and number of wear particles are determined by the microscopic wear mode which is controlled by the microscopic fracture mode and its probability.

Various types of shape and a wide size distribution of wear particles were observed by ferrography and scanning electron microscopy (SEM) [5, 6]. The microscopic surface topography of a wear particle observed by SEM showed the fracture mode for its generation in a wide range of particle sizes [7]. Large thin-film wear particles of steel looked transparent in the scanning electron microscope [8]. Fine wear particles smaller than 1.0 $\mu$m in diameter showed a crystal structure in transmission electron microscopy (TEM) [1], the size of which seemed to correspond to that of cells or subgrains in the subsurface layer observed by TEM [9].

In this way, a wear particle provides a lot of information about the wear mode for its generation. Therefore, its micro-wear mechanism in abrasive friction should give a fundamental understanding of the sliding wear mechanisms of metals.

In these circumstances a microscopic approach to wear mechanisms, the *in-situ* observation of the wear process at high magnification with the scanning electron microscope was started. It gave a new understanding about the mechanisms of groove formation and wear particle generation.

In the first stage of *in-situ* SEM wear studies, various types of wear particles and their generating processes were carefully observed [10–17], the first one appearing in 1974. The effect of repeated sliding on surface grooving and the initiation of wear was also observed [18, 19].

In the second stage, the friction coefficient was measured and plastic theory was introduced for the dynamic analysis of wear modes [20–22], and the wear mode diagram was introduced with the result of the analysis [23]. The three-dimensional approach was also tried in a similar way [24]. The microscopic wear rate was calculated with a theory based on this wear mode diagram [25–27].

The classification of microscopic wear modes and the introduction of the wear mode diagram stimulated the analysis of wear mode transition process in repeated sliding. A video system was connected to the scanning electron microscope for this purpose, and the process of wear mode transition in repeated sliding was analyzed with many successive observations [28]. Thus the *in-situ* wear study was developed from the single pass of sliding to multi-passes of sliding, which gave more practical information about the wear mechanism.

In the third stage, the wear process under lubrication was observed *in situ*. The surface and wear particles were well observed without charging in the scanning electron microscope under the lubrication of a thin grease film which was enough to decrease the friction and change the wear mode in vacuum [22–24]. The standard scanning electron microscope was modified with a valve/gauge system and good resolution images of liquid-lubricated surfaces were produced routinely [29]. It enabled the *in-situ* SEM study of wear in boundary lubrication [30]. These observations show that the *in-situ* SEM study of wear under lubrication of grease or oil will provide a new aspect for the understanding of the lubricated wear mechanism.

In the fourth stage, SEM was combined with a particle counter whose resolution was about 0.2 $\mu$m. The number and size distribution of the wear particles generated at one contact point were measured together with the observation of wear modes and the measurement of friction coefficient in SEM [31–33]. The wear volume will be related quantitatively to the number and size distribution of wear particles through this approach.

The analysis of the observed results requires an advanced theory of wear which should be closely related to the microstructure of the surface layer [9] and the related microscopic fracture modes and their probabilities. The fourth stage of *in-situ* SEM wear studies will open a new field of microscopic wear theory in this meaning, and it will contribute to the new needs of tribology in super-clean technology.

The *in-situ* SEM wear studies in those four stages were mainly for metals because of their utility in industries and conductivity for SEM observation.

In the fifth stage of the *in-situ* SEM wear studies, the analysis of wear mechanisms of ceramics was started. The modern advanced scanning electron microscope of field emission type is necessary for this purpose. Otherwise, only silicon carbide is a good ceramic material for the observation with standard SEM.

Observations on silicon carbide, alumina and silicon nitride showed some interesting wear mechanisms different from those of metals [34–36]. It seems promising from these results that the *in-situ* SEM wear studies of ceramics will help rapid development of ceramic wear theory.

Microscopic observations in these five stages are summarized and a general view of micro-mechanisms of wear is described in this review. Comprehensive coverage of the wear mechanisms is not intended, only theories of sliding wear.

## 2. The abrasive asperity and groove formation

Because of work hardening, phase transitions or third body formation, the micro-hardness on the wear surface can be about three times larger than the initial bulk hardness depending on the indenting point.

Figure 1 shows the distribution of micro-hardness on sliding wear surfaces of a pin and a ring which are made of 0.45% carbon steel [37].

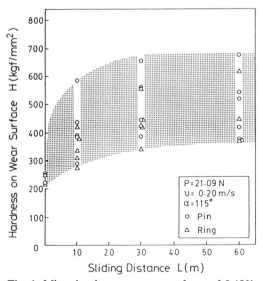

Fig. 1. Micro-hardness on wear surfaces of 0.45% carbon steel [37].

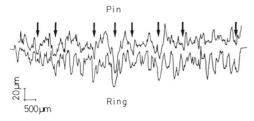

Fig. 2. Cross-sections of the mating wear surfaces of 0.45% carbon steel after pin-on-ring type sliding [37].

$$\alpha = 93°$$

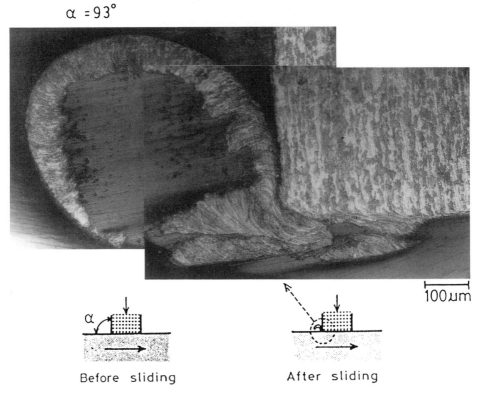

Before sliding                After sliding

Fig. 3. Micro-cutting at the leading edge of a pin specimen of 0.45% carbon steel sliding on the same steel [37].

Figure 2 shows cross-sections of the mating wear surfaces of a pin and a ring, where the peak on the pin mates to the valley on the ring and *vice versa*.

Figure 3 shows the leading edge of a pin at the entrance of the interface where a ribbon-like wear particle is being generated in the wear mode of cutting.

When the attack angle $\alpha$ at the leading edge of a pin in Fig. 4 is changed, the wear rate changes drastically (shown in Fig. 5).

It is confirmed from these observations that grooves are formed on the wear surface by a combination of the attack angle of the asperity and its micro-hardness. A third body at the contact interface would work in the same way. If the attack angle

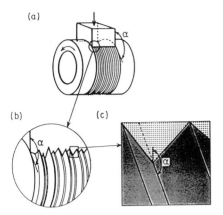

Fig. 4. Attack angle $\alpha$ at the leading edge of a pin specimen.

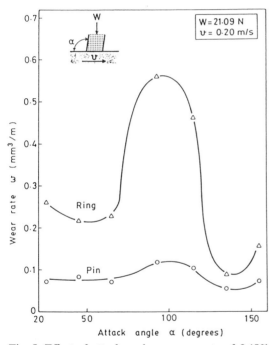

Fig. 5. Effect of attack angle on wear rate of 0.45% carbon steel in unlubricated sliding.

$\theta$ and the micro-hardness ratio $r$ ($=H_2/H_1$) between the two contact surfaces are defined as are shown in Fig. 6, the asperity can groove the lower surface when $\theta$ and $r$ are in the groove region in Fig. 7 [20, 21] ($\theta=\pi-2\alpha$). In the yield region, the asperity deforms plastically and cannot groove the mating surface. The theoretical solid line in the figure assumes the shearing strength at the contact interface being zero and it is shifted a little if a certain amount of shearing strength is introduced.

Figure 7 shows that the asperity of large $\theta$ grooves the mating surface even when the hardness ratio $r$ is very close to unity. This is further evidence to show the high possibility of groove formation at the sliding interface between similar metals.

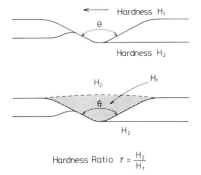

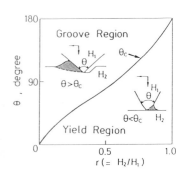

Fig. 6. Hardness ratio $r$ at a contact point.

Fig. 7. Yield criterion of an abrasive asperity [20].

## 3. The abrasive wear mode diagram

In the single pass of sliding of an abrasive model asperity on metals, three wear modes of cutting, wedge formation and ploughing were observed as in Fig. 8 [14, 22].

The degree of penetration $D_p$ of an asperity was introduced to describe the three-dimensional severity of contact for wear, which was defined by the following equation

$$D_p = \frac{h}{a} = R\left(\frac{\pi H}{2W}\right)^{1/2} - \left(\frac{\pi R^2 H}{2W} - 1\right)^{1/2} \tag{1}$$

where $a$ is the contract radius, $h$ is the depth of penetration, $R$ is the radius of the spherical asperity, $H$ is the hardness of the indented surface, and $W$ is the load.

The friction coefficient $\mu$ was measured together with the observation of three wear modes and it is related to $D_p$ in Fig. 9. [23]. The relative shear strength $f$ as a ratio of the shear strength of the interface and that of the bulk was calculated with the result of Fig. 9 and the slip line field solution for the abrasive friction by Challen and Oxley [38] which gives the relationship between $\mu$, $f$ and $\alpha$.

For the calculation, $D_p$ was related to $\alpha$ by the following semiempirical formula:

$$D_p = 0.8 \tan(\alpha/2) \tag{2}$$

In order to show the relationship between the wear modes and the frictional conditions, the wear mode diagram of Fig. 10 was described with the two parameters of $D_p$ and $f$. A possible wear mode under a given frictional condition can be estimated using this diagram.

## 4. The degree of wear at a groove in one pass of sliding

The groove formation develops a plastically deformed zone as side ridges around the groove. Therefore, the apparent groove depth does not simply mean the volume actually removed.

Figure 11 shows a schematic figure of a groove cross-section where $(A' - A'')$ should be the real wear volume. If the degree of wear $\beta$ at one groove is defined by the following equation:

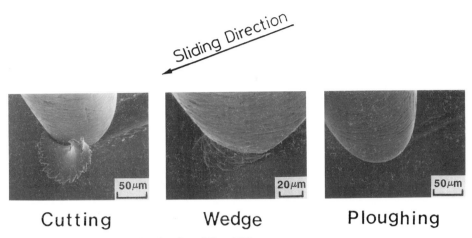

Fig. 8. Three wear modes in abrasive sliding [22].

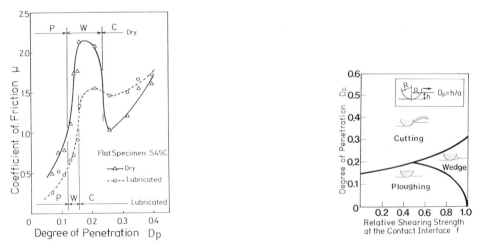

Fig. 9. Coefficient of friction as a function of the degree of penetration.

Fig. 10. Abrasive wear mode diagram.

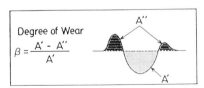

Fig. 11. Definition of degree of wear at one groove.

$$\beta = \frac{A' - A''}{A'} \tag{3}$$

The relationship between $\beta$ and $D_p$ is given by Fig. 12 for heat-treated steels [25]. The value of $\beta$ increases with $D_p$ and reaches a certain constant value $\beta_c$. The shape

284

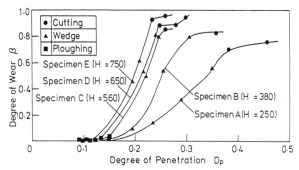

Fig. 12. The degree of wear as a function of degree of penetration. ($H$ is the hardness) [25].

of the curve changes depending on the deforming properties of the material and decreases with hardness.

A low value of $\beta$ corresponds to the ploughing mode of wear and a high value corresponds to the cutting mode. The transition range between low and high values corresponds to the wedge formation mode. Pure metals and annealed steel give lower values of $\beta$ and quenched steel gives higher values as a whole. The work hardening property seems important in determining such a $\beta$–$D_p$ relationship [39].

This relationship is expressed by the following equation for below $\beta_c$

$$\beta = cD_p{}^l \tag{4}$$

where $c$ and $l$ are experimental constants.

## 5. Estimation of the macroscopic wear rate in one pass of sliding

If the distributions of asperity tip radius $R$, micro-hardness $H$ and the load $W$ at each contact point are given at a macroscopic contact interface, the macroscopic wear rate can be estimated. However, it is generally hard now to know their values for a real contact interface. The distribution of the attack angle $\alpha$ of abrasive asperities are measured experimentally in many cases.

Figure 13 shows a representative distribution of $\alpha$ observed on hard abrasives [26]. $\alpha$ is related to the degree of penetration $D_p$ through eqn. (2) and $\beta$ is given experimentally by eqn. (4) as is shown in Fig. 12. By considering these relationships and the distribution of wear modes at all contact points, the wear volume $V$ is given by the following equation

$$V = \frac{\phi_{\text{eff}}}{k\psi_m}\left(\frac{\alpha_w\beta_w}{m_w{}^2} + \frac{\alpha_c\beta_c}{m_c{}^2}\right)\frac{WL}{H} \tag{5}$$

where $W$ is the normal load, $L$ is the sliding distance, $H$ is the hardness of the abraded material, $\phi_{\text{eff}}$ is the proportion of effective asperities, $K$, $\psi_m$ are shape factors of the asperities, $\alpha_w$, $\beta_w$, $m_w$ are factors describing the wedge formation mode of abrasive wear, $\alpha_c$, $\beta_c$, $m_c$ are factors describing the cutting mode of abrasive wear. The wear resistance defined by $WL/V$ is given as follows

$$WL/V = \frac{K\psi_m}{\phi_{\text{eff}}(\alpha_w\beta_w/m_w{}^2 + \alpha_c\beta_c/m_c{}^2)}H \tag{6}$$

285

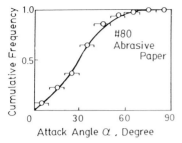

Fig. 13. Distribution of attack angle [26].

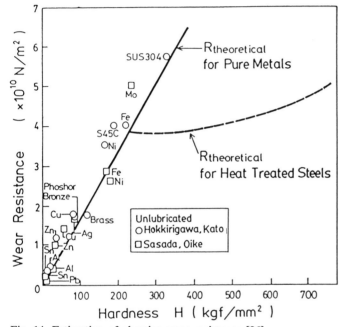

Fig. 14. Estimation of abrasive wear resistance [26].

The theoretical estimation calculated by eqn. (6) is shown in Fig. 14 [26] by a solid line together with experimental values which were observed in one pass of abrasive sliding under unlubricated conditions. Both theoretical and experimental values agree very well. The result in lubricated abrasive sliding also agreed well with the theoretical estimations from eqn. (6) [26]. Experimental values for heat-treated steels could also be well explained by developing eqn. (6) [25]. The contribution of ploughing mode to wear was neglected in all these calculations since it was relatively small.

## 6. The abrasive wear mode transition in repeated sliding

In popular machines, sliding is repeated on the same track at the interface of machine elements. The abrasive asperity is on the same groove microscopically for a long time in such a case and it is the principal situation for the initial–steady wear transition observed in the run-in period.

The successive observations of the abrasive wear process in *in-situ* SEM gave the result shown in Fig. 15. The wear mode under a load of 1.5 N, for example, made a transition from cutting to wedge formation and then to shear-tongue formation [7, 40] and finally to ploughing with the increase of friction cycle [28]. Such a process of wear mode transition is well understood from the relationship between the wear mode and the degree of penetration $D_{pn}$ at each sliding cycle, where $D_{pn}$ is defined by the following equation,

$$D_{pn} = \frac{\text{Increment of groove depth at } n\text{th cycle}}{\text{Contact length in sliding direction at } n\text{th cycle}}$$

$$= \frac{R}{(w_n{}^2 - w_{n-1}{}^2)^{1/2}} - \left(\frac{R^2}{w_n{}^2 - w_{n-1}{}^2} - 1\right)^{1/2} \tag{7}$$

where $R$ is the radius of the spherical asperity, $W_n$ is half of the contact width at the $n$th cycle, $W_{n-1}$ is half of the contact width at the $(n-1)$th cycle.

The vertical axis has the value $D_{pn}$ of this meaning. If this $D_{pn}$ is supposed to be equivalent to $D_p$ in Fig. 10, a possible mode of wear is estimated for a given value of $D_{pn}$ with Fig. 10 under the proper value of $f$. Theoretical bands of $D_{pn}$ in Fig. 15 for the modes of cutting, wedge formation and ploughing were obtained in this way with $f=0.85$. These bands agree well with the observed ones where shear tongue should be included in ploughing for comparison.

This means that the process of wear mode transition in repeated sliding can be estimated with the abrasive wear mode diagram if the degree of penetration $D_{pn}$ at each sliding cycle is given.

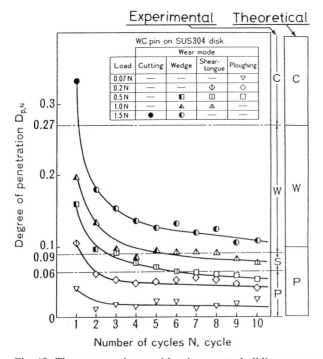

Fig. 15. The wear mode transition in repeated sliding process on a groove.

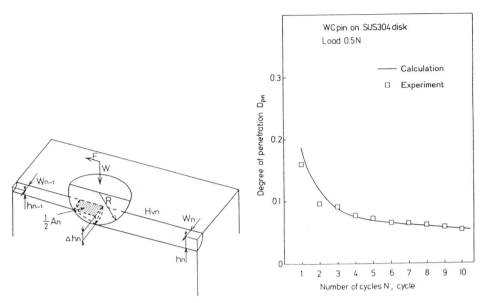

Fig. 16. Model of contact in repeated sliding.

Fig. 17. Estimation of the degree of penetration in repeated sliding process [28].

For this purpose, the values of $W_n$ and $W_{n-1}$ in eqn. (7) are calculated theoretically by the model of geometrical approximation shown in Fig. 16,

$$w_n^4 + 2w_n^3 w_{n-1} - 2w_n w_{n-1}^3 - w_{n-1}^4 = (W/H_n)^2 \qquad (8)$$

where $W$ is the load, and $H_n$ is the hardness at the $n$th cycle.

Figure 17 shows the good agreement between the observed values of $D_{pn}$ and a theoretical line calculated with Eqns. (7) and (8), where experimental values of $H_n$ were used. This means that the next problem for the estimation of the abrasive wear mode transition in repeated sliding is to know the effect of sliding repetition on hardness. If the hardness $H_n$ is given as a function of friction conditions and repeated cycles, a possible wear mode is estimated with eqns. (7) and (8) and Fig. 10.

## 7. The degree of wear at a groove in repeated sliding

After the understanding of wear mode transition in repeated sliding, the next step to estimate the macroscopic wear rate is to know the degree of wear $\beta$ at a groove. Figure 15 suggests on this point that the ploughing mode is most important in repeated sliding if we think about steady wear, since the wear mode makes a transition finally to ploughing very quickly from cutting and wedge formation under any load.

$\beta$ for modes of wedge formation and cutting were given by eqn. (4) and $\beta_c$ in Fig. 12, and $\beta$ was assumed relatively zero for ploughing mode in the calculations shown above. But for the process of repeated sliding on the same groove, we have to consider other possible wear modes together with the ploughing mode which will give a low value of $\beta$.

One is the mode of shear-tongue formation [7] where a thin flake is sheared and plucked off the surface of a groove by the adhesive transfer to the surface of an abrasive. Figure 18(a) shows a schematic figure of this mechanism and Fig. 18(b) shows two thin flakes of stainless steel transferred from the lower mating surface. Such a thin flake is called shear-tongue (once called slip-tongue) and it is formed by the combined action of ploughing and adhesive transfer.

The other is the mode of thin film formation [8] where a thin surface layer is severely deformed by repeated shear under compression and flows plastically to the direction of friction. Figure 19 shows the relationship between the amount of surface flow $\Delta D_x$ and the sliding cycles in rotational sliding contact. After the continuous

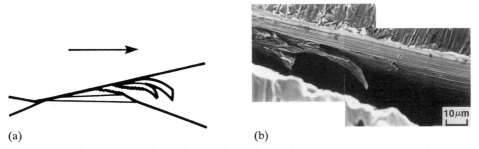

(a)                                                    (b)

Fig. 18. Two shear-tongues of stainless steel transferred from the lower surface to the upper surface by adhesion and shearing fracture [7].

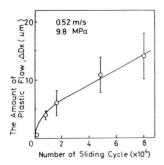

Fig. 19. The amount of plastic flow on the surface of 0.45% carbon steel caused by the repeated sliding in alkylnaphthalene oil [8].

Fig. 20. A thin-film wear particle of 0.45% carbon steel which protruded from the surface of a ridge after $8 \times 10^3$ cycles of rotational sliding in alkylnaphthalene oil [8].

plastic flow in a thin surface layer, a thin film protrudes suddenly from the surface and forms a filmy wear particle.

Figure 20 shows such a thin film protrusion from the surface of a ridge [41]. It looks transparent in the microscope and the underlying wear surface is observed through it. This type of flow wear can happen in repeated ploughing on the surface of a groove and its side ridges.

Although it is quite possible for these two modes of wear to appear in repeated ploughing, values of $\beta$ for them are not known at present. An estimation of the macroscopic wear rate in the steady state is not possible now for this reason.

## 8. The number and size distribution of wear particles

In addition to the wear mode and the groove shape, the number and size distribution of the wear particles are other important factors in practice and for the understanding of micro-mechanisms in wear.

The size distribution of wear particles was analyzed in some papers [42–48] and representative distribution functions were proposed [43, 45].

The common difficulty in the analysis of wear mechanisms in these observations is that several wear modes such as cutting, wedge formation, shear-tongue formation, plastic flow, fatigue and oxidation exist together at the same interface. In order to avoid this complexity, single point abrasive sliding was conducted in the scanning electron microscope and the size distribution of wear particles generated in repeated sliding was measured together with confirmation of the operating wear mode [31–33].

Figure 21 shows the size distribution of the wear particles observed with SEM, with a diamond pin/stainless steel disk pair after eight sliding cycles. The size and number of wear particles were measured with a laser particle counter incorporated

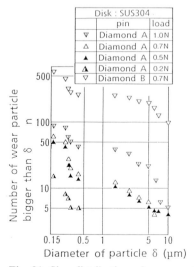

Fig. 21. Size distribution of wear particles from a groove after eight cycles of repeated sliding in ploughing mode with pin A (radius 52 $\mu$m) and cutting mode with pin B (radius 29 $\mu$m) [31].

into the scanning electron microscope. The wear mode was ploughing under pin A and cutting under pin B.

Although the total number of wear particles is different depending on the pin tip radius and the load, patterns of size distributions are almost the same as each other quantitatively. Wear particles smaller than 1.0 $\mu$m in size make up the larger part of the total number.

The total number $n$ of wear particles is shown in Fig. 22 as a function of $D_p$ for the sliding pair of diamond pin/stainless steel disk. The wear mode was continued as ploughing except for the pin of 25 $\mu$m radius. a similar result is shown in Fig. 23 for the sliding pair of tungsten carbide pin/stainless steel disk. The wear mode was wedge formation.

Experimental equations for these two results were given as follows;
ploughing mode: diamond pin/stainless steel disk

$$n = 1.0 \times 10^4 D_p^{2.5} \quad (\text{m}^{-1}) \tag{9}$$

wedge formation mode: tungsten carbide pin/stainless steel disk

$$n = 1.9 \times 10^4 D_p^{1.3} \quad (\text{m}^{-1}) \tag{10}$$

Although the physical meaning of $D_p$ for the number of wear particles is not well analyzed at present, the experimental relationships of eqns. (9) and (10) would be the first step for getting the relationship between the wear volume and the number of wear particles. $D_p$ in eqns. (9) and (10) would be replaced by $D_{pn}$ for more exact analysis. This challenge means to introduce the new theory of micro-mechanism in wear. An approach looking for the relationship between $D_{pn}$, $H_n$ and sliding cycles only would not be enough to give satisfactory explanations for eqns. (9) and (10). The microstructure of the subsurface and its change by the repetition of sliding may be related to the number of wear particles [9].

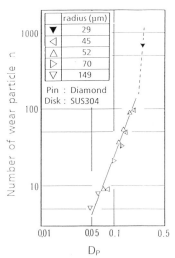 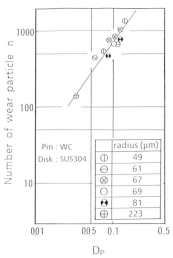

Fig. 22. The total number of wear particles as a function of degree of penetration in ploughing mode of wear (One cutting mode data) [32].

Fig. 23. The total number of wear particles as a function of degree of penetration in wedge formation mode of wear [32].

## 9. The difference of micro-mechanisms of wear between ceramics and metals

The *in-situ* SEM observations of the abrasive wear process of silicon nitride gave the result of Fig. 24 [35] where wear modes of ploughing, powder formation and flake formation were observed.

The wear modes of powder formation and flake formation are quite unique in ceramics. The style of transition from one mode to another is also different from the case of metals [28]. Observations on alumina [35] and silicon carbide [34] show similar interesting wear modes and transitions which are much different from those of metals.

The wear mode diagrams of ceramics shown in Figs. 25 and 26 [49] were drawn with those results by introducing the new parameters $S_c$ and $S_c^*$ which are given by the following equations:

$$S_c = \frac{P_{max}R_{max}^{1/2}}{K_{Ic}} \tag{11}$$

$$S_c^* = \frac{H_vR_{max}^{1/2}}{K_{Ic}} \tag{12}$$

where $P_{max}$ is the maximum contact pressure, $R_{max}$ is the maximum wear surface roughness, $K_{Ic}$ is the fracture toughness, and $H_v$ is the Vickers hardness.

These parameters $S_c$ and $S_c^*$ were introduced by developing theoretical results obtained by the fracture dynamic analysis on surface microcracks [50, 51]. They denote the severity of contact for the development of micro-cracks in the subsurface and $R_{max}$ is supposed to correspond to the maximum length of a vertical surface crack.

In Fig. 25, a theoretical condition for the transition of wear mode from flake formation to powder formation or ploughing is given by the following equation:

$$S_c = \frac{7}{1+10\mu} \tag{13}$$

In Fig. 26, a theoretical condition for the transition of wear mode from powder formation to ploughing is given by the following equation:

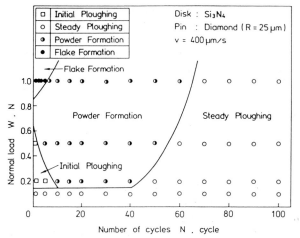

Fig. 24. The wear mode transition of silicon nitride in repeated sliding process on a groove [35].

292

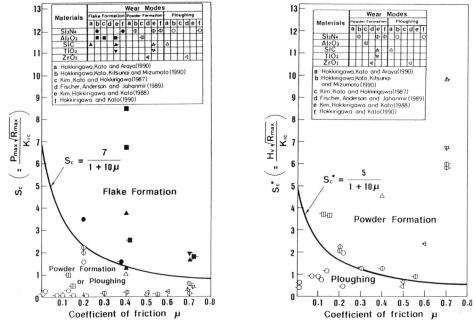

Fig. 25. Wear mode diagram of ceramics for the mode transition between flake formation and powder formation or ploughing [49].

Fig. 26. Wear mode diagram of ceramics for the mode transition between powder formation and ploughing [49].

$$S_c^* = \frac{5}{1+10\mu} \qquad (14)$$

where $\mu$ is the friction coefficient.

The good agreements between the experimental and theoretical values in Figs. 25 and 26 mean that microscopic wear modes of ceramics are mainly decided by the brittle behavior of micro-cracks in the subsurface.

In the case of rolling contact between silicon nitride rollers, the parameter $S_c$ was useful to describe the wear rate $\omega_s$ as follows:

$$\omega_s = 1.56 \times 10^{-5} S_c^{5.46} \qquad (15)$$

where $\omega_s$ has the dimensions of mm$^3$ m$^{-1}$ [52].

## 10. Discussion

Abrasive wear mode diagrams drawn with $D_p$ and $f$ for metals worked well to estimate the possible wear modes under given frictional conditions. $D_p$ was an effective parameter which gives empirical formulas for the degree of wear and the number of wear particles at one groove. But the abrasive wear mode diagram does not include the effect of frictional heating. The effect of $f$ on the wear rate in one mode is also not clear.

In the macroscopic wear mechanism map for steels by S. C. Lim and M. F. Ashby [53], however, the effect of frictional heating was introduced by a unique parameter of normalized velocity.

T. Childs, who attempted to make a wear map for steels [54], suggests that a combination of $a/f$ and pressure $\times$ velocity wear mechanism maps offers a useful way of visually presenting information for the better understanding of wear [55].

When we start the next step of the wear map, a high-speed abrasive test of one groove will become necessary. The result of a single pass pendulum grooving test [56] tells us its importance.

## 11. Conclusions

The micro-mechanisms of wear were studied by observing the wear process microscopically with the SEM-Tribosystem which is combined with a video tape recorder. The wear mode, friction coefficient, size distribution of wear particles, number of wear particles and wear rate were mainly measured.

A parameter $D_p$ ( = penetrating depth/contact radius) was introduced to describe the severity of contact for metals and a parameter $S_c$ ( = maximum contact pressure $\times$ (maximum roughness)$^{1/2}$/fracture toughness) for ceramics.

Observations and parameters introduced give the following conclusions:

(1) An abrasive wear mode diagram of metals is drawn with $D_p$ and the shearing strength at the interface $f$ for wear modes of cutting, wedge formation and ploughing.

(2) The relationship between abrasive wear resistance of metals and their hardness in one pass of sliding is explained quantitatively with a model of proposed abrasive wear mode diagram.

(3) The abrasive wear mode undergoes transitions from cutting to wedge formation and then ploughing in the process of repeated sliding. This process of wear mode transition is well estimated theoretically with the abrasive wear mode diagram.

(4) The number of wear particles in abrasive wear of metal is proportional to $D_p{}^m$, where $m$ is an experimental constant.

(5) A wear mode diagram of ceramics is drawn with $S_c$ (or $S_c{}^*$) and the friction coefficient $\mu$ for the wear modes of flake formation, powder formation and ploughing.

## Acknowledgments

The author thanks Mr. K. Adachi and Dr. K. Hokkirigawa for their cooperation in finishing this review work.

## References

1  D. A. Rigney, Sliding wear of metals, *Ann. Rev. Mater. Sci., 18* (1988) 141.
2  M. Godet, The third-body approach: A mechanical view of wear, *Wear, 100* (1984) 437.
3  T. Sasada, M. Oike and N. Emori, The effect of abrasive grain size on the transition between abrasive and abrasion wear, *Wear, 97* (1984) 291.
4  K. Komvopoulos, N. P. Suh and N. Saka, Wear of boundary-lubricated metal surface, *Wear, 107* (1986) 107.
5  D. Scott, W. W. Seifert and V. C. Westicott, The particles of wear, *Sci. Am., 230* (1974) 88.

6   L. E. Samuels, E. D. Doyle and D. M. Twley, *Fundamentals of Friction and Wear of Materials*, ed. D. A. Rigney, Am. Soc. Met., Metals Park OH, 1980, p. 13.

7   T. Kayaba and K. Kato, The adhesive transfer of the slip-tongue and the wedge, *ASLE Trans.*, *24* (1981) 164.

8   T. Akagaki and K. Kato, Simulation of flow wear in boundary lubrication using a Vickers Indentation method, *Tribol. Trans.*, *31* (1987) 310.

9   K. Kato, T. Kayaba and Y. Ono, Dislocation density and cell structure produced in the surface layer of aluminium during sliding wear, *ASME, Proc. Int. Conf. on Wear of Materials, 1985*, p. 463.

10  T. R. Bates, K. C. Ludema and W. C. Brainard, A rheological mechanism of penetrative wear, *Wear, 30* (1974) 309.

11  W. A. Brainard and D. H. Buckley, Dynamic SEM wear studies of tungsten carbide cermets, *ASLE Trans., 19* (1976) 309.

12  T. Kayaba and K. Kato, The analysis of adhesive wear mechanisms by successive observation of the wear process in SEM, *ASME, Proc. Int. Conf. on Wear of Materials, 1979*, p. 45.

13  Y. Tsuya, K. Saito, R. Takagi and J. Akaoka, *In-situ* observation of wear process in a scanning electron microscope, *ASME, Proc. Int. Conf. on Wear of Materials, 1979*, p. 57.

14  T. Kayaba, K. Kato and Y. Nagasawa, Abrasive wear in stick–slip motion, *ASME, Proc. Int. Conf. on Wear of Materials, 1981*, p. 439.

15  S. J. Calabrase, F. F. Ling and S. F. Murray, Dynamic wear tests in the SEM, *ASLE Trans., 26* (1983) 455.

16  L. Ahman and A. Oberg, Mechanism of micro-abrasion *in-situ* studies in SEM, *ASME, Proc. Int. Conf. on Wear of Materials, 1983*, p. 112.

17  S. C. Lim and J. H. Brunton, A dynamic wear rig for the scanning electron microscope, *Wear, 101* (1985) 81.

18  W. A. Gleaser, Wear experiments in the scanning electron microscope, *Wear, 73* (1981) 371.

19  S. V. Prasad and T. H. Kosel, *In-situ* SEM scratch tests on white cast iron with round quartz abrasive, *ASME, Proc. Int. Conf. on Wear of Materials, 1983* p. 121.

20  T. Kayaba, K. Kato and K. Hokkirigawa, Theoretical analysis of plastic yielding of a hard asperity sliding on a soft flat surface, *Wear, 87* (1983) 151.

21  T. Kayaba, K. Hokkirigawa and K. Kato, Experimental analysis of the yield criterion for a hard asperity sliding on a soft flat surface, *Wear, 96* (1984) 255.

22  T. Kayaba, K. Hokkirigawa and K. Kato, Analysis of the observed wear processes in a scanning electron microscope, *Wear, 110* (1986) 419.

23  K. Hokkirigawa and K. Kato, An experimental and theoretical investigation of ploughing, cutting and wedge formation during abrasive wear, *Tribol. Int., 21* (1988) 51.

24  K. Kato, K. Hokkirigawa, T. Kayaba and Y. Endo, three dimensional edge effect on abrasive wear, *Trans. ASME, J. Tribol., 108* (1986) 346.

25  K. Hokkirigawa and K. Kato and Z. Z. Li, The effect of hardness on the transition of the abrasive wear mechanism of steels, *Wear, 123* (1988) 241.

26  K. Hokkirigawa and K. Kato, Theoretical estimation of abrasive wear resistance based on microscopic wear mechanism, *ASME, Proc. Int. Conf. on Wear of Materials, Denver, CO, Vol. 1, 1989*, p. 1.

27  K. Hokkirigawa, The analysis of the transition of abrasive wear by the change of hardness ratio, *Proc. EUROTRIB 89, 1989*, p. 50.

28  H. Kitsunai, K. Kato, K. Hokkirigawa and H. Inoue, The transition between microscopic wear modes during repeated sliding friction observed by SEM-Tribosystem, *Wear, 135* (1990) 237.

29  W. Holzhauer and S. J. Calabrese, Modification of SEM for *in-situ* liquid-lubricated sliding studies, *ASLE, Trans., 30* (1986) 302.

30  W. Holzhauer and F. F. Ling, *In-situ* SEM study of boundary lubricated contacts, *ASME Trans., 31* (1987) 359.

31  M. Mizumoto, K. Kato and H. Inoue, The relationship between the size distribution of wear particles and the wear modes, *Proc. 32nd JAST Conf. Tokyo, 1988* p. 41 (in Japanese).

32  M. Mizumoto, K. Kato and H. Inoue, The relationship between the number of wear particles and the wear modes, *proc. 33rd JAST Conf., Okayama, 1988,* p. 253 (in Japanese).

33  M. Mizumoto, K. Kato and H. Inoue, How to decrease wear particles in abrasive wear, *Proc. EUROTRIB 89, 1989,* p. 334.

34  K. Kato, S. Araya and K. Hokkirigawa, The transition of microscopic wear mode of silicon carbide by the repeated sliding friction in SEM, *Proc. 33rd JAST Conf., Tokyo, 1989,* p. 1 (in Japanese).

35  K. Hokkirigawa, K. Kato, M. Mizumoto and H. Kitsunai, The transition of microscopic wear modes of silicon nitride and alumina by the repeated sliding friction in the SEM, *Proc. 33rd JAST Conf. Tokyo, 1989,* p. 5 (in Japanese).

36  K. Kato, Tribology of ceramics, *Proc. EUROTRIB 89,* and *Wear, 136* (1990) 117.

37  Y. C. Chiou and K. Kato, Wear mode of micro-cutting in dry sliding friction between steel pairs (Part 1), *J. Japanese Society of Lubrication Engineers, 32* (1987) 41.

38  J. M. Challen and P. L. B. Oxley, An explanation of the different regimes of friction and wear using asperity deformation modes, *Wear, 53* (1979) 229.

39  K. H. Zum Gahr, *Microstructure and Wear of Materials, Tribology Series 10,* Elsevier, Amsterdam, 1987, p. 132.

40  D. A. Rigney, *Fundamentals of Friction and Wear of Materials, 1980,* Am. Soc. of Metals, Metals Park, OH, 1981, p. 16.

41  T. Akagaki and K. Kato, Wear mode diagram in lubricated sliding friction of carbon steel, *Wear, 129* (1989) 303.

42  E. Rabinowicz, *Friction and Wear of Materials,* Wiley, New York, 1965, Sections 6.3–6.5.

43  Y. Kimura, A simple method of estimation the mean volume of a wear fragment, *J. Japanese Society of Lubrication Engineers, 17* (1972) 53 (in Japanese).

44  N. Soda, Y. Kimura and K. Tanaka, Wear of some f.c.c. metals during unlubricated sliding, Part 2: Effect of normal load, sliding velocity and atmospheric pressure on wear fragment, *Wear, 35* (1975) 331.

45  T. Sasada and H. Kondo, Formation of wear particles by mutual transfer and growth process, *J. JSLE, 17* (1972) 96 (in Japanese).

46  K. Nakyama and J. Okamoto, Wear particle distribution and its relation to the wear transition under boundary lubrication, *Wear, 70* (1981) 152.

47  M. Kar and S. Bahadur, Estimation of wear particle thickness in polymer–metal sliding, *Wear, 63* (1980) 105.

48  T. Kayaba, K. Kato and T. Akagaki, Ferrographic study of wear, first report: The fundamental characteristics of magnetic wear debris separation analysis, *J. Japanese Society of Lubrication Engineers Int. Edn., 6* (1958) 39.

49  K. Hokkirigawa, Wear map of ceramics, *ASME, Wear of Materials, 1991,* p. 353.

50  S. S. Kim, H. Abé, K. Hayashi, K. Kato and K. Hokkirigawa, Analysis of rolling wear mechanisms of ceramics based on fracture mechanics — Part 2, *Proc. 32nd Japanese Society of Lubrication Engineers Conf., 1988,* p. 289.

51  S. S. Kim, K. Kato and K. Hokkirigawa, Analysis of rolling wear mechanism of ceramics based on fracture mechanics — Part 3, *Proc. 32nd Japanese Society of Lubrication Engineers Conf., 1988,* p. 293.

52  S. S. Kim, K. Kato, K. Hokkirigawa and H. Abé, Wear mechanism of ceramic materials in dry rolling friction, *Trans. ASME J. Tribol., 108* (1986) 522.

53  S. C. Lim and M. F. Ashby, Wear mechanism map, *Acta Metall., 35* (1987) 1.

54  T. H. C. Childs, The sliding wear mechanism of metals, mainly steels, *Tribol. Int.* (1980) 285.

55  T. H. C. Childs, The mapping of metallic sliding wear, *Proc. Inst. Mech. Eng., 202 C6* (1988) 397.

56  O. Vingsbo and S. Hogmark, Single-pass pendulum grooving — A technique for abrasive testing, *Wear, 100* (1984) 489.

*Wear, 153* (1992) 297–299

# Notes on Contributors

Thierry A. Blanchet: will complete his Doctoral Degree in engineering sciences at Dartmouth College's Thayer School of Engineering during the 1991–1992 academic calendar. He is the holder of the degrees of Bachelor of Science (mechanical engineering) from the University of Vermont, and Master of Science (engineering sciences) from Dartmouth College. He is also the holder of a NASA Graduate Student Researchers Program Fellowship and conducts research related to polymer tribology both at Dartmouth College and the Surface Science Branch of the NASA-Lewis Research Center. He has also held nearly two years of internships with Hercules Corporation/Champlain Cable Company and Dow Chemical Company Central Research, working in fields such as radiation processing of polymers and evaluation of high-temperature tribological fluids.

You Lung Chen: received his M.Sc. in chemical engineering from the Illinois Institute of Technology (Chicago) and is currently carrying out his Ph.D. research in the area of surface forces in non-aqueous media at the University of California, Santa Barbara.

Horst Czichos: is vice-president of the Federal Institute of Materials Research and Testing (Bundesanstalt für Materialprüfung, BAM) Berlin–Dahlem and adjunct professor (Honorar-Professor) at the Technische Fachhochschule Berlin. He was educated in both engineering and physics and worked for several years in the optical industry until he joined BAM in 1966. He received a degree (Ing.-grad.) in precision engineering from the Polytechnic Ingenieurakademy Gauss Berlin, an M.Sc. (Dipl.-Phys.) in physics from the Free University and a doctor's degree from the Technical University of Berlin. He has published extensively on various topics in tribology and on the application of modern measuring techniques and systems analysis to this field.

Mark Gee: holds an honours degree in physics from Oxford and a D.Phil. in Metallurgy on the creep crack behaviour of low alloy steels. In 1979 he joined the National Physical Laboratory where his initial interests were in the diffusion joining of hardmetals and ceramics, and in the statistical description of the variability properties for hard, brittle materials. The main current research interest is in the development and standardisation of robust wear test methods for ceramics and cermets, and in the fundamental mechanisms of wear for ceramics.

Andrei Ya. Grigoriev: graduated as an engineer in mechanics in 1985 and received his Ph.D. in tribology in 1990. Main area of interest: surface topography and morphology analysis, image processing. Since 1979 he has been with the Metal–Polymer Research Institute, Byelorussian Academy of Sciences.

Jacob Israelachvili: received his B.A. and M.A. in physics from the University of Cambridge, UK and also carried out his Ph.D. research work there in the Surface Physics Department of the Cavendish Laboratory. He received his Ph.D. in 1972. After a two-year European Molecular Biology Organization (EMBO) research fellowship at the University of Stockholm, he left for Australia where, from 1974 to 1986, he set up and directed an experimental research laboratory devoted to measuring the forces between surfaces in liquids and vapors at the molecular distance resolution, and was also involved in theoretical work on intermolecular forces in colloidal systems and the self-assembly of surfactant and lipid molecules into micelles, bilayers, vesicles and biological membranes. In 1986 he joined the faculty of the University of California at Santa Barbara where he holds a joint appointment as professor in the Department of Chemical and Nuclear Engineering and the Materials Department.

Koji Kato: received a Bachelor's degree and Master's degree from the Department of Mechanical Engineering of Tohoku University in Sendai, Japan. He received a Doctoral degree from the same university in 1974. He worked as a research associate of Tohoku University until 1980 and then as an associate professor until 1987. He was promoted to full professor in 1987 in the Department of Mechanical Engineering of the same university. The majority of his research work has been in the area of tribology. He is especially interested in the micromechanisms of friction and wear, and in applications of fundamental tribology from the viewpoint of engineering. He has studied the tribological properties of materials under extreme operating conditions such as ultra-high vacuum. Currently he is studying the tribological properties of ceramic materials and coatings.

Francis E. Kennedy, Jr: is professor of engineering at Dartmouth College's Thayer School of Engineering, Hanover, NH. He was educated at Worcester Polytechnic Institute (B.S.), Stanford University (M.S.), and Rensselaer Polytechnic Institute (Ph.D.). He joined the faculty at Dartmouth College in 1974. He has also been a visiting scholar at the following institutions: Polytechnic Institute of Bucharest, Romania, NASA-Lewis Research Center, Institut National des Sciences Appliquées, Lyon, France, and Asian Institute of Technology, Bangkok, Thailand. His research activity has been in the following areas: thermal and thermo-mechanical phenomena in dry sliding contacts, experimental and numerical methods in contact mechanics and heat transfer, wear of polymers, ceramics and ceramic coatings, friction of ice, and tribology of computer disk/ head interactions.

Oleg V. Kholodilov: graduated in 1974 as a physicist. Has received a Ph.D. in tribology in 1982. His main areas of interest are acoustic phenomena in tribology; wear diagnostics and surface topography analysis. Since 1974 he has been with Metal–Polymer Research Institute, Byelorussian Academy of Sciences.

Dieter Klaffke: studied physics at the Technical University in Berlin. He received the degree of doctor of engineering from the same university in 1978. He joined the Federal Institute of Material Testing in 1970 and worked in the field of fatigue of metals. Since 1980 he has been working in the field of tribology; mainly fretting wear with special interest in ceramics and coatings.

Tonya Kuhl: is currently carrying out her Ph.D. research in the area of surface interactions between metal and biological surfaces in aqueous media at the University of California, Santa Barbara.

Uzi Landman: received his D.Sc. in chemistry from the Technion–Israel Institute of Technology in 1969. In 1977 he joined the School of Physics at the Georgia Institute of Technology where he is a Regents' and Institute professor. He has served as the associate dean of research for the College of Science and Liberal Arts. His interests are in the area of condensed matter, solid-state, and surface physics, materials science, chemical physics, statistical mechanics, and the development of computational and simulation methods. He is the editor of the new *Journal of Computational Materials Science*, published by Elsevier.

William David Luedtke: received his Ph.D. in physics from the Georgia Institute of Technology in 1984. He joined Professor Landman's condensed matter theory group at Georgia Institute of Technology in 1984, where he is currently a research scientist. His interests are in the areas of condensed matter and solid-state physics, materials science, and computational physics.

Nickolai K. Myshkin: graduated as an engineer in electromechanics in 1971 and received his Ph.D. in tribology in 1977 and D.Sc. in tribology in 1985. Since 1977 he has worked in the Metal–Polymer Research Institute, Byelorussian Academy of Sciences. His main areas of interest include: wear diagnostics, electrical contacts, surface topography and morphology analysis.

T. F. J. Quinn: is a physicist with a strong engineering bias. He obtained his D.Sc. from London University in 1979 for his many contributions to tribology, several of which involved the application of physical analytical techniques to tribosystems. His extensive experience in physical analysis was obtained in several leading industrial and academic tribological research laboratories, including those of Associated Electrical Industries at Aldermaston in the UK and those of Southwest Research Institute and Georgia Institute of Technology in the USA. He was reader in tribology at Aston University, UK, from 1974 to 1983. His current interest is the modelling of wear mechanisms.

Eric M. Ringer: received his B.Sc. degree in physics from the University of California at Irvine in 1985. He is currently completing his studies towards a Ph.D. degree in physics, at the Georgia Institute of Technology, on surface superionic conductivity, deformations of ionic solids, and tip-substrate interactions.

Rolf Wäsche: studied mineralogy at the University of Göttingen. He received a Ph.D. in material science from the Technical University of Berlin. For two years he was working with the Robert Bosch Corporation in the field of ceramic materials. In 1987 he joined the BAM tribology group. Since then he is working in the field of tribology of ceramic coatings and of high temperature solid lubrication of ceramic materials.

# Author Index of Volume 153/1

Biographic notes about the authors concerned can be found on p. 297.

Elsevier Sequoia

*Wear*, 153 (1992) 303–304

# Subject Index of Volume 153/1

Elsevier Sequoia